Use of Meta-Heuristic Techniques in Rainfall-Runoff Modelling

Special Issue Editor
Kwok-wing Chau

MDPI

Guest Editor
Kwok-wing Chau
Department of Civil and Environmental Engineering,
The Hong Kong Polytechnic University
Hong Kong

Editorial Office
MDPI AG
St. Alban-Anlage 66
Basel, Switzerland

This edition is a reprint of the Special Issue published online in the open access journal *Water* (ISSN 2073-4441) from 2015–2016 (available at: http://www.mdpi.com/journal/water/special_issues/rainfall-runoff-model).

For citation purposes, cite each article independently as indicated on the article page online and as indicated below:

Author 1; Author 2; Author 3 etc. Article title. *Journal Name*. **Year**. Article number/page range.

ISBN 978-3-03842-326-3 (Pbk)
ISBN 978-3-03842-327-0 (PDF)

Table of Contents

About the Guest Editor..v

Preface to "Use of Meta-Heuristic Techniques in Rainfall-Runoff Modelling"....................vii

Kwok-wing Chau
Use of Meta-Heuristic Techniques in Rainfall-Runoff Modelling
Reprinted from: *Water Water* **2017**, *9*(3), 186; doi: 10.3390/w9030186
http://www.mdpi.com/2073-4441/9/3/186 1

Víctor Salas-Aguilar, Antonia Macedo-Cruz, Fernando Paz, Enrique Palacios, Carlos Ortiz and Abel Quevedo
Regional Patterns of Baseflow Variability in Mexican Subwatersheds
Reprinted from: *Water* **2016**, *8*(3), 98; doi: 10.3390/w8030098
http://www.mdpi.com/2073-4441/8/3/98 7

Muhammad Ajmal, Taj Ali Khan and Tae-Woong Kim
A CN-Based Ensembled Hydrological Model for Enhanced Watershed Runoff Prediction
Reprinted from: *Water* **2016**, *8*(1), 20; doi: 10.3390/w8010020
http://www.mdpi.com/2073-4441/8/1/20 23

Soojun Kim, Yonsoo Kim, Narae Kang and Hung Soo Kim
Application of the Entropy Method to Select Calibration Sites for Hydrological Modeling
Reprinted from: *Water* **2015**, *7*(12), 6719-6735; doi: 10.3390/w7126652
http://www.mdpi.com/2073-4441/7/12/6652 41

Chien-Lin Huang, Nien-Sheng Hsu and Chih-Chiang Wei
Coupled Heuristic Prediction of Long Lead-Time Accumulated Total Inflow of a Reservoir during Typhoons Using Deterministic Recurrent and Fuzzy Inference-Based Neural Network
Reprinted from: *Water* **2015**, *7*(11), 6516-6550; doi: 10.3390/w7116516
http://www.mdpi.com/2073-4441/7/11/6516 58

Nan-Ching Yeh, Chung-Chih Liu and Wann-Jin Chen
Estimation of Rainfall Associated with Typhoons over the Ocean Using TRMM/TMI and Numerical Models
Reprinted from: *Water* **2015**, *7*(11), 6017-6038; doi: 10.3390/w7116017
http://www.mdpi.com/2073-4441/7/11/6017 87

Ming-Chang Wu and Gwo-Fong Lin
An Hourly Streamflow Forecasting Model Coupled with an Enforced Learning Strategy
Reprinted from: *Water* **2015**, *7*(11), 5876-5895; doi: 10.3390/w7115876
http://www.mdpi.com/2073-4441/7/11/5876 106

Gang Li, Chen-Xi Liu, Sheng-Li Liao and Chun-Tian Cheng
Applying a Correlation Analysis Method to Long-Term Forecasting of Power Production at Small Hydropower Plants
Reprinted from: *Water* **2015**, *7*(9), 4806-4820; doi: 10.3390/w7094806
http://www.mdpi.com/2073-4441/7/9/4806 123

Chun-Tian Cheng , Zhong-Kai Feng, Wen-Jing Niu and Sheng-Li Liao
Heuristic Methods for Reservoir Monthly Inflow Forecasting: A Case Study of Xinfengjiang
Reservoir in Pearl River, China
Reprinted from: *Water* **2015**, *7*(8), 4477-4495; doi: 10.3390/w7084477
http://www.mdpi.com/2073-4441/7/8/4477 136

Chun-tian Cheng, Wen-jing Niu, Zhong-kai Feng, Jian-jian Shen and Kwok-wing Chau
Daily Reservoir Runoff Forecasting Method Using Artificial Neural Network Based on
Quantum-behaved Particle Swarm Optimization
Reprinted from: *Water* **2015**, *7*(8), 4232-4246; doi: 10.3390/w7084232
http://www.mdpi.com/2073-4441/7/8/4232 152

Yun Wang, Shenglian Guo, Lihua Xiong, Pan Liu and Dedi Liu
Daily Runoff Forecasting Model Based on ANN and Data Preprocessing Techniques
Reprinted from: *Water* **2015**, *7*(8), 4144-4160; doi: 10.3390/w7084144
http://www.mdpi.com/2073-4441/7/8/4144 165

Der-Chang Lo, Chih-Chiang Wei and En-Ping Tsai
Parameter Automatic Calibration Approach for Neural-Network-Based Cyclonic Precipitation
Forecast Models
Reprinted from: *Water* **2015**, *7*(7), 3963-3977; doi: 10.3390/w7073963
http://www.mdpi.com/2073-4441/7/7/3963 179

Sungwon Kim and Vijay P. Singh
Spatial Disaggregation of Areal Rainfall Using Two Different Artificial Neural Networks Models
Reprinted from: *Water* **2015**, *7*(6), 2707-2727; doi: 10.3390/w7062707
http://www.mdpi.com/2073-4441/7/6/2707 192

Weijian Guo, Chuanhai Wang, Xianmin Zeng, Tengfei Ma and Hai Yang
Subgrid Parameterization of the Soil Moisture Storage Capacity for a Distributed
Rainfall-Runoff Model
Reprinted from: *Water* **2015**, *7*(6), 2691-2706; doi: 10.3390/w7062691
http://www.mdpi.com/2073-4441/7/6/2691 210

Jui-Yi Ho and Kwan Tun Lee
Grey Forecast Rainfall with Flow Updating Algorithm for Real-Time Flood Forecasting
Reprinted from: *Water* **2015**, *7*(5), 1840-1865; doi: 10.3390/w7051840
http://www.mdpi.com/2073-4441/7/5/1840 224

About the Guest Editor

Kwok-wing Chau was awarded a First Class Honours Bachelor degree in Science in Civil Engineering by the University of Hong Kong, a Master degree with distinction in Science in Civil Engineering by the University of Hong Kong, and a Doctor degree in Philosophy by University of Queensland in Australia. He is currently a Professor in the Department of Civil and Environmental Engineering of The Hong Kong Polytechnic University. He is very active in undertaking research works and the scope of his research interest is very broad, covering numerical flow modeling, water quality modeling, hydrological modeling, knowledge-based system development and artificial intelligence applications. Prof. Chau has published over 160 Science Citation Index journal papers and the total number of non-self-citations is over 7000. He has acquired many prestigious research awards, including National Natural Science Class 2 Award, Natural Science Class 1 Award and Dean's Award for Outstanding Publication Achievement.

Preface to "Use of Meta-Heuristic Techniques in Rainfall-Runoff Modelling"

Each year, extreme floods, which appear to be occurring more frequently in recent years (owing to climate change), lead to enormous economic damage and human suffering around the world. It is therefore imperative to be able to accurately predict both the occurrence time and magnitude of peak discharge in advance of an impending flood event. The use of meta-heuristic techniques in rainfall-runoff modeling is a growing field of endeavor in water resources management. These techniques can be used to calibrate data-driven rainfall-runoff models to improve forecasting accuracies. This book, being also a Special Issue of the journal *Water*, is designed to fill the analytical void by including papers concerning advances in the contemporary use of meta-heuristic techniques in rainfall-runoff modeling. The information and analyses are intended to contribute to the development and implementation of effective hydrological predictions, and thus, of appropriate precautionary measures. Being the editor of this book, I would like to thank all authors contributing to the fourteen chapters as well as the reviewers involved and who have provided constructive comments on these articles during the reviewing process.

Kwok-wing Chau
Guest Editor

water MDPI

Article

Use of Meta-Heuristic Techniques in Rainfall-Runoff Modelling

Kwok-wing Chau

Department of Civil and Environmental Engineering, The Hong Kong Polytechnic University, Hunghom, Kowloon, Hong Kong; cekwchau@polyu.edu.hk; Tel.: +852-2766-6014

Academic Editor: Arjen Y. Hoekstra
Received: 20 December 2016; Accepted: 2 March 2017; Published: 6 March 2017

Abstract: Each year, extreme floods, which appear to be occurring more frequently in recent years (owing to climate change), lead to enormous economic damage and human suffering around the world. It is therefore imperative to be able to accurately predict both the occurrence time and magnitude of peak discharge in advance of an impending flood event. The use of meta-heuristic techniques in rainfall-runoff modeling is a growing field of endeavor in water resources management. These techniques can be used to calibrate data-driven rainfall-runoff models to improve forecasting accuracies. This Special Issue of the journal *Water* is designed to fill the analytical void by including papers concerning advances in the contemporary use of meta-heuristic techniques in rainfall-runoff modeling. The information and analyses can contribute to the development and implementation of effective hydrological predictions, and thus, of appropriate precautionary measures.

Keywords: rainfall-runoff; meta-heuristic; data-driven; modeling; flood; prediction

---

1. Introduction

Around the world each year, extreme floods, which appear to be occurring more frequently in recent years (owing to climate change), lead to enormous economic damage and human suffering. As such, it is imperative to be able to accurately predict both the occurrence time and magnitude of peak discharge in advance of an impending flood event. The use of meta-heuristic techniques in rainfall-runoff modeling is a growing field of endeavor in water resources management [1–12]. These techniques can be used to calibrate data-driven rainfall-runoff models to improve forecasting accuracies.

The papers contained within this Special Issue entitled Use of Meta-Heuristic Techniques in Rainfall-Runoff Modelling are designed to fill the analytical void by including papers concerning advances in the contemporary use of meta-heuristic techniques in rainfall-runoff modeling. The information and analyses can contribute to the development and implementation of effective hydrological predictions, and thus, of appropriate precautionary measures. The papers cover a number of applications of different novel meta-heuristic techniques in addressing a variety of hydrological modelling problems, tailored for different areas of geography and climatic conditions.

2. Contributors

The correlation between landscape and climate with the data availability is a difficult problem in sub-watershed hydrology. Salas-Aguilar et al.'s work [13] employs a top-down approach to develop a generalized baseflow model in order to assess the annual recession curves and to correlate the recession parameter with hydrological and geographical attributes of twenty-one sub-watersheds in Mexico, covering a variety of climatic conditions. Results indicate that the recession parameter increases with longitude but decreases with latitude and it exhibits a consistent non-linear behavior dependent upon the precipitation rate and evapotranspiration in the sub-watersheds. The non-linear baseflow model is able to separate baseflow from direct flow more accurately in sub-watersheds. It can adequately address the relationship amongst recharge, storage and discharge and can thus be used in basins with insufficient data availability.

The key drawbacks of the conventional curve number model are the vulnerability to instability in the direct runoff results owing to its reliance on the original abstraction level and the absence of the procedure on pre-storm soil moisture accounting for ungauged watersheds. Ajmai et al. [14] integrate the conventional curve number model with a French four-parameter model with a varying original abstraction level, in order to address this issue. Inherent parameters are assigned in the novel parameterization procedure. Its performance is assessed by comparing results with several benchmarking conventional models for observed data in thirty-nine watersheds employing different statistical metrics. Results indicate that the novel model is able to generate better and more consistent outcomes than its counterparts.

It is difficult to optimize the number of calibration sites in hydrologic modeling and, currently, the most often employed method is the trial and error method. Kim et al. [15] put forward an entropy method to attain automatic optimization of the number of calibration sites with application in a Korean river basin. The entropy method is first applied to group different combinations of runoff discharge stations and to determine the best one amongst them. The optimal set of parameters of the developed hydrologic model is then calibrated by employing a genetic algorithm. Calibration results corroborate that the model with the combination and site number recommended by the entropy method outperforms the others. Besides, it is proven to be able to substantially shorten the time required on model calibration.

In real-time discharge forecasting, particularly during typhoon attacks, the difficulties mostly encountered include high uncertainty and long lead time. Huang et al. [16] couple a real-time recurrent learning neural network, an adaptive network-based fuzzy inference system, and some heuristic techniques to address this problem. Heuristic inputs are utilized to enhance the spatial and temporal precision. Results indicate that this proposed model performs much better than the adaptive network-based fuzzy inference system, in terms of both forecasting error at long lead-time and solution stability. The prediction lead-time of the former can be up to forty-nine hours with an average error percentage smaller than 10% while for the latter, the corresponding values are six hours and 20% to 40% respectively.

In their paper Estimation of Rainfall Associated with Typhoons over the Ocean Using Tropical Rainfall Measuring Mission (TRMM)/TRMM Microwave Imager (TMI) and Numerical Models, Yeh et al. [17] couple much numerical weather research and forecasting as well as radiative transfer models with the Tropical Rainfall Measuring Mission/ Precipitation Radar data from 2002 to 2010 to predict rainfall resulting from a typhoon in the northwestern Pacific Ocean. A microwave radiative transfer model is developed to mimic fifteen typhoons and to generate a posterior probability distribution function. The precipitation rate resulting from a typhoon can then be determined by entering the TMI with attenuation indices at specific frequency into the posterior probability distribution function. Results show that the locations of the simulated rainband with the heaviest precipitation agree well with field observations. This paper contributes towards a feasible solution in providing a quick and accurate prediction of rainfall resulting from a typhoon.

The paper by Wu and Lin [18] entitled An Hourly Streamflow Forecasting Model Coupled with an Enforced Learning Strategy documents how to enhance the accuracy of hourly streamflow prediction by integrating an enforced learning strategy with four different neural network-based models, namely, the support vector machine, radial basis function network, back propagation network, and self-organizing map. The performances of these neural network-based models, with and without the enforced learning strategy, are compared under real-life application. Results indicate that, among different neural network-based models, the support vector machine and self-organizing map outperform the radial basis function network and back propagation network. Besides, the incorporation of the enforced learning strategy is able to enhance the performance of all types of neural network-based models in hourly streamflow prediction. As such, it is concluded that the proposed methodology is promising in enhancing neural network-based streamflow prediction models.

It is important to be able to predict the long-term power production of small hydropower plants for successive integration with power production of large to medium hydropower plants. However, a recognized prediction model for this purpose does not exist. Li et al. [19], in their paper Applying a Correlation Analysis Method to Long-Term Forecasting of Power Production at Small Hydropower Plants, employ a correlation analysis method to predict the power production of small hydropower plants. Analysis is performed on the correlation between small hydropower plants and large to medium hydropower plants which reveals that they have similar interval inflows. As such, a regression model is built to predict the power production of small hydropower plants on the basis of the inflows of large to medium hydropower plants. The proposed method is successfully applied to small hydropower plants in the Yunnan Power Grid.

The prediction of reservoir monthly inflow is significant owing to the purposes of water resource management as well as the stability of long-term reservoir operation. In their paper Heuristic Methods for Reservoir Monthly Inflow Forecasting: A Case Study of Xinfengjiang Reservoir in Pearl River, China, Cheng et al. [20] employ two heuristic prediction methods, namely, artificial neural networks and the support vector machine, to predict reservoir monthly inflow. In these models, a genetic algorithm is used to select and calibrate the optimized set of model parameters. A hybrid prediction two-stage model coupling the above two methods is also developed in this study. In the first stage, each method is employed to predict the reservoir monthly inflow values, both of which are used as the input variables of a second artificial neural network model for refined prediction in the second stage. These three models are applied to predict monthly reservoir inflow in Xinfengjiang reservoir from 1944 to 2014. Results indicate that the hybrid method outperforms both artificial neural networks and the support vector machine in terms of five performance evaluation metrics.

Whilst the artificial neural network has been proven to be one of the most effective methods in daily discharge prediction, its drawbacks of slow training speed and vulnerability to being trapped in the local optimum cannot be neglected in real-life application. Cheng et al. [2], in their paper Daily Reservoir Runoff Forecasting Method Using Artificial Neural Network Based on Quantum-behaved Particle Swarm Optimization, address this problem by investigating the use of the artificial neural network model based on quantum-behaved particle swarm optimization in daily discharge prediction. In this model, quantum-behaved particle swarm optimization is utilized to determine the optimal set of synaptic weights and thresholds of the artificial neural network. The hybrid model is able to couple the advantages of both methods and thus to improve the performance of the prediction model. It is applied to Hongjiadu reservoir in China for the period from 2006 to 2014. Results illustrate that the proposed hybrid model outperforms the original artificial neural network model and hence proves its feasibility in daily discharge prediction.

Wang et al. [21], in their paper Daily Runoff Forecasting Model Based on ANN and Data Preprocessing Techniques, examine the effect of applying a data preprocessing technique, namely, singular spectrum analysis, to the input data on the performance of the artificial neural network model for daily discharge prediction. Benchmark comparison is then made with the original artificial neural network model as well as a nonlinear perturbation model based on the artificial neural network. Field data of eight real watersheds are used for model calibration and comparison. Results show that the artificial network model with singular spectrum analysis outperforms both benchmarking models whilst the integration of a nonlinear perturbation model to the artificial neural network can also induce some performance enhancement, though to a lesser extent. Besides, models with the input combination comprising both rainfall and previous runoff perform better than their counterparts with the input combination considering rainfall solely.

In their paper Parameter Automatic Calibration Approach for Neural-Network-Based Cyclonic Precipitation Forecast Models, Lo et al. [22] propose a neural network-based precipitation prediction model coupled with a parameter automatic calibration approach in determining the training parameters of the neural network. It is applied to Dawu station in Taiwan, with data on a typhoon and ground weather as model inputs. A multiple linear regression model and a multilayer perception neural network model are employed as the benchmark for comparison of the performance of the proposed model. For the multilayer perception neural network model, the trial-and-error method is used for tuning and calibrating the training parameters manually. Results demonstrate that the neural network-based model with a parameter automatic calibration approach outperforms all the benchmarking models. Results also show that, if the increment number in the parameter ranges increases, the computing efficiency of the proposed model will decrease but its accuracy will increase.

The paper by Kim and Singh [23] entitled Spatial Disaggregation of Areal Rainfall Using Two Different Artificial Neural Networks Models presents the development of two artificial neural network models, namely, the multilayer perceptron and Kohonen self-organizing feature map, for spatial disaggregation of areal precipitation in the Wi-stream catchment in South Korea. For the three-layer multilayer perceptron model, three training algorithms, namely, Levenberg–Marquardt, conjugate gradient and quickprop, are employed to compute areal precipitation. Results show that the Levenberg–Marquardt training algorithm is more sensitive to the number of hidden nodes than the other two training algorithms. The network architectures of 11-3-1 for the Levenberg–Marquardt algorithm and 11-5-1 for both the conjugate gradient and quickprop algorithms perform the best amongst all tried structures. As such, their corresponding inverse networks represent the best multilayer perceptron model for spatial disaggregation of areal precipitation. Results also indicate that both the multilayer perceptron and Kohonen self-organizing feature map are feasible for spatial disaggregation of areal precipitation.

In nonlinear hydrologic processes, spatial variability has a very significant role. In most grid-based rainfall-runoff models, the often assumed uniform subgrid variability results in scale-dependence. In their paper Subgrid Parameterization of the Soil Moisture Storage Capacity for a Distributed Rainfall-Runoff Model, Guo et al. [24] study the effect of scale on the Grid-Xinanjiang model at Yanduhe Basin and propose a subgrid parameterization method in order to integrate the subgrid variability of the soil moisture storage capacity, which has significant effects on discharge partitioning and generation in the model. Correlation is performed between the soil moisture storage capacity and the topographic index because their spatial patterns are quite similar. Results illustrate that the proposed method outperforms the original Grid-Xinanjiang model in terms of consistency and precision. It is able to eliminate the recalibration process when there is any change to the resolution of the digital elevation model and enhance the use of the model even in an ungauged basin.

Previous research indicates that adaptive algorithms are key in deterministic flood prediction models owing to the intrinsic non-stationary nature of the rainfall-runoff process. Ho and Lee [25], in their paper Grey Forecast Rainfall with Flow Updating Algorithm for Real-Time Flood Forecasting, develop a real-time flood prediction system by coupling a precipitation prediction model, a geomorphology-based discharge model and an updating algorithm. Observed hourly precipitation data are employed in the grey precipitation prediction model. The watershed discharge model is able to mimic the effects of changing geo-hydrological conditions. Validation of the system is performed at two watersheds in Taiwan and one in the United States. Results demonstrate that the proposed system is promising in simulating the observed hydrographs in several sets of rainfall-runoff cases covering different conditions and will be useful in reducing human and economic losses in advance of flooding incidents.

3. Conclusions

The fourteen papers contained in the Special Issue entitled Use of Meta-Heuristic Techniques in Rainfall-Runoff Modelling cover a wide range of applications of different novel meta-heuristic methodologies and techniques in addressing a variety of hydrological modelling problems, tailored for different areas of geography and climatic conditions in order to resolve both local and regional pertinent issues as well as in different time scales. They are demonstrated to be able to fill the analytical void by enriching the advances in the contemporary use of meta-heuristic techniques in rainfall-runoff modeling. It is apparent, from the abovementioned collection of papers, that novel applications of meta-heuristic techniques in rainfall-runoff modeling will be required for proper water resources management. The information and analyses can certainly contribute to the development and implementation of effective hydrological predictions, and thus, of appropriate precautionary measures.

Acknowledgments: The author of this editorial, who served as Guest Editor of this Special Issue of *Water*, thanks the journal editors for their time and resources, the many authors of the papers for their contributions, and the numerous referees for their hard work that improved the various versions of the manuscripts leading to high quality published papers.

Conflicts of Interest: The author declares no conflict of interest.

References

1. Saeidifarzad, B.; Nourani, V.; Aalami, M.T.; Chau, K.W. Multi-site calibration of linear reservoir based geomorphologic rainfall-runoff models. *Water* **2014**, *6*, 2690–2716. [CrossRef]
2. Cheng, C.T.; Niu, W.J.; Feng, Z.K.; Shen, J.J.; Chau, K.W. Daily Reservoir Runoff Forecasting Method Using Artificial Neural Network Based on Quantum-behaved Particle Swarm Optimization. *Water* **2015**, *7*, 4232–4246. [CrossRef]
3. Wu, C.L.; Chau, K.W.; Fan, C. Prediction of rainfall time series using modular artificial neural networks coupled with data-preprocessing techniques. *J. Hydrol.* **2010**, *389*, 146–167. [CrossRef]
4. Wang, W.C.; Xu, D.M.; Chau, K.W.; Lei, G.J. Assessment of river water quality based on theory of variable fuzzy sets and fuzzy binary comparison method. *Water Resour. Manag.* **2014**, *28*, 4183–4200. [CrossRef]
5. Olyaie, E.; Banejad, H.; Chau, K.W.; Melesse, A.M. A comparison of various artificial intelligence approaches performance for estimating suspended sediment load of river systems: A case study in United States. *Environ. Monit. Assess.* **2015**, *187*, 189. [CrossRef] [PubMed]
6. Xu, D.M.; Wang, W.C.; Chau, K.W.; Cheng, C.T.; Chen, S.Y. Comparison of three global optimization algorithms for calibration of the Xinanjiang model parameters. *J. Hydroinform.* **2013**, *15*, 174–193. [CrossRef]
7. Gholami, V.; Chau, K.W.; Fadaee, F.; Torkaman, J.; Ghaffari, A. Modeling of groundwater level fluctuations using dendrochronology in alluvial aquifers. *J. Hydrol.* **2015**, *529*, 1060–1069. [CrossRef]
8. Taormina, R.; Chau, K.W. Data-driven input variable selection for rainfall-runoff modeling using binary-coded particle swarm optimization and Extreme Learning Machines. *J. Hydrol.* **2015**, *529*, 1617–1632. [CrossRef]
9. Wu, C.L.; Chau, K.W.; Li, Y.S. Methods to improve neural network performance in daily flows prediction. *J. Hydrol.* **2009**, *372*, 80–93. [CrossRef]
10. Wang, W.C.; Chau, K.W.; Xu, D.M.; Chen, X.Y. Improving forecasting accuracy of annual runoff time series using ARIMA based on EEMD decomposition. *Water Resour. Manag.* **2015**, *29*, 2655–2675. [CrossRef]
11. Chen, X.Y.; Chau, K.W.; Busari, A.O. A comparative study of population-based optimization algorithms for downstream river flow forecasting by a hybrid neural network model. *Eng. Appl. Artif. Intell.* **2015**, *46*, 258–268. [CrossRef]
12. Chau, K.W.; Wu, C.L. A Hybrid Model Coupled with Singular Spectrum Analysis for Daily Rainfall Prediction. *J. Hydroinform.* **2010**, *12*, 458–473. [CrossRef]
13. Salas-Aguilar, V.; Macedo-Cruz, A.; Paz, F.; Palacios, E.; Ortiz, C.; Quevedo, A. Regional Patterns of Baseflow Variability in Mexican Subwatersheds. *Water* **2016**, *8*, 98. [CrossRef]
14. Ajmal, M.; Khan, T.; Kim, T. A CN-Based Ensembled Hydrological Model for Enhanced Watershed Runoff Prediction. *Water* **2016**, *8*, 20. [CrossRef]
15. Kim, S.; Kim, Y.; Kang, N.; Kim, H. Application of the Entropy Method to Select Calibration Sites for Hydrological Modeling. *Water* **2015**, *7*, 6719–6735. [CrossRef]
16. Huang, C.; Hsu, N.; Wei, C. Coupled Heuristic Prediction of Long Lead-Time Accumulated Total Inflow of a Reservoir during Typhoons Using Deterministic Recurrent and Fuzzy Inference-Based Neural Network. *Water* **2015**, *7*, 6516–6550. [CrossRef]
17. Yeh, N.; Liu, C.; Chen, W. Estimation of Rainfall Associated with Typhoons over the Ocean Using TRMM/TMI and Numerical Models. *Water* **2015**, *7*, 6017–6038. [CrossRef]

18. Wu, M.; Lin, G. An Hourly Streamflow Forecasting Model Coupled with an Enforced Learning Strategy. *Water* **2015**, *7*, 5876–5895. [CrossRef]

19. Li, G.; Liu, C.; Liao, S.; Cheng, C. Applying a Correlation Analysis Method to Long-Term Forecasting of Power Production at Small Hydropower Plants. *Water* **2015**, *7*, 4806–4820. [CrossRef]

20. Cheng, C.; Feng, Z.; Niu, W.; Liao, S. Heuristic Methods for Reservoir Monthly Inflow Forecasting: A Case Study of Xinfengjiang Reservoir in Pearl River, China. *Water* **2015**, *7*, 4477–4495. [CrossRef]

21. Wang, Y.; Guo, S.; Xiong, L.; Liu, P.; Liu, D. Daily Runoff Forecasting Model Based on ANN and Data Preprocessing Techniques. *Water* **2015**, *7*, 4144–4160. [CrossRef]

22. Lo, D.; Wei, C.; Tsai, E. Parameter Automatic Calibration Approach for Neural-Network-Based Cyclonic Precipitation Forecast Models. *Water* **2015**, *7*, 3963–3977. [CrossRef]

23. Kim, S.; Singh, V. Spatial Disaggregation of Areal Rainfall Using Two Different Artificial Neural Networks Models. *Water* **2015**, *7*, 2707–2727. [CrossRef]

24. Guo, W.; Wang, C.; Zeng, X.; Ma, T.; Yang, H. Subgrid Parameterization of the Soil Moisture Storage Capacity for a Distributed Rainfall-Runoff Model. *Water* **2015**, *7*, 2691–2706. [CrossRef]

25. Ho, J.; Lee, K. Grey Forecast Rainfall with Flow Updating Algorithm for Real-Time Flood Forecasting. *Water* **2015**, *7*, 1840–1865. [CrossRef]

water

MDPI

Article

Regional Patterns of Baseflow Variability in Mexican Subwatersheds

Víctor Salas-Aguilar, Antonia Macedo-Cruz *, Fernando Paz, Enrique Palacios, Carlos Ortiz and Abel Quevedo

Colegio de Postgraduados, Carretera México-Texcoco, Km 36.5 Montecillo, 56230 México, Mexico; vsalasaguilar@gmail.com (V.S.-A.); ferpazpel@gmail.com (F.P.); epalacio@colpos.mx (E.P.); ortiz@colpos.mx (C.O.); anolasco@colpos.mx (A.Q.)

* Correspondence: macedoan@colpos.mx; Tel.: +52-595-952-0200 (ext. 1164)

Academic Editor: Kwok-wing Chau
Received: 1 December 2015; Accepted: 3 March 2016; Published: 11 March 2016

Abstract: One of the challenges faced by subwatershed hydrology is the discovery of patterns associated with climate and landscape variability with the available data. This study has three objectives: (1) to evaluate the annual recession curves; (2) to relate the recession parameter (RP) with physiographic characteristics of 21 Mexican subwatersheds in different climate regions; and (3) to formulate a Baseflow (BF) model based on a top-down approach. The RP was calibrated utilizing the largest magnitude curves. The RP was related to topographical, climate and soil variables. A non-linear model was employed to separate the baseflow which considers RP as a recharge rate. Our results show that RP increases with longitude and decreases with latitude. RP displayed a sustained non-linear behavior determined by precipitation rate and evapotranspiration ($\frac{P}{E}$) over years and subwatersheds. The model was fit to a parameter concurrent with invariance and space-time symmetry conditions. The dispersion of our model was associated with the product of ($\frac{P}{E}$) by the aquifer's transmissivity. We put forward a generalized baseflow model, which made the discrimination of baseflow from direct flow in subwatersheds possible. The proposed model involves the recharge-storage-discharge relation and could be implemented in basins where there are no suitable ground-based data.

Keywords: runoff; invariance; non-linear model; recession parameter; symmetry

---

1. Introduction

Baseflow (BF) is an essential component for the hydrological balance of a basin. Its study is necessary for different purposes, such as aquatic systems' preservation, hydroelectric energy generation and pollutant transportation, and it also includes the effects of plant coverage changes on surface runoff [1–3]. Long-term hydrological balance within the basin depends on water and energy availability [4]. Budyko's model considers this relation and associates actual and potential evapotranspiration (energy) with precipitation (water). This model and its derivations have been proven reliable through validation in different climate and physiographic conditions around the world [5–8].

This approach has been utilized to predict BF; for instance, Wang and Luo [9] found an association between the aridity index and perennial stream. The baseflow recession parameter (RP) has also been related by means of this model; van Dick [2] noted how the parameter decreased exponentially as the aridity index value increased. Furthermore, Beck *et al.* [3] observed the same trend when they correlated climate, topography, plant coverage, geology and soil type with the baseflow recession parameter. Their results indicated non-linear and heteroscedastic relations with satisfactory fits ($R^2 > 0.72$). Similar studies associated the baseflow index with geographical, climate and edaphic patterns [10,11].

This model has the disadvantage of disregarding underwater storage, making it impractical to model the water balance at temporal scales [12]. According to Istambulluoglu *et al.* [13], the model correlates negatively as the aridity index increases, which points out the need to include the baseflow component into Budyko-like hydrological balances on an interannual basis.

Other studies have described how hydrological balance variability and interaction within and among subwatersheds follow similar patterns [14]. For instance, the precipitation-runoff relations on a monthly and an annual basis tend to display non-linear behaviors, varying only in magnitude, as shown by Ponce and Shetty [15]. These studies describe a space-time dependence that can be labeled as symmetry, where observations from different regions can be utilized for the construction of a generalized model with invariance principles [16,17]. The recession master curve is a symmetric model for studying BF; however, according to Tallaksen [18], it is inconvenient due to its grouping of n different recession curves along the year, a procedure that turns out to be time consuming if many years are to be analyzed.

Although there are simplifications based on linear reservoirs utilized to separate baseflow [19,20], the linear algorithm can only be successful when short periods of recession are adjusted. According to He *et al.* [21], in most cases of unconfined aquifers, the storage-discharge relationship in an aquifer represented by the curve of recession is set to a concave shape, indicating the non-linearity of the process.

Moreover, the problem of calibrating and validating mechanistic models in Mexico is that there is not enough data to feed these models [22]. Therefore, this research aimed at discovering new hydrological patterns that incorporate within them the effects of the natural heterogeneity found in different subwatersheds [14], responding to the hypothesis of a robust hydrological model, sustained on physical limits and based on easily accessible data that can be replicated in any zone.

Therefore, the proposal of this study can be divided into three different objectives. The first one was to evaluate the annual recession curve with a non-linear model; the second one was to relate the recession parameter with subwatershed physiographics; and the last one was to formulate a baseflow model supported by the symmetry and invariance principles. Our base hypothesis was that working with annual data enables a separation of baseflow into shorter time scales.

2. Materials and Methods

2.1. Input Data

Daily runoff registers (converted into mm· d^{-1}) from 21 Mexican subwatersheds were gathered; the source of this information was El Banco Nacional de Datos de Aguas Superficiales [23]. The subwatersheds were selected so as to represent different climate characteristics (aridity index, seasonality, humidity), as shown by Garcia *et al.* [24], and landscape characteristics (topography, soil and plant coverage).

An additional criterion was that the subwatersheds were located in National Parks and Biosphere Reserves, in order to avoid as much as possible extraneous influences on the hydrological regime (water extraction, urban development, storage works, *etc.*) (Figure 1). The subwatersheds areas ranged from 42 to 23,475 km^2. The analyzed period went from 1950 to 2011, which is the period of available hydrometric data in Mexico.

Hydrological vector data for Mexico were available at the hydrologic region, basin, subwatershed and micro-basin levels according to the Instituto Nacional de Estadística y Geografía (Natonal Institute of Statistics and Geography, INEGI) and the Comisión Nacional para el Conocimiento y Uso de la Biodiversidad (National Commission for Knowledge and Use of Biodiversity, CONABIO) [25,26]. To convert flow in m^3· s^{-1} to depth in mm· day^{-1}, it is necessary to know the area of the subwatershed that uses the gauging station present as its reference.

The INEGI and CONABIO vectors failed to consider the previous data, which led to conversion overestimations or underestimations. Therefore, subwatersheds were digitized based on their hydrometric station [27]; the former Hydraulic Resources Secretary [28] hydrological bulletins were used as the reference.

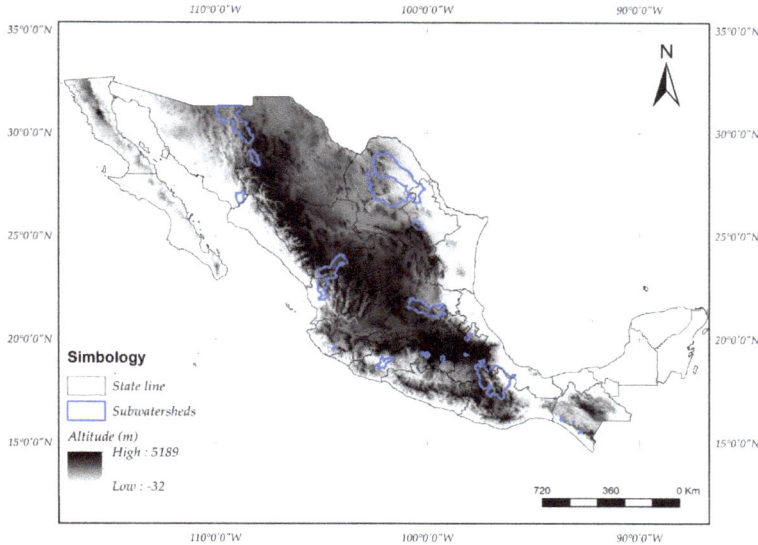

Figure 1. Locations for the 20 Mexican subwatersheds included in this study.

Daily precipitation and temperature data were obtained from the National Climate Grid [29]. The grid consisted of 3147 nodes distributed across the country and separated by 27 km from one another, which have registered daily information on precipitation and minimum and maximum temperature from 1950 to 2013. The information in the climate grid was processed in order to estimate potential evapotranspiration using the Hargreaves [30] method.

The data were transformed into an annual scale to enable interpolation through a cubic method. The Python 2.7[RM] (Python Software Foundation, Amsterdam, The Netherlands) programming language was utilized to obtain the annual average values for each subwatershed and each variable. The soil texture records were obtained from the Food and Agriculture Organization of the United Nations [31] Soil Database v 1.2.

2.2. Recession Curves' Selection

The traditional analytic method for obtaining the master curve required discrimination of *n* curves per year, which led to a slow and operator-biased extraction process (e.g., Figure 2a). This research proposed to select one annual recession curve per subwatershed, the one with the largest magnitude, which makes the consideration of climate variability among the selected subwatersheds possible (Figure 2b). Recession curves were selected, considering at least three years of hydrometric records. The selected annual curves fit the non-linear model put forward by [32]:

$$Qt = Qo \left[1 + \frac{(1-b)\,Qo^{1-b}}{ab} t \right]^{\frac{1}{b-1}} \qquad (1)$$

where *Qt* is the recession curve for a non-linear reservoir (mm· day^{-1}), *Qo* is the initial discharge, *t* is time measured in days and *a* (RP) and *b* are the model's parameters.

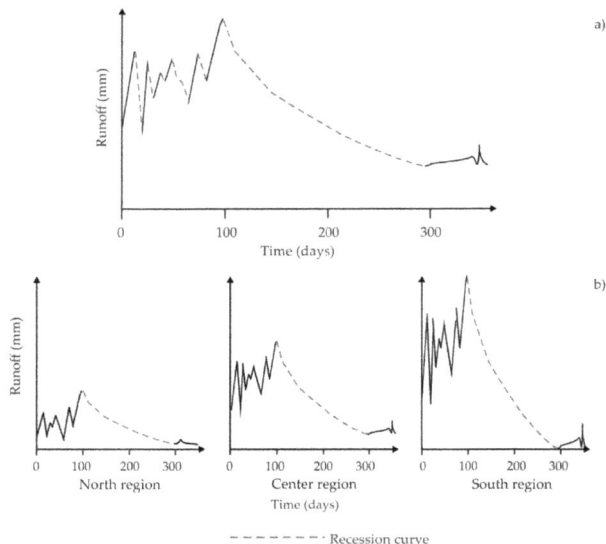

Figure 2. Recession curves' selection through the master curve method (dotted line through the year) (**a**); proposed annual recession curves selection (annual dotted line) (**b**).

The *b* exponent value ranges from 0 to 1, corresponding to studies by [32–34]. For regionalization purposes, this exponent can be fixed to average conditions *b* = 0.5, which is a standard value in unconfined aquifers [35,36].

A contribution of this work, as compared to the aforementioned non-linear models, is that the *a* (RP) value was fitted and associated with a physiographic characteristic inherent to its subwatershed, adding physical significance to the model.

The Hastie [37] criterion (Z) was applied to minimize errors in the objective function and to optimize *a*:

$$Z = ||y - \tilde{y}|| + a \sum wi \tag{2}$$

where $\tilde{y}$ is the fitted recession curve, *a* is the RP and *wi* is the prediction error.

2.3. Spatial Predictors of the Response of Baseflow and Symmetry in the Process

The area and average slope were analyzed for each subwatershed using topographical variables. The variables obtained from the soil database were percentages for sand, slit and clay. Finally, precipitation due to potential evapotranspiration (NP = $\frac{P}{E}$) was normalized. The processed spatial characteristics were related to RP.

$$RP = f\,[Climate,\; Soil,\; Topography]$$

The analysis involved the correlation of variables with RP. A threshold of ±0.40 (equivalent to $R^2 = 0.20$) was considered a potentially meaningful correlation [2]. Potential, exponential and linear functions were calculated for all predictors. The fitting criteria were based on the R^2 determination coefficient and the root-mean-square error (RMSE). To avoid multiple methods to evaluate data fit, these two criteria were chosen because they are the most widely used in various hydrological calibrations [2,3,15,21].

2.4. Baseflow Separation

The use of a recession curve approach as done by Wittenberg [33] required inverting Equation (1), and the baseflow was calculated by combining the recursive filters back and forward. This method assumes that the first and last values of the hydrometric time series represent the baseflow.

This kind of model only displays a statistical array harmonically representing the low frequencies of the surface flow, since it considers neither the intrinsic balances within a subwatershed (water and energy balance) nor the displacement or retention that flow may be affected by (e.g., soil, vegetation and basin shape).

The aim of this study was to find a logical relation between the recession parameter and variables inherent to subwatersheds in order to separate the baseflow. Salas *et al.* [38] found non-linear trends of the recession parameter over the baseflow. Therefore, we proposed to implement a non-linear function in order to estimate the baseflow (BF) in reference to previously-estimated parameters and associate the (α) model dispersion with hydrological characteristics available from the subwatersheds.

$$BF = f\left[\frac{P}{E}, \alpha\right] \tag{3}$$

The aquifers selected for this analysis were the only ones for which average transmissivity was reported. Table 1 shows hydrogeological values for each subwatershed and its corresponding aquifer.

Table 1. Subwatershed hydrogeological characteristics [39–45].

Hydrometric Station	Aquifer Identifier	Aquifer Type	Transmissivity ($m^2 \cdot s^{-1}$)	Rock Type
9080	0859 [39]	unconfined	0.0241	Riolite-tuff-acid, basalt, alluvial
11,012	1802 [40]	unconfined	0.0131	Riolite-tuff-acid, basalt, alluvial
12,601	1502 [41]	unconfined	0.0370	Alluvial, riolite
18,271	1701 [42]	unconfined	0.0180	Basalt, sandstone
23,022	0711 [43]	unconfined	0.0018	Basalt
24,038	0512 [44]	unconfined	0.1761	Limestone, sandstone
24,150	0507 [45]	unconfined	0.0902	Alluvial, limestone

3. Results

3.1. Recession Curves

The average recession curves for 21 Mexican subwatersheds were obtained. Table 2 presents calibration results for the curve model. In general, the observed data fit well to the proposed model ($R^2 > 0.88$). The largest magnitude curve was found to be located in the southwest part of the country (San Pedro, Chiapas, hydrometric station Number 30,067), whereas the lowest value was located in a subwatershed in the Mexican northwest (Río Salado-Anahuac, hydrometric station Number 24,038).

Table 2. Average recession constant fitting summary.

Hydrometric Station	Subwatershed Name	Longitude (°)	Latitude (°)	Number of Recessions	Surface (km^2)	Fitted Value	R^2
9010	R. Bavispe-Angostura	−109.36	30.61	3	14,188	6.4	0.92
9080	R. Papigochic	−108.30	29.13	4	1856	14.3	0.96
10,098	R. Alamos	−108.76	26.59	4	1813	12.7	0.91
11,012	R. San Pedro	−105.14	21.96	4	11,924	36.0	0.92
15,010	R. Purificación	−104.50	19.56	4	168	54.8	0.93
18,157	R, Atoyac	−98.23	19.23	6	258	125.3	0.95

Table 2. *Cont.*

Hydrometric Station	Subwatershed Name	Longitude (°)	Latitude (°)	Number of Recessions	Surface (km^2)	Fitted Value	R^2
18,169	R. Tilostoc	−100.11	19.17	4	154	212.6	0.93
18,271	R. Apatlaco	−99.22	18.84	6	364	15.3	0.88
18,466	R. Tilostoc-Anahuac	−100.25	19.27	3	124	100.0	0.91
18,489	R. Tilostoc-set	−100.12	19.22	3	317	113.4	0.95
23,011	R. Zanatenco	−93.74	16.08	6	166	43.0	0.96
23,022	R. Sesecapa	−92.87	15.46	3	125	90.9	0.90
24,038	R. Salado	−100.13	27.22	3	23,475	4.0	0.97
24,150	R. Salado de Nadadores	−100.94	27.42	6	21,520	25.0	0.94
24,198	R. Monterrey	−100.36	25.66	6	5412	91.0	0.94
26,268	R. Tampán	−99.21	21.65	4	8722	22.0	0.92
27,083	R. Necaxa	−97.87	20.25	5	562	140.3	0.98
28,135	R. Papaloapan	−95.84	18.30	3	20,263	87.5	0.92
30,067	R. San Pedro Mar	−93.09	16.06	5	42	235.0	0.92
12,574	R. Gavia	−99.87	19.42	5	37	3.5	0.93
12,601	R. Sila	−99.71	19.77	3	36	12.5	0.96

Note: R. = River.

Figure 3 shows the recession pattern spatial trend based on geographical location. It was demonstrated that the RP increases both ways, by decreasing longitude and increasing latitude. The RP values were rescaled to one.

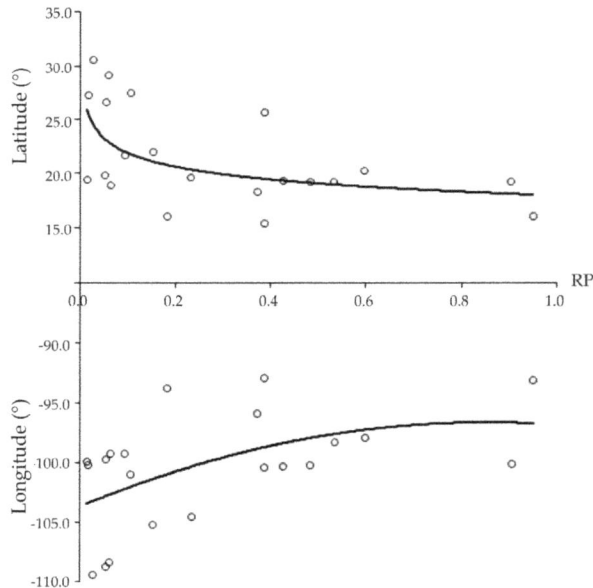

Figure 3. Relation between the recession parameter (RP) and corresponding longitude and latitude.

3.2. Baseflow Response Spatial Predictors

The dependence of the RP on climate and topographical variables is presented in Figure 4. The relation between the percentages of sand, slit and clay and RP was weak ($R^2 < 0.14$), indicating that the soil variables considered do not affect the fitted parameter. Area and slope were slightly predictive of the parameter ($R^2 > 0.30$); however, these variables were not statistically significant ($p > 0.05$). With regard to normalized precipitation (NP), a marked non-linear trend with RP was observed ($R^2 > 0.43$), and so, this climate variable was chosen as the principal parameter predictor. The remaining 57% of variance was not explained by this variable. Equation (5) represents this dispersion in the model.

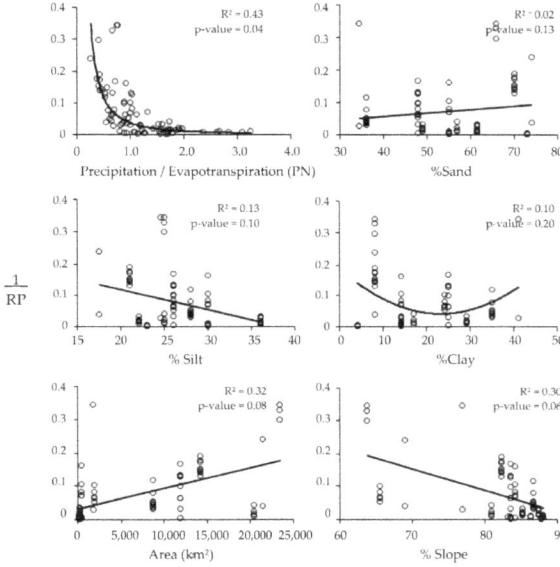

Figure 4. Relation between recession parameter and landscape and climate variables among subwatersheds.

Figure 5 presents the fitting of the proposed model (Equation (4)), and it shows the variability among subwatersheds (represented by their hydrometric station) and the annual variability of the RP and NP relation for 21 selected subwatersheds. Figure 5a shows the long-term average for RP and NP. Figure 5b presents the corresponding interannual relation. Both relations fit better to the following exponential model:

$$\frac{1}{a} = 1 - \left(1 - exp^{\left(\frac{P}{E}\right)^{-\alpha}}\right) \tag{4}$$

A closer fitting was found for the long-term relation ($R^2 = 0.51$, RMSE = 0.12) as compared to the interannual relation ($R^2 = 0.35$, RMSE = 0.71). The interannual variability showed a higher dispersion than the average long-term variation; even so, this trend and the α fitted parameter were similar in both cases (3.88 *vs.* 4.22). In this study, the model dispersion (Equation (4)) was associated with the predominant type of rock in each subwatershed and its transmissivity. Transmissivity data were available for only seven subwatersheds.

Figure 6a presents this relation; the storage-discharge relation for subwatersheds with limestone and sandstone surface structures was the most direct (higher RP and transmissivity values), such as the Río Salado and Río Salado de Nadadores subwatersheds (hydrometric station Numbers 24,038 and 24,150). On the other hand, subwatersheds where basalt and crystal rocks are predominant revealed low RP values (e.g., Río Sesecapa, station Number 23,022). At subwatersheds presenting a mixture of permeable and impermeable rock types, the recession curve values were intermediate (e.g., Río Apatlaco, station Number 18,271).

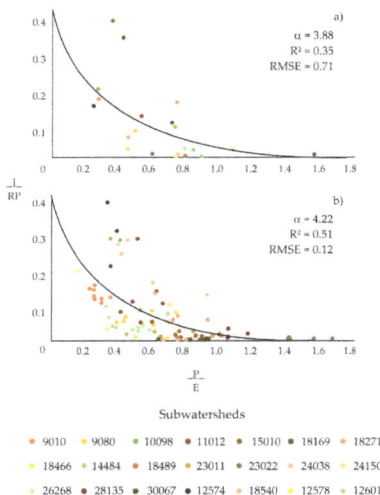

Figure 5. Subwatershed variability (identified through hydrometric stations) at (**a**) an interannual scale and (**b**) subwatershed average long-term variability.

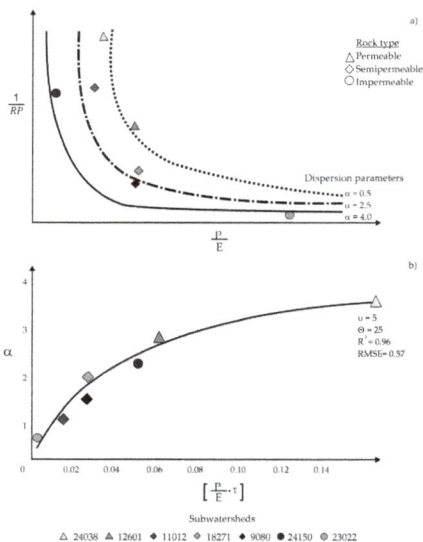

Figure 6. Subwatershed variability (identified through hydrometric station) and rock type. Relation between the dispersion parameter estimated in the model (**a**); Equation (4) and the product of $\frac{P}{E}$ and transmissivity (**b**).

Figure 6b shows the relation between the model's (Equation (4)) α parameter and the product of $\dfrac{P}{E}$ by the average transmissivity for each aquifer (τ). A potential model (Equation (5)) was proposed in order to fit this trend ($R^2 = 0.96$, RSME $= 0.57$). The model depends on two parameters: μ is the maximum reported transmissivity for Mexican aquifers (which could be fixed), and θ is the model's variation rate in relation to $\dfrac{P}{E}$.

$$\alpha = \mu \left[\left(\frac{\theta\left(\frac{P}{E} * \tau\right)}{1 + \left(\theta * \left(\frac{P}{E} * \tau\right)\right)}\right)\right] \tag{5}$$

3.3. Baseflow Separation

The daily rainfall and streamflow time series were compared to each other. Generally, a more or less one-day lag-time was observed between maximum precipitation events and runoff. We proposed an exponential model, Equation (9), contemplating the recession curve based on $\dfrac{P}{E}$ in order to separate the baseflow with the following frontier conditions:

$$P > Qd > BF \tag{6}$$

$$QF \rightarrow Qd, \ if: \ \frac{P}{E} \rightarrow 0 \tag{7}$$

$$Max\left(\frac{P}{E}\right)_{t-2} \rightarrow Max\,(Qd)_{t-1} \rightarrow Max\,(BF) \tag{8}$$

Precipitation (P) will always be larger than surface runoff (Qd), which in turn will be larger than baseflow (BF; Equation (6)). The exponential function (Equation (9)) of the model allows BF to come closer to direct flow when $\dfrac{P}{E}$ is zero (Equation (7)).

The maximum BF events continued after a day with the highest surface runoff and after two days of maximum precipitation (Equation (8)). The proposed generalized model depends on only one parameter estimated in Equation (5):

$$BF = Qdt_{t-1}\left[Exp\left(-1-\left(exp^{\left(-1-\left(\frac{P}{E}\right)_{t-2}^{-\alpha}\right)}\right)\right)\right]^{-1/\alpha} \tag{9}$$

The BF separation for two subwatersheds with different climate conditions can be observed in Figure 7. The baseflow index (IFB), a proportion of total flow and BF, ranged from 0.39 to 0.36 at the Zanatenco and El Tecolote subwatersheds (hydrometric Stations 23,011 and 15,010).

Our results were justified and based on accurate observations of each area. The Zanatenco subwatershed has a precipitation rate higher than 3000 mm per year, whereas the El Tecolote subwatershed presented an annual mean precipitation of 1000 mm. This is the reason why we observed a difference in runoff magnitude in Figure 7.

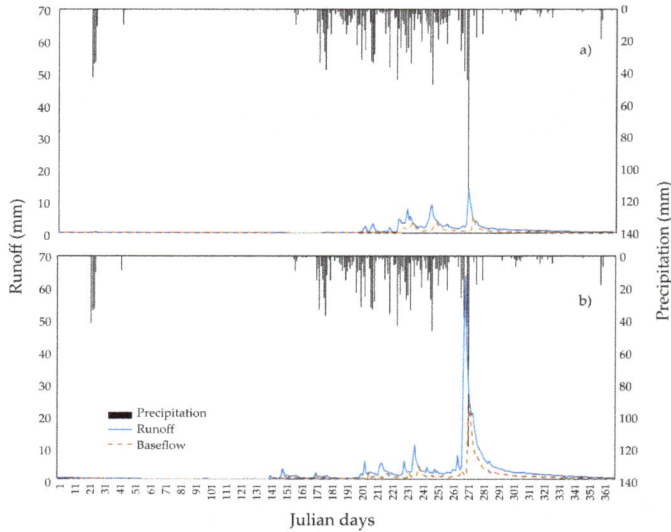

Figure 7. Separation of baseflow by the generalized baseflow model in the sub-basins: (**a**) El Tecolote, located in the state of Jalisco, Mexico; and (**b**) Zanatenco, located in the state of Chiapas, México.

4. Discussion

Estimating baseflow is a key challenge for hydrological research in Mexico, since there is a lack of large-scale information on subterranean waters dynamics. This study proposed a model based on precise analytical observations of different subwatersheds in the country to estimate baseflow with easily available information and a pragmatic approach.

The model proposed in this research is based on the observation of patterns of invariance and symmetry between sub-basins, rather than empirical adjustments. The response variable (rainfall-evapotranspiration) is hypothesized to be dependent on the availability of water and energy by exponential models, providing a physical explanation to the modeling, besides being feasible to implement, since these variables are readily available at the most basic climatological station.

4.1. Recession Curve

Generally, recession curve analysis is one of the most accurate methods for estimating BF [30]. Considering the top-down approach by Sivapalan [46] and Sivapalan´s proposal of a unified hydrological theory [14], this study proposes analyzing different hydrographs per year and subwatershed, which allowed us to obtain recession curves for different climate, topographic and edaphic conditions more efficiently than the master curve method.

Parametrization of recession curves usually implies the use of linear models, where the aquifer's storage is to be directly proportional to its retention parameter [47]. As occurred in Wittemberg and Gan and Luo [33,35], it was observed that recession curves in actual conditions have a concave shape and the estimated parameter steadily increases with decreasing runoff, a strong indication of the non-linearity of the process.

While Thomas *et al.* [48] compared the characteristics of the recession curve between linear and nonlinear models, the results were inconsistent in the linear model, and the authors recommended applying the nonlinear algorithm in sub-basins of New Jersey, USA. Stewart [49] showed that the direct flow and base flow in New Zealand watersheds have (non-linear) quadratic characteristics in their relations.

Equation (1) estimates recession curves based on a power law function and invariance properties for scale changes. On various watersheds around the world, authors, such as Wittenberg [32] and Wittenberg [50], as well as Wittenberg and Sivalapan [51], have tested that the *b* parameter is 0.5 on average. This condition allowed us to only estimate RP and keep *b* invariant, even with heterogeneous magnitudes of flow in different subwatersheds.

In simple terms, the RP parameter was related to the maximum flow of hydrometric records as observed by Salas *et al.* [38]. This revealed information about the humidity and drought of the subwatershed [52]. The maximum values of RP were found in high latitudes where arid climate prevails, as observed in Figure 3. Although, low RP values were found in humid climates south of Mexico.

Therefore, our result revealed that RP exhibits a trend associated with spatial location. RP increases when angular coordinates decrease. This trend was also found by Sivalapan *et al.* and Beck *et al.* [3,16], who found patterns in the spatial distribution of their fitted parameters allowing them to separate subwatersheds with similar conditions.

4.2. Baseflow Spatial Patterns and Model Parameterization

Different BF response spatial predictors were tested; the NP variable ($\frac{P}{E}$) showed the closest fitting. The importance of using NP lies in potential evapotranspiration (E) varying much less than precipitation (P). Given that the E depends on solar radiation, temperature and latitude, it is a function of energy, and therefore, no major variations are expected through the years. Thus, the E is converted as a scale natural factor for precipitation [53].

The climate index commonly used to predict the recession constant is the index of aridity. According to Wang and Wu [9], Peña *et al.* [54] and Longombardi and Villani [11], it was concluded that the baseflow patterns can be completely modeled with this index, because it considers water and energy limits on its implementation; this type of modeling is feasible by virtue of its physical representation of the phenomenon; and the allure of using a single parameter is that it can be applied in countries where there is not enough data to reproduce a spatially-explicit model [7].

Meanwhile, van Dick [2] and Lacey and Grayson [55] found that the humidity index (HI) was the most closely related variable to the baseflow constant; their studies reported a negative relationship between baseflow and HI. Beck *et al.* [3] found that E, mean temperature, forest coverage and mean subwatershed altitude had the strongest impact on BF. On the other hand, Fan *et al.* [56] stated that precipitation is the main recharge source for aquifers and that baseflow's response to precipitation depends on the season.

In contrast to Santhi *et al.* [10], this study did not find a significant impact of soil texture on RP on an annual basis (Figure 4). Other studies, such as He *et al.* [21] and Sanchez *et al.* [57], found no relationship between recession constant and soil characteristics, but found a relation with climatic variables. The results matched those of Haberland *et al.* [58], who found that the IFB was related to rainfall and topography, but they did not observe an influence of the properties of soil type or cover in the subwatershed.

Unlike the long-term analysis, higher variability and lower model fitting were found in the interannual analysis. Variability was dependent on the interacting dynamics of energy and water balances [8,53]. Furthermore, the low model fitting is due to temporary effects, such as temporary storage, as well as macroclimate conditions, which are reflected by means of the estimated model's parameter in Equation (5). The marked symmetry between RP and NP exhibits climate variability among basins and over years [6,16], suggesting that the observed trend will carry on in different regions and that applying the same model with the previously-calibrated parameters is feasible [15].

The hydrological balance trend depends on climate conditions, and its variability was attributed to landscape conditions [59]. This study associated the predominant rock type in each subwatershed with its transmissivity, which in turn was associated with the model's parameter (Equations (9)). Tague and Gran [60] assert that subwatershed geology is a primary control in the baseflow-generation process.

A more direct storage-discharge relation was found at subwatersheds whose soils were formed by permeable rocks.

According to Price [61], permeable or fractured rocks can store large amounts of water, as opposed to crystalline or very compact rocks. At subwatersheds where low-permeability rocks are predominant, RP values were lower. The results agree with Walton [62]; this author noted that the basins with greater groundwater discharge speed are those with low-permeability rocks. Meanwhile, Sanchez *et al.* [57] found that subwatersheds with basaltic rock presence tended to be drier and to have shorter recession times. These basins are also characterized by a low value of the index of aridity, which can accelerate the recession rate.

4.3. Baseflow Separation

The analyzed subwatersheds were selected by virtue of their minimum anthropogenic disturbances. Therefore, it is feasible to assume that the flow that feeds the outflow during a period of recession corresponds to the BF.

Our research showed that the recession parameter clearly exhibited spatial patterns across subwatersheds [63]. Subwatersheds within the same climatic conditions (similar values of $\frac{P}{E}$) exhibited different RP values, which according to Brooks *et al.* [64] depend on local landscape features, although in our work, it depended on the dominant lithology of each subwatershed. On account of its trend, the recession parameter is assumed to be an aquifer's recharge rate, which includes the intrinsic properties of each aquifer (hydraulic conductivity, porosity, transmissivity and surface) [35].

Analyzing the RP over time, Salas *et al.* [38] observed that the recession curve is the scale parameter modeling the separation of baseflow from direct flow by means of a non-linear function. This observation is similar to that presented by Paz *et al.* [22,65]. When analyzing potential functions, they concluded that if parameters match at one common point, it means that the parameters are correlated (fit a linear function). In this case, analytical modeling can be simplified to a single parameter, and setting one *a priori* value is avoided. This approach will be addressed in future research aimed at making comparable methods of setting *b* subjectively or estimating it analytically.

The daily time series of rainfall and streamflow were compared. Generally, a more or less one-day lag-time was observed between maximum precipitation events and runoff. According to Caro and Eagleson [66], the lag-time is due to an increased hydraulic charge within the aquifer accelerating the stored water exfiltration towards the main currents. The exponential model proposal complies with the principle of BF never being equal to direct flow, due to the ground storage-evapotranspiration interaction, even with no precipitation [67].

This research is based on a top-down approach, that is to say, with the information available and hydrological support, it is possible to infer a complex phenomenon, which is commonly analyzed under a reductionist approach [14]. One example of this is given by Gholami *et al.* [68], who analyzed subterranean water fluctuations using dendrochronology with satisfactory results. These examples challenged the paradigm of always using the same variables in hydrological studies and offered an alternative to apply these conditions in future research.

The proposed BF generalized model requires only precipitation and evapotranspiration variables to estimate baseflow; these variables are readily available across the country, making its operational implementation feasible. The model has one additional distinct advantage: the maximum Qb events correspond to the recession curve initial value. According to Aksoy and Wittemberg [34], the aforementioned feature involves an aquifer's recharge-storage-discharge interactions. The advantages of applying this type of model are the possibility of interpreting parameters by their association with observable physical features and operative parsimony [69].

The analysis presented in this paper separated the BF for 21 Mexican subwatersheds. Furthermore, a coherent digitalization for each acquisition area was obtained, *i.e.*, the measuring station was deemed the starting and ending point for determining each subwatershed surface, which contrasts with current basin cartographic products in the country.

The climate grid contains information under quality control standards, which allows for certainty regarding input data. Furthermore, the basin-to-basin analysis of annual recession curves showed the intrannual interaction within those basins due to climate variability.

Although information on vegetation and groundwater levels is not available operationally in the country, this study was directed towards the discovery of patterns in the obtainable data and the formulation of hypotheses concerning subwatershed interactions, aiming to avoid the redundancy of using observations to calibrate *a priori* constructed models [14].

5. Conclusions

The results of this study demonstrate that baseflow (BF) can be separated from direct flow by using a single-parameter non-linear model. The higher variability and low model fitting of our proposed model was related to subwatershed geology and climate variables. This allowed us to use variables that are easily available in the country. It was feasible to calibrate the non-linear model using only the longer duration recession curve, unlike the traditional approach using the master curve.

The recession curve maintains a symmetric trend over years and within measured subwatersheds located in protected natural areas with diverse landscapes and climate conditions in Mexico. The BF generalized model is a result of accurate observations from different geographic regions in the country, and so, it can be utilized for separating BF in non-measured basins. Our ensuing research considers analyzing the interaction of BF with available ground humidity for short time scales.

Despite the limited information, the generalized BF model may represent a baseline for the generation of alternative modeling approaches. Such an accomplishment should include functional elements that explore the baseflow behavior based on multiple spatial and temporal scales. In order to improve the calibration model, we recommend incorporating local variables (e.g., canopy, soil moisture, groundwater levels), and we also suggest including subwatersheds affected by anthropogenic activity, so as to analyze flow changes ascribable to climate oscillation or human influence.

Acknowledgments: The authors would like to thank the CONACyT for financing the doctoral studies. This work has been partially support by Colegio de Postgraduados, Secretaria de Agricultura, Ganaderia, Desarrollo Rural, Pesca y Alimentación (SAGARPA).

Author Contributions: The research presented was developed in collaboration of all of the authors. Salas-Aguilar and Paz had the original idea for the study. Macedo-Cruz, Palacios, Ortiz and Quevedo conducted the research methods. All authors discussed the structure and commented on the manuscript at all stages.

Conflicts of Interest: The authors declare no conflict of interest.

References

1. Campolo, M.; Soldati, A.; Andreussi, P. Forecasting river flow rate during low-flow periods using neural networks. *Water Resour. Res.* **1999**, *35*, 3547–3552. [CrossRef]
2. Van Dijk, A.I. Climate and terrain factors explaining streamflow response and recession in Australian catchments. *Hydrol. Earth Syst. Sci.* **2010**, *14*, 159–169. [CrossRef]
3. Beck, H.L.; van Dijt, A.; Miralles, D.G.; McVicar, T.R.; Schellekens, J. Global patterns in baseflow index and recession based on streamflow observations from 3394 catchments. *Water Resour. Res.* **2013**, *49*, 7843–7863. [CrossRef]
4. Budyko, M.I. *Climate and Life*; Academics: New York, NY, USA, 1974.
5. Fu, B.P. On the calculation of the evaporation from land surface. *Sci. Atmos.* **1981**, *1*, 23–31. (In Chinese)
6. Zhang, L.; Dawes, W.R.; Walker, G.R. Response of mean annual evapotranspiration to vegetation changes at catchment scale. *Water Resour. Res.* **2001**, *3*, 701–708. [CrossRef]
7. Gerrits, A.M.J.; Savenije, H.H.G.; Veling, E.J.M.; Pfister, L. Analytical derivation of the Budyko curve based on rainfall characteristics and a simple evaporation model. *Water Resour. Res.* **2009**, *45*. [CrossRef]
8. Troch, P.A.; Carrillo, G.; Sivapalan, M.; Wagener, T.; Sawlez, K. Climate-vegetation-soil interactions and long-term hydrologic partitioning: Signatures of catchment co-evolution. *Hydrol. Earth Syst. Sci.* **2013**, *17*, 2209–2217. [CrossRef]

9. Wang, L.; Wu, L. Similarity of climate control on baseflow and perennial stream density in the Budyko framework. *Hydrol. Earth Syst. Sci.* **2013**, *17*, 315–324. [CrossRef]

10. Santhi, C.; Allen, P.; Muttiah, M.R.S.; Arnold, J.G.; Tuppad, P. Regional estimation of base flow for the conterminous United States by hydrologic landscape regions. *J. Hydrol.* **2008**, *351*, 139–153. [CrossRef]

11. Longobardi, A.; Villani, P. Baseflow index regionalization analysis in a mediterranean area and data scarcity context: Role of the catchment permeability index. *J. Hydrol.* **2008**, *355*, 63–75. [CrossRef]

12. Wang, T.; Istanbulluoglu, E.; Lenters, J.; Scott, D. On the role of groundwater and soil texture in the regional water balance: An investigation of Nebraska Sand Hills. *Water Resour. Res.* **2009**, *45*. [CrossRef]

13. Istanbulluoglu, E.; Tiejun, W.; Wright, O.; Lenters, J.D. Interpretation of hydrologic trends from a water balance perspective: The role of groundwater storage in the Budyko's hypothesis. *Water Resour. Res.* **2012**, *48*. [CrossRef]

14. Sivapalan, M. Pattern, process and function: Elements of a unified theory of hydrology at the catchment scale. In *Encyclopedia of Hydrological Sciences*; Jhon Wiley Ltd.: West Sussex, UK, 2005; Chapter 13, pp. 193–219.

15. Ponce, V.M.; Shetty, A.V. A conceptual model of catchment water balance: Formulation and calibration. *J. Hydrol.* **1995**, *173*, 27–40. [CrossRef]

16. Sivapalan, M.; Yaeger, M.A.; Ciaran, H.J.; Xiangyu, X.; Troch, P.A. Functional model of wáter balance variablity at the catchment scale: 1. Evidence of hydrologic similiraty and space-time symmetry. *Water Resour. Res.* **2011**, *47*. [CrossRef]

17. Harman, C.J.; Troch, P.A.; Sivapalan, M. Functional model of water balance variability at the catchment scale: 2. Elasticity of fast and slow runoff components to precipitation change in the continental United States. *Water Resour. Res.* **2011**, *47*. [CrossRef]

18. Tallaksen, L. A review of baseflow recession analisys. *J. Hydrol.* **1995**, *165*, 349–370. [CrossRef]

19. Eckhardt, K. How to construct recursive digital filters for Baseflow separation. *Hydrol. Process.* **2005**, *19*, 507–515. [CrossRef]

20. Huyck, A.; Pauwels, V.; Vershoest, N. A baseflow separation algorithm based on the linearized boussinesq equation for complex hillslopes. *Water Resour. Res.* **2005**, *41*. [CrossRef]

21. He, S.; Li, S.; Xie, R.; Lu, J. Baseflow separation based on a metereology corrected nonlinear algorithm in typical rainy agricultural watershed. *J. Hydrol.* **2016**, *535*, 418–428. [CrossRef]

22. Paz, F.; Odi, M.; Cano, A.; Bolaños, M.; Zarco, A. Equivalencia ambiental en la productividad de la vegetación. *Agrociencia* **1999**, *43*, 635–648. (In Spanish).

23. Banco Nacional de Datos de Aguas Superficiales, 2011. Consulta de Datos Hidrométricos, de Presas y Sedimentos. Comisión Nacional del Agua: México. Available online: www.conagua.gob.mx/CONAGUA07/contenido/documentos/portada%20bandas.htm (accessed on 25 January 2015).

24. García, E. *Climas, 1:4000 000. IV.4.10 (A). Atlas Nacional de México Vol. II*; Instituto de Geografía, UNAM.: Ciudad de México, México, 1990. (In Spanish)

25. Instituto Nacional de Estadística, Geografía e Informática (INEGI). Red Hidrográfica Escala 1:50,000 Edición 2.0. Available online: http://www.inegi.org.mx/geo/contenidos/topografia/regiones_hidrograficas.aspx (accessed on 16 Junuary 2016).

26. Comisión Nacional para el Conocimiento y Uso de la Biodiversidad (CONABIO). Subcuencas Hidrológicas. Available online: http://www.conabio.gob.mx/informacion/metadata/gis/subcu1mgw.xml?_httpcache=yes&_xsl=/db/metadata/xsl/fgdc_html.xsl&_indent=no (accessed on 15 January 2015).

27. Programa Mexicano del Carbono (PMC). *Digitalización de Subcuencas Escala 1,50000*; Programa Mexicano del Carbono: Texcoco, Estado de México, México, 2014.

28. Secretaria de Recursos Hidráulicos (SRH). *Boletines Hidrológicos*; Gerencia de Aguas Superficiales: Ciudad de México, México, 1970.

29. Programa Mexicano del Carbono (PMC). *Malla Climática Nacional*; Programa Mexicano del Carbono (PMC): Texcoco, México, 2015. (In Spanish)

30. Hargreaves, G.H.; Samani, Z.A. Reference crop evapotranspiration from temperature. *Appl. Eng. Agric.* **1985**, *1*, 96–99. [CrossRef]

31. Food and Agriculture Organization of the United Nations (FAO). Harmonized Database of Soil. Available online: http://www.fao.org/soils-portal/levantamiento-de-suelos/mapas-historicos-de-suelos-y-bases-de-datos/base-de-datos-armonizada-de-los-suelos-del-mundo-v12/es/ (accessed on 10 January 2015).

32. Wittenberg, H. Nonlinear analysis of flow recession curves. *IAHS Publ.* **1994**, *221*, 61–67.

33. Wittenberg, H. Baseflow recession and recharge as nonlinear storage processes. *Hydrol. Process.* **1999**, *13*, 715–726.

34. Aksoy, H.; Wittenberg, H. Nonlinear baseflow recession analysis in watersheds with intermittent streamflow. *Hydrol. Sci. J.* **2011**, *56*, 226–237. [CrossRef]

35. Gan, R.; Luo, Y. Using the nonlinear aquifer storage-discharge relationship to simulate the baseflow of glacir—And snowmelt-dominated basins in northwest China. *Hydrol. Earth Syst. Sci.* **2013**, *17*, 3577–3586. [CrossRef]

36. Aksoy, H.; Wittenberg, H. Baseflow Recession Analysis for Flood-Prone Black Sea Watersheds in Turkey. *Clean Air Soil Water* **2015**, *42*, 1–10. [CrossRef]

37. Hastie, T.; Tibshirani, R.; Friedman, J. *The Elements of Statistical Learning: Prediction, Inference and Data Mining*, 2nd ed.; Springer Verlag: New York, NY, USA, 2009.

38. Salas, A.V.; Paz, F.; Macedo, C.; Ortiz, C.; Palacios, E. Modelación no lineal del flujo base en tres subcuencas de México. *Terra Latinoam.* **2015**, *33*, 285–297. (In Spanish)

39. Comisión Nacional del Agua (CONAGUA). *Determinación de la Disponibilidad de Agua Subterránea en el Acuífero 0859*; Subdirección General Técnica de Aguas Subterraneas: Madera, México, 2013.

40. Comisión Nacional del Agua (CONAGUA). *Actualización de la Disponibilidad de Agua Subterránea en el Acuífero 1802*; Subdirección General Técnica de Aguas Subterraneas: San Pedro Tuxpan, México, 2009.

41. Comisión Nacional del Agua (CONAGUA). *Actualización de la Disponibilidad de Agua Subterránea En el Acuífero 1502*; Subdirección General Técnica de Aguas Subterraneas: Ixtlahuaca-Atlacomulco, México, 2009.

42. Comisión Nacional del Agua (CONAGUA). *Determinación de la Disponibilidad de Agua en el Acuífero 1701*; Subdirección General Técnica de Aguas Subterraneas: Cuernavaca, México, 2013.

43. Comisión Nacional del Agua (CONAGUA). *Actualización de la Disponibilidad Media Anual de Agua Subterránea Acuífero 0711*; Subdirección General técnica de Aguas Subterraneas: Arriaga-Pijijiapan, México, 2009.

44. Comisión Nacional del Agua (CONAGUA). *Actualización de la Disponibilidad de Agua Subterránea en el Acuífero 0512*; Subdirección General Técnica de Aguas Subterraneas: Región Carbonífera, México, 2013.

45. Comisión Nacional del Agua (CONAGUA). *Actualización de la Disponibilidad de Agua Subterránea en el Acuífero 0507*; Subdirección General Técnica de Aguas Subterraneas: Monclova, México, 2013.

46. Sivapalan, M. Prediction of ungauged basin: A gran challenge for theoretical hydrology. *Hydrol. Process.* **2003**, *17*, 3163–3170. [CrossRef]

47. Pedersen, T.J.; Peters, J.C.; Helweg, O. Hydrographs by single linear reservoir model. *J. Hydraul. Div. ASCE* **1980**, *106*, 837–852.

48. Thomas, B.; Voegel, R.; Famiglietti, J. Objetive hydrograph Baseflow recession analysis. *J. Hydrol.* **2015**, *525*, 102–112. [CrossRef]

49. Stewart, M.K. Promising new Baseflow separation and recession analysis methods applied to streamflow at Glendhu Catchment, New Zealand. *Hydrol. Earth Syst. Sci.* **2015**, *19*, 2587–2603. [CrossRef]

50. Wittenberg, H. Effects of season and man-made changes on baseflow and flow recession: Case studies. *Hydrol. Process.* **2003**, *17*, 2113–2123. [CrossRef]

51. Wittenberg, H.; Sivapalan, M. Watershed groundwater balance estimation using streamflow recession analysis and baseflow separation. *J. Hydrol.* **2003**, *219*, 20–33. [CrossRef]

52. Dralle, D.; Karst, N.; Thompson, S. a, b careful: The challenge of scale invariance for comparative analyses in power law models of the streamflow recession. *Geophys. Res. Lett.* **2015**, *42*, 9285–9293. [CrossRef]

53. Carmona, A.M.; Sivalapan, M.; Yaeger, M.A.; Poveda, G. Regional patterns variability of catchment water balances across the continental U.S.: A Budyko framework. *Water Resour. Res.* **2014**, *50*. [CrossRef]

54. Peña-Arancibia, J.L.; van Dijk, A.I.J.M.; Mulligan, M.; Bruijnzeel, L.A. The role of climatic and terrain attributes in estimating baseflow recession in tropical catchments. *Hydrol. Earth Syst. Sci.* **2010**, *14*, 2193–2205. [CrossRef]

55. Lacey, G.; Grayson, R. Relating baseflow to catchment properties in south-eastern Australia. *J. Hydrol.* **1998**, *204*, 231–250. [CrossRef]

56. Fan, Y.; Chen, Y.; Li, W. Increasing precipitation and baseflow in Aksu River since 1950s. *Quat. Int.* **2014**, *336*, 26–34. [CrossRef]

57. Sanchez, R.; Brooks, E.; Elliot, W.; Gazel, E.; Boll, J. Baseflow recession analysis in the inland Pacific Northwest of the United States. *Hydrogeol. J.* **2015**, *23*, 287–303. [CrossRef]

58. Haberlandt, U.; Klocking, B.; Krysanova, V.; Becker, A. Regionalisation of the baseflow indexfrom dynamically simulated flow components—A case study in the Elbe River Basin. *J. Hydrol.* **2001**, *248*, 35–53. [CrossRef]

59. Yang, D.; Shao, W.; Yeh, P.; Yang, H.; Kanae, S.; Oki, T. Impact of vegetation coverage on regional water balance in the nonhumid regions of China. *Water Resour. Res.* **2009**, *45*, 1–13. [CrossRef]

60. Tague, C.; Grant, G.E. A geological framework for interpreting the low-flow regimes of Cascade streams, Willamette River Basin, Oregon. *Water Resour. Res.* **2004**, *40*, 150–178. [CrossRef]

61. Price, K. Effects of watershed topography, soils, land use and climate on baseflow hydrology in humid regions: A review. *Prog. Phys. Geogr.* **2011**, *4*, 465–492. [CrossRef]

62. Walton, W.C. *Ground Water Recharge and Runoff in Illinois*; Report of Investigation; Illinois State Water Survey; State Water Survey Division: Champaign, IL, USA, 1965; p. 55.

63. Voepel, H.; Rudell, B.; Shumer, R.; Troch, P.; Brooks, P.; Neal, A.; Durcik, M.; Sivapalan, M. Quantifying the role climate and landscape characteristics on hydrologic partitioning and vegetation response. *Water Resour. Res.* **2011**, *47*, 1–13. [CrossRef]

64. Brooks, P.D.; Troch, P.A.; Durcik, M.; Gallo, E.L.; Moravec, B.G.; Schlegel, M.E.; Carlson, M. Quantifying regional-scale ecosystem response to changes in precipitation: Not all rain is created equal. *Water Resour. Res.* **2011**, *47*. [CrossRef]

65. Paz, F.; Odi, M.; Cano, A.; Lopez, E.; Bolaños, M.; Zarco, A.; Palacios, E. Elementos para el desarrollo de una hidrologia operacional con sensors remotos: Mezcla suelo-vegetación. *Tecnol. Cienc. Agua* **2009**, *24*, 69–80.

66. Caro, R.; Eagleson, P.S. Estimating aquifer recharge due to rainfall. *J. Hydrol.* **1981**, *53*, 185–211. [CrossRef]

67. Bart, R.; Hope, A. Inter-seasonal variability in base flow recession rates: The role of aquifer antecedent storage in central California watersheds. *J. Hydrol.* **2014**, *519*, 205–213. [CrossRef]

68. Gholami, V.; Chau, K.; Fadaee, F.; Torkaman, J.; Ghaffari, A. Modeling of groundwater level fluctuations using dendrochronology in alluvial aquifers. *J. Hydrol.* **2015**, *529*, 1060–1069. [CrossRef]

69. Archontoulis, S.; Miguez, F. Nonlinear regression models and applications in agricultural research. *Agron. J.* **2015**, *105*, 1–13. [CrossRef]

water

MDPI

Article

A CN-Based Ensembled Hydrological Model for Enhanced Watershed Runoff Prediction

Muhammad Ajmal [1,2], Taj Ali Khan [1] and Tae-Woong Kim [3,*]

[1] Department of Agricultural Engineering, University of Engineering and Technology, Peshawar 25120, Pakistan; engr_ajmal@uetpeshawar.edu.pk or ajmal@hanyang.ac.kr (M.A.); taj_marwat@yahoo.com (T.A.K.)
[2] Department of Civil and Environmental Engineering, Hanyang University, Seoul 04763, Korea
[3] Department of Civil and Environmental Engineering, Hanyang University, Ansan 15588, Korea
*   Correspondence: twkim72@hanyang.ac.kr; Tel.: +82-31-400-5184

Academic Editor: Kwok-wing Chau
Received: 2 October 2015; Accepted: 11 January 2016; Published: 15 January 2016

Abstract: A major structural inconsistency of the traditional curve number (CN) model is its dependence on an unstable fixed initial abstraction, which normally results in sudden jumps in runoff estimation. Likewise, the lack of pre-storm soil moisture accounting (PSMA) procedure is another inherent limitation of the model. To circumvent those problems, we used a variable initial abstraction after ensembling the traditional CN model and a French four-parameter (GR4J) model to better quantify direct runoff from ungauged watersheds. To mimic the natural rainfall-runoff transformation at the watershed scale, our new parameterization designates intrinsic parameters and uses a simple structure. It exhibited more accurate and consistent results than earlier methods in evaluating data from 39 forest-dominated watersheds, both for small and large watersheds. In addition, based on different performance evaluation indicators, the runoff reproduction results show that the proposed model produced more consistent results for dry, normal, and wet watershed conditions than the other models used in this study.

Keywords: hydrological model; pre-storm soil moisture; runoff prediction; variable initial abstraction

---

1. Introduction

The one-parameter traditional curve number (CN) model (CN model) developed by the U.S. Soil Conservation Service (SCS) now known as Natural Resources Conservation Service (NRCS), has enjoyed a long history of application as a lumped hydrological model. Its simplicity, versatility, and the availability of the necessary data have made it popular worldwide, as reported in [1], and an essential component in various hydrologic models, including water balance and storm routing models. Obviously, the CN model is reputable in the realm of applied hydrology, and CN is a mature concept that will remain in the forefront of engineering design. Its different versions, despite the complicated forms that result from introducing new parameters, cannot apply directly in approximating real situations because of the problem of model closure. Therefore, the CN model has been one of the most appealing and popular models for watershed runoff estimation for more than six decades [2]. The unavailability of any other simple contender has allowed this model to enjoy a long application history [3]. The widespread application of the CN model has led to its inclusion in hydrological software for surface runoff computations, such as CREAMS, CELTHYM, EPIC, HELP, L-THIA, PRZM, SWAT, SWIM [4], AGNPS, EPA-SWMM, GLEAMS, HEC-HMS, NLEAP, WinTR20, and WinTR55 [5]. Furthermore, the absence of hydrologic gauging stations and the high cost of gauging station installations lead hydrologists to estimate the surface direct runoff for ungauged watersheds using various techniques, and the CN model plays the leading role in such a situation [6].

Nonetheless, the CN model is not without its shortcomings. Despite its wide applications, the CN model has some limitations and misapprehensions caused mainly by its basic empirical assumptions [5].

For example, it considers a three-step CN variation based on three antecedent moisture conditions (AMCs), dry, normal, and wet, which permit unreasonable sudden jumps in runoff estimation [7]. Using tabulated CNs also underestimates most of the storm surface direct runoff in steep slope watersheds [8]. Furthermore, application of the CN model for forested watersheds can result in an inaccurate estimate of runoff from a given storm rainfall [9–11]. Thus, despite the long history, the CN model requires further study to develop and introduce a more robust model to better estimate runoff. Among other researchers, [1] and [11] modified the CN model to improve its runoff prediction capability. The modification proposed by [1] introduced storm-to-storm variation by incorporating a new parameter (M_c) to account for soil moisture before rainfall occurrence. However, this parameter sometimes results in negative values, which limits its applications [1]. The simplified one-parameter modified model suggested by [11] claimed improved runoff prediction. Nevertheless, that model has been criticized for not preventing the sudden jumps in runoff estimation [4,5,12]. To avoid sudden jumps in runoff estimation, simulated soil moisture (SM) has been employed using the soil water balance equation [13]. Further the parameter S (maximum potential retention) of the CN model has been determined by means of an experimentally derived relationship between S and SM as $S = a(1-\theta_e)$, where θ_e is the simulated relative SM at the beginning of the rainfall storm event and a is a parameter to be optimized. However, due to limited data in ungauged watersheds, neither θ_e nor a can be estimated and hence this reduces the application of the CN model only for gauged watersheds. Recognizing the limitations of the traditional CN model and its modified versions, we set out to develop a new ensembled lumped model that accounts for a continuous initial abstraction and prevents sudden jumps in runoff estimation. In addition, by using a small number of required parameters, we intended for our new conceptualization to be less sensitive to CN variation and structurally more consistent than the traditional CN model and its modified versions.

2. Materials and Methods

2.1. Study Area and Data

To analyze the runoff reproduction, we selected 39 South Korean forest-dominated mountainous watersheds. The selected watersheds represent the overall hydro-meteorological setting of South Korea and their corresponding characteristics are described in [14]. The selected watersheds vary in size from 42.32 to 888.01 km² and are characterized by low to high elevations (26 to 911 m above mean sea level) with average slopes from 7.50% to 53.53%. In Table 1, we differentiated the watersheds as small (Area ⩽ 250 km²) and large (Area > 250 km²) following [9]. The land cover is mainly forests, followed by agricultural and urbanized land as illustrated in Table 1. Loam and sandy loam are the two major soil textures with some fractions of silt loam.

We collected 30 min time-step rainfall data from the Korea Meteorological Administration (KMA) whereas observed discharge data at the same time step came from the Hydrological Survey Center (HSC) of Korea. We used land cover information from the Ministry of Land, Infrastructure, and Transport (MOLIT). The collected measurements constitute 1804 rainfall-runoff events from 39 watersheds between 2005 and 2012. Figure 1 gives the locations of the large watersheds in the study area; the small watersheds can be seen in [14].

To separate baseflow and direct runoff from discharge, we used the straight-line hydrograph method [15]. We first screened the measured data to exclude small storm rainfall events ($P < 25.4$ mm) to prevent bias in estimating runoff using the traditional CN model [16]. We applied the P_5 (the accumulated prior five days rainfall) criterion to determine the watershed antecedent condition to adjust the CN and its corresponding S values from normal to dry and wet conditions [12]. We took the composite CN by applying the procedure documented in the NRCS [17] based on the watersheds' land cover characteristics, which we considered to be the same for all models. According to [18], hydrological models are more reliable when they reproduce satisfactory measurements, especially from watersheds with limited data. To make the models applicability more realistic in ungauged watersheds, we did not calibrate any of the parameters used in this study. Some statistics regarding the measured and predicted data are shown in Table 2.

Table 1. Watersheds and data description.

WS ID	Watershed Name	Major Land Cover Distribution (km²)				Area (km²)	NOE	ME (m)	α (%)	CN
		Forests	Agriculture	Urbanized	Grass					
Small watersheds, Area ⩽ 250 km²										
WS01	Cheonwang	97.05	57.51	30.82	3.86	42.32	29	26	13.40	66
WS02	Daeri	47.31	1.67	0.39	0.25	60.45	39	424	48.13	75
WS03	Janggi	36.76	23.80	2.44	1.11	62.80	42	146	21.50	70
WS04	Dopyeong	106.03	27.75	15.42	3.70	138.36	34	173	28.71	64
WS05	Chunyang	105.06	23.66	2.69	5.20	143.10	40	197	34.30	60
WS06	Cheongju	14.95	14.48	17.23	0.50	161.44	70	202	20.10	69
WS07	Boksu	119.09	30.83	5.02	1.30	161.90	26	343	35.50	60
WS08	Donghyang	111.34	44.76	4.51	2.67	164.66	68	911	35.09	64
WS09	Maeil	152.06	20.79	0.48	0.13	174.86	60	517	39.65	53
WS10	Yulgeuk	42.41	110.95	15.47	3.72	179.95	38	113	7.50	71
WS11	Toigyewon	137.55	37.86	14.06	6.05	200.45	44	285	26.70	64
WS12	Jungrang	94.17	15.54	83.26	2.01	208.41	42	219	17.30	67
WS13	Soochon	79.46	108.11	18.42	2.09	223.19	31	76	15.40	73
WS14	Guryong	163.71	65.18	7.08	3.95	245.50	33	244	26.60	65
WS15	Yoosung	167.64	48.15	17.64	7.29	249.63	65	349	27.30	71
Large watersheds, Area > 250 km²										
WS01	Kyeongan	153.70	44.73	37.15	11.50	256.91	89	165	22.86	63
WS02	Jeonju	169.78	59.36	39.36	5.03	278.00	72	168	28.33	70
WS03	Cheoncheon	183.91	72.31	8.18	16.85	284.03	89	554	32.23	58
WS04	Gwanchon	217.56	62.11	7.90	7.65	301.26	49	420	33.70	70
WS05	Gapyeong	274.05	18.52	5.28	2.21	305.12	39	490	45.40	69
WS06	Heukcheon	232.82	57.19	13.04	3.75	307.82	19	253	32.70	59
WS07	Heungcheon	124.45	135.52	31.07	7.32	309.08	28	112	13.80	67
WS08	Bookcheon	377.04	123.35	36.04	15.97	330.20	38	733	53.53	52
WS09	Changchon	280.95	35.50	5.64	2.45	335.07	83	523	41.82	68
WS10	Ohsoo	210.60	118.95	11.00	3.92	350.09	61	243	24.60	62
WS11	Wangsungdong	374.02	20.97	1.33	2.12	378.67	24	866	47.80	61
WS12	Sanganmi	350.57	40.55	4.31	2.62	402.45	26	778	39.40	61
WS13	Shinan	301.16	87.52	9.36	3.32	411.96	56	244	31.25	71
WS14	Janghowon	181.36	182.02	23.52	10.92	431.23	26	678	16.80	65
WS15	Youngjung	288.93	101.36	30.87	12.28	445.36	29	268	27.00	61
WS16	Sangyegyo	331.21	134.62	13.42	3.29	496.30	35	268	29.40	71
WS17	Cheongmi	215.69	219.85	29.82	14.12	514.66	30	147	16.70	78
WS18	Hwachon	443.38	50.85	6.45	0.91	523.20	59	499	41.40	57
WS19	Banglim	448.67	56.84	5.81	3.30	527.12	30	763	40.20	63
WS20	Joocheon	449.10	68.49	5.74	1.90	533.23	65	608	38.12	58
WS21	Hoideok	362.89	105.74	94.04	23.68	609.15	41	170	25.70	70
WS22	Songcheon	455.78	131.15	11.86	4.54	612.17	54	386	33.25	64
WS23	Pyeongchang	609.60	79.87	8.92	4.47	697.67	64	734	40.30	64
WS24	Panwoon	757.06	99.67	11.18	6.29	888.01	37	678	40.88	60

WS ID, NOE, ME, and α are the watershed identification, number of events, mean elevation, and mean slope, respectively.

Table 2. Statistics of model outputs from the combined data set from 39 watersheds.

Data Type	Parameter/ Model	Statistics							
		Min	Mean	Median	Max	SD	Skewness	25th Percentile	75th Percentile
	P (mm)	25.12	78.94	58.32	519.68	60.89	2.32	40.03	94.02
Observed data	P_5 (mm)	0.00	58.18	34.80	629.80	75.12	2.63	6.95	79.00
	T (h)	1.50	19.62	16.00	154.00	13.96	2.71	11.00	24.00
	Q_o (mm)	0.17	37.26	19.36	364.38	46.81	2.46	8.10	46.96
Modeled data (Q_c(mm))	CNM	0.00	24.36	6.22	415.63	44.50	3.50	1.49	24.48
	MCM	0.56	44.56	26.08	487.31	55.02	2.63	7.71	56.38
	MRM	0.00	30.84	11.42	432.04	48.60	3.01	1.17	37.64
	AJM	1.62	34.69	20.05	375.63	41.52	2.97	9.95	40.47

Other parameters are defined in the text, T is the storm duration.

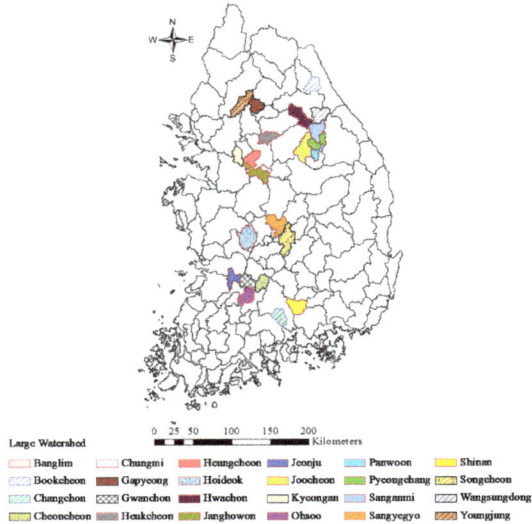

Figure 1. Location of large watersheds (Area > 250 km^2) in the study area. Small watersheds (Area ⩽ 250 km^2) can be seen in [14].

2.2. Development of a New Hydrological Model

2.2.1. The Traditional CN Model (CNM)

For a given P and its corresponding initial abstraction, I_a, the traditional CN model in general is expressed as:

$$Q = \frac{(P - I_a)^2}{P - I_a + S} = \frac{(P - \lambda S)^2}{P - \lambda S + S} \tag{1}$$

where Q, P, I_a, λ and S are surface direct runoff (mm), total rainfall (mm), initial abstraction (mm), initial abstraction coefficient (dimensionless), and potential maximum retention (mm), respectively. The standard $I_a = 0.20S$ [19] and its one modified version for comparable improved runoff prediction is $I_a = 0.05S$ [20]. Different researchers have found structural inconsistencies in the traditional CN model, such as sudden jumps in S with corresponding runoff values for dry, normal, and wet conditions [11,12]. Similarly the standard $I_a = 0.20S$ has been found to be unreasonably high; and researcher across the globe suggested $I_a < 0.2S$ (e.g., [1,14,20–23]). For the CNM, we estimated the weighted composite CN for watershed characteristics and calculated the transformed S using the following Equation:

$$S = 25.4 \left(\frac{1000}{CN} - 10 \right) \tag{2}$$

2.2.2. Mishra *et al.* Model (MRM)

To prevent unreasonable sudden jumps in runoff estimation, the relationship for I_a was modified by incorporating a new parameter (M_c) to account for soil moisture content before the rainfall occurrence [1]. The modified I_a is expressed as:

$$I_a = \frac{\lambda S^2}{S + M_c} \tag{3}$$

The new parameter (M_c) can be found from the prior five days accumulated rainfall (P_5), λ and S as $M_C = -0.5\left[(1+\lambda)S - \sqrt{(1-\lambda)^2 S^2 + 4P_5 S}\right]$ or with a more simplified version $M_C = \beta\sqrt{P_5 S}$ where $\beta = 0.72$ is the optimized coefficient. Despite some improvements in runoff prediction, the application of M_c in [1] sometimes causes negative Q values, which is the major drawback of that formulation. Therefore, the model should be revisited to eliminate this complication when estimating runoff. For runoff estimation, the MRM can be expressed as:

$$Q = \frac{(P - I_a)(P - I_a + M_c)}{P - I_a + M_c + S} \tag{4}$$

In Equation (4), $M_C = 0.72\sqrt{P_5 S}$ which is one of the best versions presented in [1] and I_a is calculated using Equation (3) ($\lambda = 0.2$).

2.2.3. Michel *et al.* Model (MCM)

For $\lambda = 0.2$, the simplified forms of the MCM for dry (AMC-I), normal (AMC-II), and wet conditions (AMC-III), respectively, are as follows:

$$Q = \frac{P^2}{P + S} \tag{5}$$

$$Q = P\left(\frac{0.48S + 0.72P}{S + 0.72P}\right) \tag{6}$$

$$Q = P\left(\frac{0.79S + 0.46P}{S + 0.46P}\right) \tag{7}$$

Similarly, a simplification of the model parameters reported in [11] also considers a three-step S parameter and cannot eradicate the problem of sudden jumps in runoff prediction.

2.2.4. The Proposed Model (AJM)

To circumvent the sudden jumps and other inconsistencies, we here derived a new model ensembling the traditional CN and GR4J models [23] with the pre-storm moisture content concept [11] and further introduced a continuous S formulation. The GR4J (which stands for modèle du génie rural à 4 paramé tres journalier) is a French daily lumped four-parameter rainfall-runoff model that belongs to the family of soil moisture accounting models. It determines four parameters for daily runoff prediction: maximum storage capacity, groundwater exchange coefficient, one day prior maximum routing storage capacity, and time base of unit hydrograph. More details on the GR4J model are available in [23].

We replaced the M_c in Equation (3) with V_o adopted from [11], to make the following relationship:

$$I_a = \frac{\lambda S^2}{S + V_o} \tag{8}$$

where V_o is the soil moisture content before a storm event. Different values of V_o are found for different AMCs [11] which are differentiated based on P_5 [14]. Using the available CN adjustment formulae from normal (AMC-II) to dry (AMC-I) and wet (AMC-III) conditions, the expression for V_o becomes [4]:

$$V_o = \gamma S \quad \text{for AMC-II} \tag{9}$$

$$V_o = \gamma\left[\frac{S}{2.3}\right] = 0.435\gamma S \quad \text{for AMC-I} \tag{10}$$

$$V_o = \gamma \left[\frac{S + 289.56}{0.43} \right] \quad \text{for AMC-III} \tag{11}$$

where γ is the fraction to link V_o and S that can be optimized from measured data. After testing the measured rainfall-runoff data from 140 French watersheds with different surface and variable moisture conditions, V_o as some fraction of S was simplified for dry, normal and wet conditions as; $V_o = 0.33S$, $V_o = 0.61S$, $V_o = 0.87S$, respectively. Taking $\lambda = 0.20$, as generally assumed for practical applications in the traditional CN model, and substituting V_o from Equations (12)–(14), respectively into Equation (8) gives:

$$I_a = \frac{0.2S^2}{S + 0.33S} = 0.150S \quad \text{for AMC-I} \tag{12}$$

$$I_a = \frac{0.2S^2}{S + 0.61S} = 0.124S \quad \text{for AMC-II} \tag{13}$$

$$I_a = \frac{0.2S^2}{S + 0.87S} = 0.107S \quad \text{for AMC-III} \tag{14}$$

To incorporate the new initial abstraction formulation, we conceptualized a new model by combining the CN model, the PSMA procedure [11], and the event-based empirical GR4J model. To do this, we initialized V_o as the soil moisture store level at the onset of an event and V as the moisture level corresponding to the total rainfall P [11].

$$V = V_o + P - Q \tag{15}$$

Substituting Q from Equation (1) into Equation (15) yields

$$V = V_o + P - \frac{(P - I_a)^2}{P - I_a + S} = V_o + \frac{(S + I_a) P - I_a^2}{(P - I_a + S)} \tag{16}$$

Now the simplified form of the GR4J runoff model described in [11] can be expressed in its cumulative form as:

$$Q = (P - PE) \times \left(\frac{V}{S + S_a} \right)^2 \quad P > PE \tag{17}$$

Here PE is the daily potential evapotranspiration and is assumed negligible because the runoff from rainfall usually lasts for an event of sufficiently limited duration [24]. Hence, the above equation becomes:

$$Q = P \times \left(\frac{V}{S + S_a} \right)^2 \tag{18}$$

Equation (18) yields $Q = P$ for $V = S + S_a$ as a maximum capacity of V, where S_a is an intrinsic parameter equal to; $S_a = V_o + I_a$ [11]. Substituting the expression for V from Equation (16) into Equation (18) and simplifying yields

$$Q = P \times \left[\frac{V_o (P - I_a + S) + (S + I_a) P - I_a^2}{(P - I_a + S)(S + V_o + I_a)} \right]^2 \tag{19}$$

Now, substituting $I_a = 0.15S$ from Equation (12) and $V_o = 0.33S$ (assuming the watershed dry condition), after simplification Equation (19) becomes:

$$Q = P \times \left[\frac{1.48PS + 0.258S^2}{1.48PS + 1.258S^2} \right]^2 \quad \text{or} \quad Q = P \times \left[\frac{P + 0.174324S}{P + 0.85S} \right]^2 \tag{20}$$

It is interesting that Equation (20) is a simple, one-parameter model like the traditional CN model. Using the traditional CN model, as in Equation (1), after substituting I_a from Equation (13) could improve runoff prediction if S is taken as the transformed value from the dimensionless CN assessed as a function of land use/cover, soil types, and AMCs (differentiated from P_5). However, many researchers of various Mediterranean watersheds reported limitations and drawbacks to that approach, and it inconsistently displays pre-storm soil moisture temporal variations (e.g., [19,25–27]). Some researchers (e.g., [26,28]) have specifically mentioned that the cumulative rainfall in the previous five days is not a good proxy of the wetness conditions of the catchment before a flood event. Similarly, the use of a fixed I_a in the traditional CN model causes unusual sudden jumps in runoff estimation [1,4,11,12]. To circumvent this issue, we present a continuous spatio-temporal expression for the initial abstraction by replacing the S value in the proposed model with a new expression; $S \times \left(\dfrac{P}{P + P_5}\right)$. Assuming a watershed in dry condition, Equation (12) for the new I_a becomes

$$I_a = 0.15S \left(\frac{P}{P + P_5}\right) \tag{21}$$

Substituting Equation (21) into Equation (19), and retaining $V_o = 0.33S$ for dry watershed condition and simplifying gives:

$$Q = P \times \left(\frac{P_5 + P + 0.17432\mathrm{4}S}{P_5 + P + 0.85S}\right)^2 \quad \text{for} \quad P > 0.15S \left(\frac{P}{P + P_5}\right) \tag{22}$$

For $P_5 \to \infty$ then $Q \to P$ which means the watershed is fully saturated by pre-storm soil moisture content and it has no more capacity to retain water. Hence all rainfall will be converted to runoff. In the case of $S \to 0$, then $Q = P$, whereas, if $S \to P$ and $P_5 = 0$ (dry condition), then $Q = 0.40P$. Using this new model (Equation (22)) does not require any adjustment for S values from normal to dry or wet conditions, because the P_5 variation accounts for the I_a adjustment associated to different pre-storm soil moisture responses in a watershed.

From this point, we investigated four models in this study: the traditional CN model (CNM), the model proposed in [11] as Michel model (MCM) and in [1] Mishra model (MRM), and our proposed model (AJM). Details of the different models are given in Table 3.

Table 3. Models and their corresponding parameters identification.

Model ID	λ	CN	Model Expression	Remarks
CNM	0.20	NEH-4 Tables	Equations (1) and (2)	Original CN model in [17]
MCM	-do-	-do-	Equations (2), (5), (6) and (7)	Modification in [11]
MRM	-do-	-do-	Equations (2)–(4)	Modification in [1]
AJM	-do-	-do-	Equations (2) and (22)	Proposed Model

-do- means as above.

3. Models' Goodness-of-Fit Evaluation

A vital step in evaluating and inferring model results is creating graphs to display them and determining goodness-of-fit indicator values to quantify model performance in terms of prediction accuracy [29]. No formal standards evaluate goodness-of-fit to data visually or numerically through quantitative assessment. This leads to considerable variability in the techniques used, which are frequently decided based on applications in previous similar studies. According to [30], model evaluation (validation) and sometimes performance are judged by comparing calculated values with measured benchmark data. Commonly, evaluations of model performance are based on several statistics and techniques. To assess models' prediction accuracy quantitatively, the most commonly used methods are the root mean squares error (RMSE) [15,31–33], Nash-Sutcliffe efficiency (NSE) [32–34], and Percent Relative Error (PRE) [35] expressed as:

$$RMSE = \left[\frac{1}{N} \sum_{i=1}^{N} (Q_o - Q_c)_i^2 \right]^{0.5} \tag{23}$$

$$NSE = \left[1 - \left(\frac{RMSE}{SD} \right)^2 \right] \tag{24}$$

$$PRE = \left[\frac{\sum_{i=1}^{N} (Q_o - Q_c)_i}{\sum_{i=1}^{N} (Q_o)_i} \right] \times 100 \tag{25}$$

where Q_{oi} and Q_{ci} are the observed and estimated runoff values for storm events i to N and SD is the standard deviation of observed data. Smaller RMSE values (optimum = 0.0) depict better model runoff estimation. Here, $\overline{Q}_o$ represents the mean of observed runoff values for storm events i to N. A model is deemed satisfactory if its NSE > 0.50 [35]. Another recent study considered a hydrologic model satisfactory if NSE > 0.65 [36].

We further tested the appropriateness of each model based on the best-fit distribution and its corresponding statistic for the cumulative observed and modeled runoff from the 39 watersheds. To do so, we analyzed the observed and modeled data using three different tests: Kolmogorov-Smirnov test, Anderson Darling test, and chi-squared test [37]. We used those tests to identify that the data belong to a specific distribution. We identified the best-to-worst fit distribution for those three tests from rank 1 to rank 18 after analyzing for 18 different distribution fittings. The model depicting the same distribution fit as exhibited by the measured runoff would be the best alternative for runoff prediction in the study area. Significant agreement between the measured and modeled runoff can be further validated in comparing models based on closeness of statistical values from any of the aforementioned three tests.

Beside the above evaluation indicators, to examine the model performance, the time series data for measured and modeled runoff were compared for two example watersheds selected from the study area. In addition, percent errors on peak discharge (E_{Qp}) [13] were also calculated to identify the physical behaviors of the models in estimating runoff.

$$E_{Qp} = \left[\frac{\max(Q_o) - \max(Q_c)}{\max(Q_o)} \right] \times 100 \tag{26}$$

where max (Q_o) and max (Q_c) are the maximum peak discharge values for the observed and modeled runoff.

4. Results and Discussion

To select an appropriate physical relationship between P_5 and I_a we assessed the watersheds' runoff-producing response for the common discrete (fixed) $I_a = 0.2S$ and the proposed variable (continuous) formulation. This assessment was accomplished once the pre-storm soil moisture was adjusted in I_a based on the recommendation from [11] and was subsequently adopted by other researchers in their studies (e.g., [4,5,12]). In our analysis, we kept the CN as a major parameter obtained from watershed characteristics under normal conditions fixed for all models. The measured rainfall-runoff events we used in the model assessments were characterized by a complex pattern to represent a diverse response. Considering P and CN as the fundamental and common parameters and other physiographic characteristics as shown in Table 1, all the models compared in this study both structurally differ from each other and lie within the parameter space of the traditional CN model.

Figure 2 illustrates the variation of fixed and variable I_a used in the CNM and AJM respectively. For the CNM, the evident high I_a and sudden jumps in S were the two major reasons for underestimating runoff from steep slope watersheds like in South Korea. As illustrated [9], the traditional CN model should be employed cautiously in watersheds larger than 250 km². Keeping in mind this criteria, the model's analysis was carried out for small (Area $\leqslant$ 250 km²) and large (Area > 250 km²) watersheds as well as based on pre-storm watershed hydrological conditions (dry, normal and wet). As shown in Figure 3a, for small watersheds, the MCM showed no evident improvement in terms of mean (median) RMSE (mm) values of 22.66 (23.25) compared to the CNM values of 22.07 (20.15). However, the spread of RMSE values in those watersheds between the 25th and 75th percentiles depicted improvement followed by the MRM with mean (median) RMSE of 20.79 (18.78). Contrarily, the AJM indicated more accurate mean (median) RMSE of 13.13 (12.34). The improved results by the AJM indicate the reliability of the proposed variable I_a in estimating runoff from mountainous watersheds compared to the CNM and the models presented in [1] and [11].

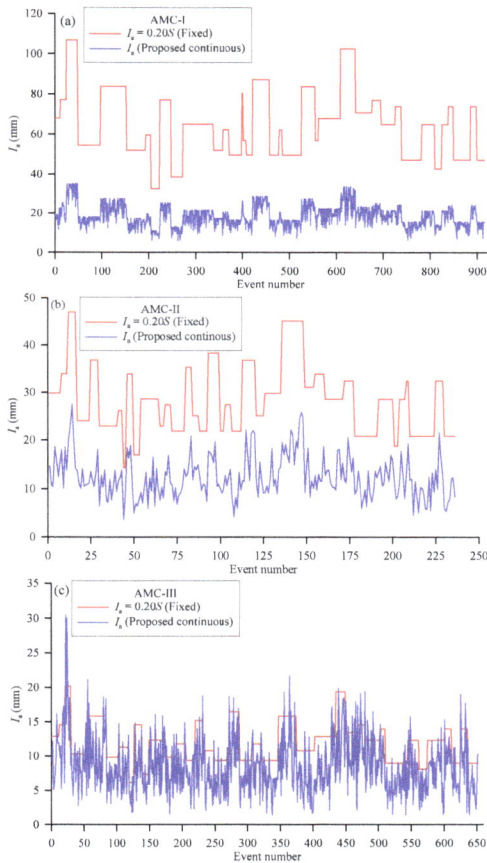

Figure 2. Variation of fixed and variable initial abstraction (I_a) for rainfall events in (**a**) dry condition; (**b**) normal condition; and (**c**) wet condition.

To assess the model's efficacy in large watersheds, as shown in Figure 3b, it is similar to that for small watersheds, as depicted in Figure 3a. The mean (median) RMSE for the CNM, MCM, MRM, and AJM were 27.94 (24.85), 27.00 (25.86), 25.50 (23.48) and 17.40 (16.16), respectively. The MCM showed almost no improvement over the CNM and the MRM exhibited modest improvement, whereas the

AJM indicated significantly lower RMSE values in all watersheds. The cumulative RMSE values for all types of events, shown in Figure 3c, support that the AJM has more reliable results than the other contenders. The consistently lower RMSE values evidenced by the AJM for all kinds of events (combined dry, normal, and wet conditions from 39 watersheds) indicate its superiority.

Analyzing the runoff prediction efficacy illustrated by different models using NSE as the performance indicator demonstrated modest improvement by the MCM followed by the MRM, as shown in Figure 4a. The mean NSE (0.57) for the MCM showed almost no improvement compared to the CNM mean NSE (0.57), but the spread of the NSE from this figure indicates good model performance by the MCM. Moreover, the MRM mean NSE (0.63) indicated some increases in the model's overall efficacy compared to the CNM and MCM. Nevertheless, the AJM had the highest NSE values (mean 0.85) indicating its reliability for accurate runoff estimation in small watersheds. Figure 4b evidences a similar pattern of performance for large watersheds. Here, the mean NSE for the CNM, MCM, MRM, and AJM were 0.64, 0.65, 0.71, and 0.86, respectively. The higher NSE values in both small and large watersheds confirmed the AJM enhanced runoff prediction. According to the NSE criteria in [35], the CNM, MCM, MRM, and AJM had respectively, good to very good results 46.67%, 33.33%, 60.00%, and 100% of small watersheds. Similarly, the models respectively fulfilled the same performance rating in 41.67%, 54.17%, 58.33%, and 100% of large watersheds. Considering the performance rating criteria in [36], the good to very good performance by the CNM, MCM, MRM, and AJM respectively, was in 26.67%, 6.67%, 26.67%, and 66.67% of small watersheds. Likewise, those ratings respectively were met in 25.00%, 16.67%, 37.50%, and 87.50% of large watersheds.

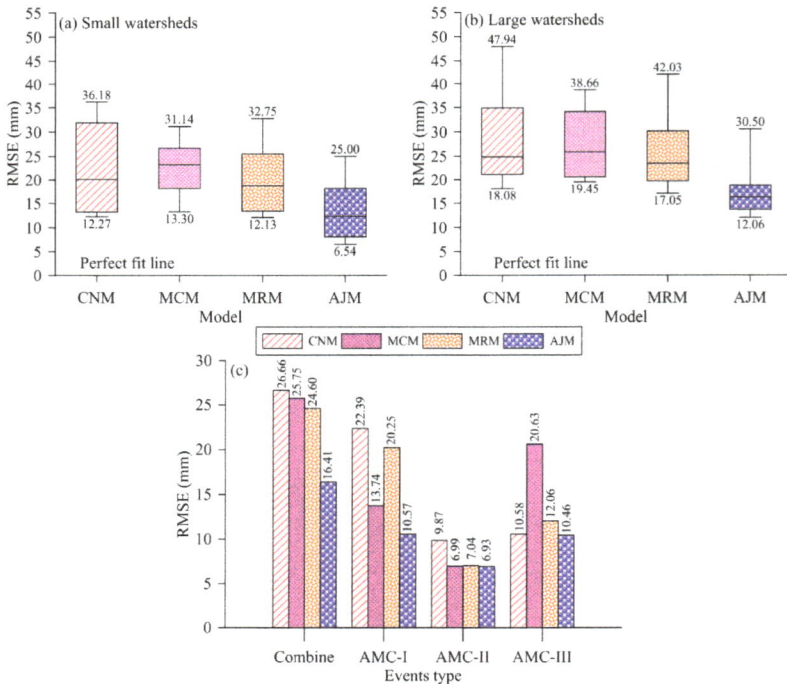

Figure 3. Model performance based on root mean squares error (RMSE) (**a**) in small watersheds (Area < 250 km^2); (**b**) in larger watersheds (Area > 250 km^2) and (**c**) for different types of events (dry, normal, and wet).

For cumulative events, all AMC-I, AMC-II and AMC-III events from 39 watersheds, the CNM showed improvement from AMC-I to AMC-II and AMC-III. However, the MCM exhibited improvement in AMC-II events compared to AMC-I but worse results in AMC-III. The MRM increased in efficiency from AMC-I to AMC-II and AMC-III events. Nonetheless, the higher and consistent NSE values exhibited by the AJM indicated superior performance in all watersheds for all types of events. This performance can be attributed to the incorporation of the variable I_a in the CN model in the AJM.

The RMSE and NSE cannot indicate over- or underestimation of the model runoff. Therefore, we assessed the models' performances using the PRE statistic. Figure 5a,b show that the CNM most underestimated all events, followed by the MRM. Contrarily, the MCM overestimated runoff for the majority of the events. Both the CNM and MCM were inferior because their PRE values are in the unsatisfactory range (PRE $\geqslant$ +25 or PRE $\leqslant$ −25) [14,35]. The mean PRE (%) in small (large) watersheds for CNM, MCM, MRM and AJM respectively were 36.55 (34.64), −23.01 (−20.83), 13.04 (16.59), and 5.66 (8.26). Evidently, both in small and large watersheds, the mean PRE values for the AJM were in the very good performance range [14,35]. Using the PRE statistics, all models show better performance in large watersheds than in small watersheds in the mountainous parts of the study area.

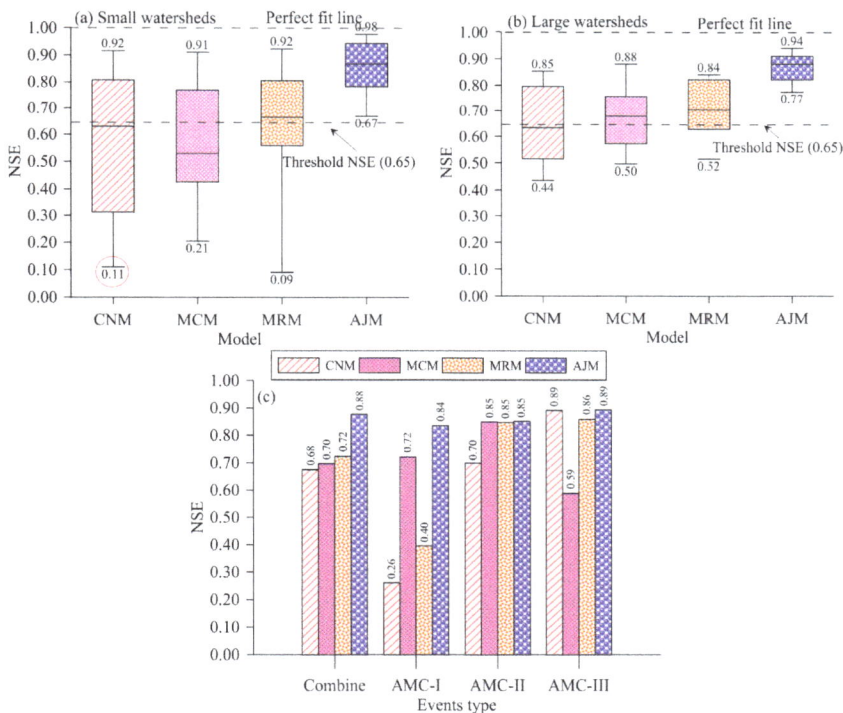

Figure 4. Model performance based on Nash-Sutcliffe efficiency (NSE) (**a**) in small watersheds (Area $\leqslant$ 250 km^2); (**b**) in larger watersheds (Area > 250 km^2) and (**c**) for different types of events (dry, normal and wet). The circled NSE value for the CNM shows the second overall value (the minimum was −0.05, which is not shown here).

For not only the cumulative events from all 39 watersheds, but also the cumulative AMC-I, II, and III events, the AJM more accurately and consistently predicted the runoff. On the contrary, the other models were inconsistent in their runoff predictions. The performance ratings of different models for runoff prediction are given in Table 4. Using different statistical indicators, the proposed model performed significantly better than the other models investigated. One reason for the CNM's inferior results might be the watersheds slope difference. The CNM was derived from rainfall-runoff data from watersheds with up to 5% slope [15], whereas the watersheds in our study area range between 7.50% and 53.53% slope (refer to Table 1). In addition, no statistical indicator showed any significant overall performance difference in predicting runoff from small or large watersheds, which indicates that the size of watershed is not a major concern for any models in this study.

Table 5 shows the best-fit distribution, ranking 1 out of 18 different continuous distributions associated with each test for observed runoff and that predicted by models. It is evident that the observed and AJM-based estimated runoff not only followed the Log-Pearson 3 (LP3) distribution with rank 1 from all three tests but also signified their association from very close test statistic values. Contrarily, the runoff modelled with the CNM and MRM were fitted to other types of distributions. The MCM output runoff values match only the LP3 test based on the Anderson Darling test with comparatively high test statistics. These distributions and their associated test statistics also showed that the proposed model (AJM) exhibited more reliable runoff prediction for steep slope watersheds in the study area than did the other models.

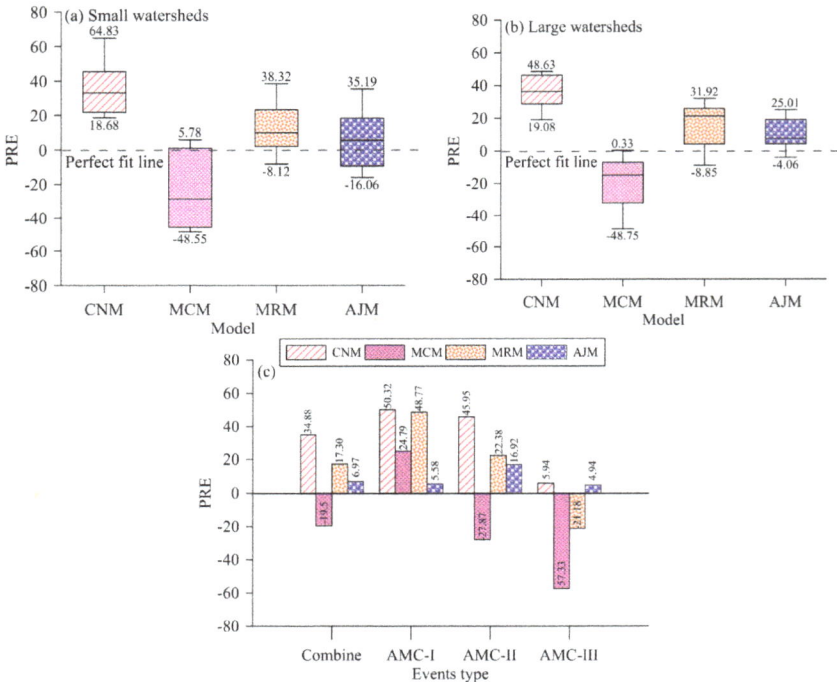

Figure 5. Model performance based on Percent Relative Error (PRE) (**a**) in small watersheds (Area ⩽ 250 km²); (**b**) in larger watersheds (Area > 250 km²); and (**c**) for different types of events (dry, normal and wet).

We also evaluated the models' performances using scatter plots (Figure 6) between the observed and modeled runoff values for all events from 39 watersheds. It is evident that the CNM and MRM underestimated the runoff and made inferior predictions for most events. The runoff estimated with the MRM exhibited modest improvement compared to the CNM. The MCM depicted better results than the CNM and MRM. However, the proposed (AJM) model produced more consistent and statistically significant results for runoff estimation. The close agreement between the measured runoff values and those modeled by the AJM can be seen from the best-fit line approaching the 1:1 line with a high coefficient of determination ($R^2 = 0.88$) compared to that for the CNM ($R^2 = 0.75$), MRM (0.76), and MCM ($R^2 = 0.82$).

A time series plot (Figure 7a,b) compares the measured and modeled runoff values for the selected events from Cheoncheon and Donghyang watersheds highlighting the performance of different models used in this study. It was found that the AJM is comparatively more consistent than the other models.

Figure 8 shows the model performance in individual watersheds and represents their cumulative frequency distribution for the total 39 watersheds in this study. The maximum peak discharge values were calculated after estimating the peak discharge for the individual storm events in the respective watersheds. The evaluation based on the percentage error in peak discharge, E_{Q_P} (Figure 8a) as well as the percentage absolute error in peak discharge, $|E_{Q_P}|$ (Figure 8b), indicated that the runoff estimated using the proposed model is in better agreement with the measured data when compared to other models. Similarly, the CNM, MCM, MRM, and AJM depicted the overall mean (median) percentage absolute peak discharge $|E_{Q_P}|$ for the 39 watersheds as 16.82 (19.19), 26.15 (25.66), 18.30 (15.99), and 14.33 (12.81), respectively. From these statistical scores the proposed model can be encouraged for application in the study area as well as other hydrological similar areas.

Table 4. Model performance ratings in 39 watersheds based on different statistical indicators.

	According to [35]			
Performance Index Range	$0.75 < \text{NSE} \leqslant 1.00$	$0.65 < \text{NSE} \leqslant 0.75$	$0.50 < \text{NSE} \leqslant 0.65$	$\text{NSE} \leqslant 0.50$
Performance Rating	Very good	Good	Satisfactory	Unsatisfactory
Model				
CNM	14	2	12	11
MCM	10	8	13	8
MRM	15	8	12	4
AJM	36	3	0	0
	According to [36]			
Performance index range	$\text{NSE} \geqslant 0.90$	$0.80 \leqslant \text{NSE} < 0.90$	$0.65 \leqslant \text{NSE} < 0.80$	$\text{NSE} < 0.65$
Performance rating	Very good	Good	Satisfactory	Unsatisfactory
Model				
CNM	2	6	8	23
MCM	1	3	14	21
MRM	1	10	12	16
AJM	13	17	9	0
	According to [4,35]			
Performance index range	$\text{PRE} < 10$	$10 \leqslant \text{PRE} < 15$	$15 \leqslant \text{PRE} < 25$	$\text{PRE} \geqslant 25$
Performance rating	Very good	Good	Satisfactory	Unsatisfactory
Model				
CNM	1	0	10	28
MCM	14	25	21	17
MRM	14	2	13	10
AJM	19	8	11	5

Table 5. Comparison of observed and modeled runoff based on best-fit distributions (statistic).

Data Type/Model		Test Type		
		Kolmogorov-Smirnov	Anderson Darling	Chi-Squared
Runoff		Best-fit distribution (Statistic)		
Observed (Q_o)		LP3 (0.023)	LP3 (1.273)	LP3 (21.821)
Modeled (Q_c)	CNM	PBW (0.033)	W (39.865)	PBW (30.628)
	MCM	W (0.021)	LP3 (8.696)	GP (48.923)
	MRM	GEV (0.145)	W (37.654)	W (89.477)
	AJM	LP3 (0.024)	LP3 (1.523)	LP3 (15.949)

LP3 = Log Pearson 3; W = Wakeby; GP = General Pareto; PBW = Phased Bi Weibull; GEV = General Extreme Value.

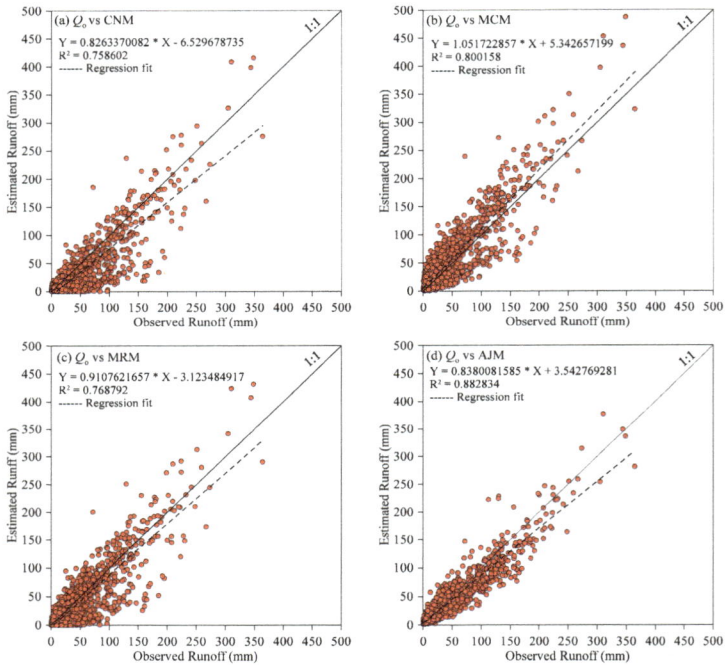

Figure 6. Comparison of events from all watersheds for (**a**) observed runoff (Q_o) *vs.* predicted with CNM; (**b**) Q_o *vs.* predicted with MCM; (**c**) Q_o *vs.* predicted with MRM; and (**d**) Q_o *vs.* predicted with AJM.

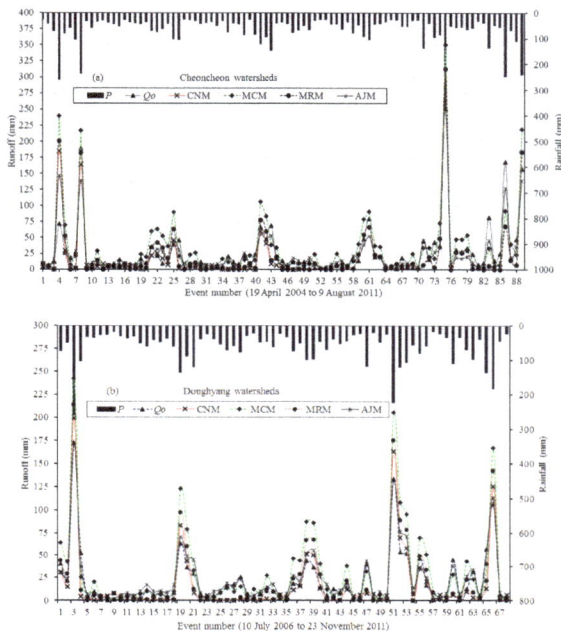

Figure 7. Comparison between the measured runoff time series values and those obtained from application of four models for (**a**) Cheoncheon watershed; and (**b**) Donghyang watershed.

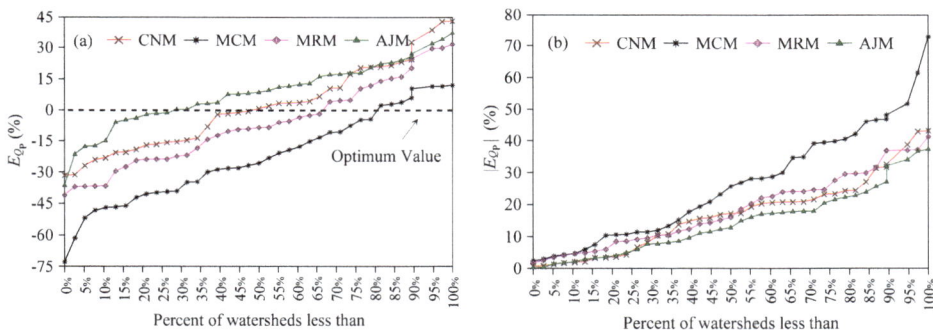

Figure 8. Model evaluation for 39 watersheds based on: (**a**) cumulative distribution of percentage error in peak discharge (E_{Qp}), and (**b**) cumulative distribution of absolute percentage error in peak discharge $|E_{Qp}|$.

5. Conclusions

We tested the rainfall and runoff data collected for 1804 selected events from 39 mountainous watersheds for runoff reproduction using our proposed model and three earlier contenders. Because it underestimated the runoff for the majority of events, the CNM was found inferior to the other models. This might be attributable to the fixed initial abstraction and the absence of a credible parameter for pre-storm soil moisture, which results in sudden jumps in runoff estimation. After testing data from 140 French watersheds [11], researchers conceptualized an intrinsic parameter and incorporated it into the CN model to enhance its runoff prediction capability. However, their simplified model was unable to circumvent sudden jumps in runoff prediction and hence overestimated the majority of events. The model's amendment presented in [1] was also unable to handle this inconsistency and provided only modest improvement on the CNM.

In the proposed model, we conceptualized a CN-based ensembled approach by amending the previously suggested formulation [1] for initial abstraction after incorporating the pre-storm soil moisture adjustment [11]. To circumvent sudden jumps in runoff estimation, we used a continuous and variable initial abstraction that depends not only on S, but also takes into account the storm magnitude and the prior rainfall effects irrespective of the three AMCs. Our modification resulted in a structurally more consistent model. Our proposed model has shown a high degree of reliability in predicting runoff from a majority of watersheds in the study area irrespective of the watershed size. Because of its simplicity and statistically reliable performance, the proposed model can be incorporated fruitfully in continuous hydrologic modeling. Nevertheless, a thorough investigation is required for watersheds of other biomes. In addition, the current study is limited to the prediction of runoff from large storm rainfall events ($P \geqslant 25.4$ mm). The application of the proposed model can be tested in future studies by estimating runoff from small storm rainfall events ($P < 25.4$ mm). It could be more interesting to compare runoff estimation based on watershed scale and the partial source areas.

Acknowledgments: Acknowledgments: Research for this paper was supported by a grant [MPSS-NH-2015-79] from the Natural Hazard Mitigation Research Group funded by the Ministry of Public Safety and Security, Korea. Special thanks to Jae-Hyun Ahn at Seokyeong University for motivating this research.

Author Contributions: Author Contributions: Tae-Woong Kim supervised the research by managing the research results and data collected from different organizations; Muhammad Ajmal had the original idea, performed the experimental work and statistical analysis, and prepared the manuscript; Taj Ali Khan discussed and reviewed the manuscript.

Conflicts of Interest: Conflicts of Interest: The authors declare no conflict of interest.

References

1. Mishra, S.K.; Sahu, R.K.; Eldho, T.I.; Jain, M.K. An improved I_a-S relation incorporating antecedent moisture in SCS-CN methodology. *Water Resour. Manag.* **2006**, *20*, 643–660. [CrossRef]
2. Chung, W.H.; Wang, I.T.; Wang, R.Y. Theory-based SCS-CN method and its applications. *J. Hydrol. Eng.* **2010**, *15*, 1045–1058. [CrossRef]
3. Garen, D.C.; Moore, D.S. Curve number hydrology in water quality modeling: Uses, abuses, and future directions. *J. Am. Water Resour. Assoc.* **2005**, *41*, 377–388. [CrossRef]
4. Durbude, D.G.; Jain, M.K.; Mishra, S.K. Long-term hydrologic simulation using SCS-CN-based improved soil moisture accounting procedure. *Hydrol. Process.* **2011**, *25*, 561–579. [CrossRef]
5. Grimaldi, S.; Petroselli, A.; Romano, N. Green-Ampt curve number mixed procedure as an empirical tool for rainfall-runoff modelling in small and ungauged basins. *Hydrol. Process.* **2013**, *27*, 1253–1264. [CrossRef]
6. Patil, J.P.; Sarangi, A.; Singh, A.K.; Ahmad, T. Evaluation of modified CN methods for watershed runoff estimation using a GIS-based interface. *Biosyst. Eng.* **2008**, *100*, 137–146. [CrossRef]
7. Wang, X.; Liu, T.; Yang, W. Development of a robust runoff-prediction model by fusing the rational equation and a modified SCS-CN method. *Hydrol. Sci. J.* **2012**, *57*, 1118–1140. [CrossRef]
8. Garg, V.; Nikam, B.R.; Thakur, P.K.; Aggarwal, S.P. Assessment of the effect of slope on runoff potential of a watershed using NRCS-CN method. *Int. J. Hydrol. Sci. Technol.* **2013**, *3*, 141–159. [CrossRef]
9. Ponce, V.M.; Hawkins, R.H. Runoff curve number: Has it reached maturity? *J. Hydrol. Eng.* **1996**, *1*, 11–19. [CrossRef]
10. Schneider, L.E.; McCuen, R.H. Statistical guidelines for curve number generation. *J. Irrig. Drain. Eng.* **2005**, *131*, 282–290. [CrossRef]
11. Michel, C.; Andréassian, V.; Perrin, C. Soil conservation service curve number method: How to mend a wrong soil moisture accounting procedure. *Water Resour. Res.* **2005**, *41*, 1–6. [CrossRef]
12. Sahu, R.K.; Mishra, S.K.; Eldho, T.I.; Jain, M.K. An advanced soil moisture accounting procedure for SCS curve number method. *Hydrol. Process.* **2007**, *21*, 2872–2881. [CrossRef]

13. Massari, C.; Brocca, L.; Barbetta, S.; Papathanasiou, C.; Mimikou, M.; Moramarco, T. Using globally available soil moisture indicators for flood modelling in Mediterranean catchments. *Hydrol. Earth Syst. Sci.* **2014**, *18*, 839–853. [CrossRef]
14. Ajmal, M.; Kim, T.-W. Quantifying excess stormwater using SCS-CN-based rainfall runoff models and different curve number determination methods. *J. Irrig. Drain. Eng.* **2015**, *141*, 04014058. [CrossRef]
15. Deshmukh, D.S.; Chaube, U.C.; Hailu, A.E.; Gudeta, D.A.; Kassa, M.T. Estimation and comparison of curve numbers based on dynamic land use land cover change, observed rainfall-runoff data and land slope. *J. Hydrol.* **2013**, *492*, 89–101. [CrossRef]
16. Hawkins, R.H.; Ward, T.J.; Woodward, D.E.; van Mullem, J.A. *Curve Number Hydrology-State of Practice*; The American Society of Civil Engineers (ASCE): Reston, VA, USA, 2009.
17. Natural Resources Conservation Service. Chapter 10: Hydrology. *National Engineering Handbook, Supplement A, Section 4*; The United States Department of Agriculture: Washington, DC, USA, 2004.
18. Seibert, J. On the need for benchmarks in hydrological modelling. *Hydrol. Process.* **2001**, *15*, 1063–1064. [CrossRef]
19. Tramblay, Y.; Bouaicha, R.; Brocca, L.; Dorigo, W.; Bouvier, C.; Camici, S.; Servat, E. Estimation of antecedent wetness conditions for flood modelling in northern Morocco. *Hydrol. Earth Syst. Sci.* **2001**, *16*, 75–86.
20. Woodward, D.E.; Hawkins, R.H.; Jiang, R.; Hjelmfelt, A.T., Jr.; van Mullem, J.A.; Quan, D.Q. Runoff curve number method: Examination of the initial abstraction ratio. In Proceedings of the World Water and Environmental Resources Congress, Philadelphia, PA, USA, 23–26 June 2003.
21. Baltas, E.A.; Dervos, N.A.; Mimikou, M.A. Technical Note: Determination of the SCS initial abstraction ratio in an experimental watershed in Greece. *Hydrol. Earth Syst. Sci.* **2007**, *11*, 1825–1829. [CrossRef]
22. D'Asaro, F.; Grillone, G. Empirical investigation of curve number method parameters in the Mediterranean area. *J. Hydrol. Eng.* **2012**, *17*, 1141–1152. [CrossRef]
23. Perrin, C.; Michel, C.; Andréassian, V. Improvement of a parsimonious model for streamflow simulation. *J. Hydrol.* **2003**, *279*, 275–289. [CrossRef]
24. Yuan, Y.; Nie, W.; McCutcheon, S.C.; Taguas, E.V. Initial abstraction and curve numbers for semiarid watersheds in southeastern Arizona. *Hydrol. Process.* **2014**, *28*, 774–783. [CrossRef]
25. Yuan, Y.; Mitchell, J.K.; Hirschi, M.C.; Cooke, R.A.C. Modified SCS curve number method for predicting subsurface drainage flow. *Trans. Am. Soc. Agric. Eng.* **2001**, *44*, 1673–1682. [CrossRef]
26. Brocca, L.; Melone, F.; Moramarco, T.; Singh, V.P. Assimilation of observed soil moisture data in storm rainfall-runoff modeling. *J. Hydrol. Eng.* **2009**, *14*, 153–165. [CrossRef]
27. Tramblay, Y.; Bouvier, C.; Martin, C.; Didon-Lescot, J.F.; Todorovik, D.; Domergue, J.M. Assessment of initial soil moisture conditions for event-based rainfall-runoff modelling. *J. Hydrol.* **2010**, *387*, 176–187. [CrossRef]
28. Beck, H.E.; de Jeu, R.A.M.; Schellekens, J.; van Dijk, A.I.J.M.; Bruijnzeel, L.A. Improving curve number based storm runoff estimates using soil moisture proxies. *IEEE J. Sel. Top. Appl. Earth Obs. Remote Sens.* **2009**, *2*, 250–259. [CrossRef]
29. Massari, L.; Brocca, L.; Moramarco, T.; Tramblay, Y.; Lescot, J.-F.D. Potential of soil moisture observations in flood modelling: Estimating initial conditions and correcting rainfall. *Adv. Water Res.* **2014**, *74*, 44–53. [CrossRef]
30. Harmel, R.D.; Smith, P.K.; Migliaccio, K.W.; Chaubey, I.; Douglas-Mankin, K.R.; Benham, B.; Shukla, S.; Muñoz-Carpena, R.; Robson, B.J. Evaluating, interpreting, and communicating performance of hydrologic/water quality models considering intended use: A review and recommendations. *Environ. Model. Softw.* **2014**, *57*, 40–51. [CrossRef]
31. Legates, D.R.; McCabe, G.J., Jr. Evaluating the use of "goodness-of-fit" measures in hydrologic and hydroclimatic model validation. *Water Resour. Res.* **1999**, *35*, 233–241. [CrossRef]
32. Chen, X.Y.; Chau, K.W.; Busari, A.O. A comparative study of population-based optimization algorithms for downstream river flow forecasting by a hybrid neural network model. *Eng. Appl. Artif. Intell.* **2015**, *46*, 258–268. [CrossRef]
33. Wu, C.L.; Chau, K.W.; Li, Y.S. Methods to improve neural network performance in daily flows prediction. *J. Hydrol.* **2009**, *372*, 80–93. [CrossRef]
34. Nash, J.; Sutcliffe, J. River flow forecasting through conceptual models part I-A discussion of principles. *J. Hydrol.* **1970**, *10*, 282–290. [CrossRef]

35. Moriasi, D.N.; Arnold, J.G.; van Liew, M.W.; Binger, R.L.; Harmel, R.D.; Veith, T. Model evaluation guidelines for systematic quantification of accuracy in watershed simulations. *Trans. Am. Soc. Agric. Biosyst. Eng.* **2013**, *50*, 885–900.

36. Ritter, A.; Muñoz-Carpena, R. Performance evaluation of hydrological models: Statistical significance for reducing subjectivity in goodness-of-fit assessments. *J. Hydrol.* **2013**, *480*, 33–45. [CrossRef]

37. EasyFit Professional (Version 5.5). Mathwave Technologies, 2004–2010. Available online: www.mathwave.com (accessed on 15 July 2015).

water

MDPI

Article

Application of the Entropy Method to Select Calibration Sites for Hydrological Modeling

Soojun Kim [1], Yonsoo Kim [2], Narae Kang [2] and Hung Soo Kim [2,*]

[1] Columbia Water Center, Earth Institute, Columbia University, New York, NY 10027, USA; soojun78@gmail.com

[2] Department of Civil Engineering, Inha University, Incheon 402-751, Korea; civil.engineer@hanmail.net (Y.K.); naraeme@naver.com (N.K.)

* Correspondence: sookim@inha.ac.kr; Tel: +82-32-860-7572; Fax: +82-32-876-9783

Academic Editor: Kwok-wing Chau

Received: 1 August 2015; Accepted: 13 November 2015; Published: 26 November 2015

Abstract: Selecting an optimum number of calibration sites for hydrological modeling is challenging. Modelers often spend a lot of time and effort on trial and error because there is no guide. We propose a novel entropy method to automate the selection of the optimum combination of calibration sites. To illustrate, the proposed entropy method is applied using discharge data from one river basin in Korea. First, different combinations of discharge-gauging sites were grouped based on the maximum information estimated by the entropy method. Then, a hydrological model was set up for the study basin and was calibrated by estimating optimal parameters using a genetic algorithm at the discharge-gauging sites. The calibration result confirmed that the model's performance was best when it was calibrated using the site number and combination suggested by the entropy method. In addition, the entropy method was useful in reducing the time and effort of model calibration. Therefore, we suggest and confirm the applicability of the entropy method in selecting calibration sites for hydrological modeling.

Keywords: calibration sites; entropy; genetic algorithm; hydrological modeling

1. Introduction

Hydrological models are increasingly used to evaluate the impacts of climate, land use, and crop management practices on the quantity of water resources [1]. The two main objectives of hydrological modeling are to explore the implications of making certain assumptions about the nature of the real-world system and to predict the system's behavior under a set of naturally occurring circumstances [2]. The successful application of any hydrological model is dependent on the quality of its calibration [3]. As a result, developing calibration strategies is a requirement for their proper application in hydrological modeling. During the calibration process, model parameters are estimated by minimizing the deviation between the measured and simulated discharges. Researchers have suggested a number of methodologies to improve calibration-related issues [4–11].

Over the past decades, information technologies, such as the Geographical Information System (GIS), have developed significantly and several GIS-based hydrological models have been created. The GIS provides spatial data as inputs for the variables needed in hydrological models. The GIS has contributed to the change in hydrology from simplified conceptual models to high-resolution distributed models. Runoff analysis, using a physically-based distributed model, gains an advantage from its ability to reflect the spatial characteristics of a watershed's physical parameters [12]. The parameters in a physically-based distributed model are classified as those set up through observation and those set up through estimation. Ideally, parameters established through observation should not require calibration; however, because of scale problems and observation errors, it is still required [4,13–17]. As the parameters are dependent on the topography, land cover and soil characteristics are allocated by a grid or a sub-basin. There have also been many studies about real-life case studies of soft computing techniques in hydrologic engineering [18–24].

Until now, the calibration of the hydrological model has focused on estimating the optimum parameters. The traditional approach to calibrating hydrological models has relied on a single objective function, such as Root-Mean-Square Error (RMSE) or Percent Bias, among others [25]. Local search methods, such as the simplex method [26], have a very low probability of success in finding the global optimum parameter set [3]. Currently available global search methods are the population-evolution-based Shuffled Complex Evolution-University of Arizona (SCE-UA) [3] and Genetic Algorithms (GA) [27]. Other studies have also been conducted on the selection of calibration sites. When runoff is calculated at multiple sites in a watershed, the most intuitive method to guarantee the physical and hydrological similarities between the watershed where the model is calibrated and the sub-basin where the model will be simulated is to calibrate the model using the stream gauges near the sub-basin outlet [15,28–31]. Choi, *et al.* [31] and Zhang, *et al.* [32] suggested the importance of calibration at multiple sites in the basin.

Recently, many discharge-gauging stations have been installed in basins to manage water resources, such as forecasting and issuing warnings for possible flooding events. When establishing and calibrating the hydrological model, the issue of selecting sites naturally arises. Of course, to select discharge-gauging sites, the spatial resolution can be considered, depending on the purpose of establishing the hydrological model and the quality or the importance of the discharge-gauging sites. However, there is no generalized guide for this even though there have been a significant number of studies as the above references, and it depends on the modeler's experience. Sometimes we do not have confidence in the calibrated results even though we spend a large amount of time and effort. The aim of this study under the problems is to confirm the applicability of the entropy method when selecting observation sites to calibrate the hydrological model in multiple sites. The basic theory of the application methodology, including the entropy method, is introduced in Section 2. Section 3 is an analysis and discussion of the application and the results of the methodology for the study basin, and Section 4 consists of the study's conclusion.

2. Methodology and Basic Theory

In this study, the procedure and methodology, as seen in Figure 1, were constructed to review and confirm the entropy method's applicability when selecting the calibration sites of the hydrological model. Data were collected at the discharge-gauging sites within the study basin, and discharge-gauging sites were combined based on the number of sites with maximum information. Then, the Soil and Water Assessment Tool (SWAT) was established for the study basin, and the entropy method was used to calibrate the model at the selected sites. GA was used to optimize the parameters for each site. Finally, the model was calibrated using the site combination with maximum information, depending on the selected number of sites, and the result was evaluated.

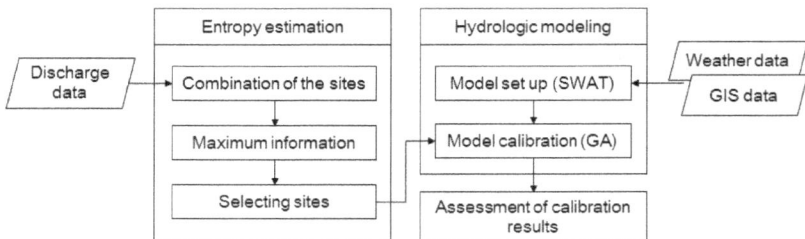

Figure 1. A schematic drawing of the analysis procedure.

Water **2015**, *7*, 6719–6735

2.1. Entropy Method for Information Measurement

Shannon and Weaver [33] defined the marginal entropy for the discrete random variable, shown in Equation (1):

$$H(X) = -\sum_{n=1}^{N} p(x_n)\ln p(x_n), \ n = 1, 2, 3, \cdots, N \tag{1}$$

where $p(x_n)$ is the occurrence probability of x_n. The marginal entropy $H(X)$ is the amount of information (or uncertainty) of X.

If there exists $y_m (m = 1, 2, \cdots, N)$ related to a random variable x_n, it may be possible to reduce the uncertainty of x_n by using y_m to estimate x_n. Using this principle, the remaining uncertainty in X with the given Y can be estimated, as shown in Equation (2):

$$H(X|Y) = -\sum_{n=1}^{N}\sum_{m=1}^{N} p(x_n, y_m)\ln p(x_n|y_m) \tag{2}$$

where $p(x_n, y_m)$ is the joint probability of $X = \{x_n\}$ and $Y = \{y_m\}$, and $p(x_n|y_m)$ is the conditional probability of X with the given Y. $H(X|Y)$ is then the conditional entropy of X with the given Y, which can also be interpreted as the information loss in the transinformation between X and Y [34]. The reduction of uncertainty in X with the given Y, or the transinformation between X and Y, is defined in Equation (3):

$$T(X, Y) = H(X) - H(X|Y) \tag{3}$$

This concept of entropy can be applied to the analysis of a hydrological time series. In this study, the variable X is defined as the daily stream flow. It is assumed that X is a continuous random variable with a probability density function $f(x)$.

If the range of X is divided by the class interval Δx, then the marginal entropy X can be computed with Equation (4):

$$H(X; \Delta x) \simeq -\int_{0}^{\infty} f(x)\ln f(x)dx - \ln \Delta x \tag{4}$$

Moreover, if the same class interval Δx is applied for Y, then the conditional entropy of X with the given Y can be computed with Equation (5):

$$H(X|Y; \Delta x) \simeq -\int_{0}^{\infty}\int_{0}^{\infty} f(x,y)\ln f(x|y)dxdy - \ln \Delta x \tag{5}$$

when X and Y follow the log-normal distribution function, the marginal entropy, the conditional entropy, and the transinformation are derived, respectively, in Equations (6)–(8) [35]:

$$H(X; \Delta x) = \mu_z + 0.5\ln(2\pi e\sigma_z^2) - \ln \Delta x \tag{6}$$

$$H(X|Y; \Delta x) = \mu_z + 0.5\left[\ln(2\pi e\sigma_z^2)\left(1 - \rho_{zw}^2\right)\right] - \ln \Delta x \tag{7}$$

$$T(X, Y) = -0.5\ln\left(1 - \rho_{zw}^2\right) \tag{8}$$

where μ_z and σ_z are the mean and the standard deviation of $z = (\ln x)$, respectively, and ρ_{zw} represents the cross-correlation coefficient between z and $w(= \ln y)$. Chapman [36] also derived the marginal entropy and the conditional entropy, like in Equations (9) and (10), while considering the varying interval $\Delta x / x$ to be proportional to the range instead of being a fixed class interval Δx. The transinformation $T(X, Y)$ between X and Y is independent of the class interval from Equation (8).

$$H(X; \Delta x/x) = 0.5\ln(2\pi e\sigma_z^2) - \ln(\Delta x/x) \tag{9}$$

$$H(X|Y; \Delta x/x) = 0.5\left[\ln(2\pi e\sigma_z^2)\left(1 - \rho_{zw}^2\right)\right] - \ln(\Delta x/x) \tag{10}$$

The decision problem in calibration for hydrological modeling minimizes the redundant information and maximizes the total information from the selected discharge-gauging sites. Thus, the objective function of this optimization problem can be formulated as shown in Equation (11) [37,38]:

$$\text{MAXI}_{\text{Total}}(X_1, X_2, \cdots, X_m; X_i, X_{ii}, \cdots, X_k) \tag{11}$$

where m is the total number of discharge-gauging sites operating in the basin and k is the number of discharge-gauging sites selected of the m discharge-gauging sites. A set of k sites $i, ii, \cdots, k$) is selected to maximize the total information, $I_{\text{Total}}(X_1, X_2, \cdots, X_m; X_i, X_{ii}, \cdots, X_k)$. Equation (11) can also be expressed as follows in Equation (12):

$$\text{MAXI}_{\text{Total}} = \text{MAX}\left[H(X_i) + H(X_{ii}) + \cdots + H(X_k) + \sum_{x=1}^{m-k}\sum_{y=i}^{k} T(X_x, X_y)\right], \; x \neq y \tag{12}$$

where $H(X_i) + H(X_{ii}) + \cdots + H(X_k)$ is the sum of the marginal entropy from the selected discharge-gauging sites, and $\sum_{x=1}^{m-k}\sum_{y=i}^{k} T(X_x, X_y)$ is the sum of transinformation between the selected and the unselected discharge-gauging sites. As the number of selected discharge-gauging sites increases, the total information obtained increases, but then decreases after hitting a threshold number of discharge-gauging sites. That is, the marginal entropy increases as the number of discharge-gauging sites increases, while the sum of transinformation decreases.

2.2. Genetic Algorithm

GA is an algorithm based on Charles Darwin's "Survival of the Fittest" theory, the most widely known evolutionary theory. GA was first proposed by Holland [39] as a search algorithm that applied the natural selection of organisms to the mechanical learning area. GA has been applied to various application fields, such as pattern recognition, including optimization, machine learning, robot engineering, and TSP, the traveling salesman problem. GA is an organic evolution model in the natural world. It is a stochastic optimization method with excellent applicability in the real world that simulates the process where, among a group of individuals forming a generation, individuals with high environmental adaptability are more likely to survive (survival of the fittest), go through crossover and mutation, and form the next generation. In hydrology, GA was used as a methodology to overcome the local optimization of parameters in the main [40–42].

2.3. SWAT for Runoff Simulation

Numerous hydrological models have been developed to assist in understanding watershed system, such as MIKE-SHE (MIKE Système Hydrologique Européen) [43], Petroleum Resources Management System (PRMS) [44], SLURP (Semi-distributed Land Use-based Runoff Processes) [45], SWAT [46] and so on. Among the models, SWAT has been successfully applied in a wide variety of data-limited studies, particularly in South Korea [47]. SWAT as open-source software has an advantage to estimate parameters with an optimization tool like GA.

SWAT is a physically based and distributed agro-hydrological model that operates on a daily time step (as a minimum) at the watershed scale. It is designed to predict the impact of management on water, sediments, and agricultural chemical yields in ungauged catchments [46]. The model is capable of continuous simulation of dissolved and particulate elements in large complex catchments with varying weather, soils, and management conditions over long periods. SWAT can analyze small or large catchments by discretizing them into sub-basins, which are then further subdivided into hydrological response units with homogeneous land use, soil type, and slope. When embedded within a GIS, SWAT can integrate various spatial environmental data including soil, land cover, climate, and topographical features. The theory and details of the hydrological and sediment transport processes integrated in SWAT are available online in the SWAT documentation (http://swatmodel.tamu.edu/).

3. Application and Results

3.1. Study Area

The study area was the Chungju Dam Basin in the Han River of the Korean peninsula. The area of the basin is approximately 6648 km², and the length of the related river is approximately 280 km. The average altitude of the basin, calculated using a 50 × 50 m² grid, is 610 m; its maximum altitude is 1560 m; its minimum altitude is 71 m; and its standard deviation is 261 m. We selected five weather-gauging sites (the red circles in Figure 2), which have collected data for five years (2008–2012), from the Korean Meteorological Agency. Table 1 shows the geographic information for the weather stations and the daily data (minimum temperature, maximum temperature, precipitation, relative humidity, wind speed, and solar radiation) from the collection period. There are 21 water-level gauging sites in the basin (the black and pink triangles in Figure 2). However, only eight discharge-gauging sites (the pink triangles in Figure 2) had discharge data for the period from 2008 to 2012, as most gauging stations were either recently installed or have not developed a relationship between water level and discharge.

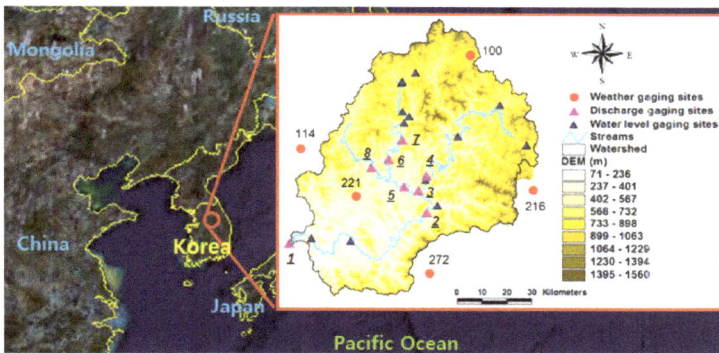

Figure 2. Study area (Chungju Dam Basin).

Table 1. Weather and discharge-gauging stations.

Stations	Code	Station Name	Latitude (°)	Longitude (°)	Elevation (m)	Period of Record (Year)
	100	Daegoanrung	37.68	128.82	772.4	2008–2012
	114	Wonju	37.34	127.95	150.7	2008–2012
Weather gauging stations	216	Taebaek	37.17	128.99	714.2	2008–2012
	221	Jecheon	37.16	128.19	263.1	2008–2012
	272	Youngju	36.87	128.52	210.5	2008–2012
	1	Chungju Dam	37.00	128.00	80.0	2008–2012
	2	Youngchun	37.10	128.51	190.0	2008–2012
	3	Youngwol 1	37.18	128.48	200.0	2008–2012
Discharge-gauging stations	4	Geowun	37.23	128.51	221.0	2008–2012
	5	Youngwol 2	37.19	128.41	383.0	2008–2012
	6	Panwoon	37.30	128.38	722.0	2008–2012
	7	Pyeongchang	37.37	128.41	762.0	2008–2012
	8	Jucheon	37.27	128.27	720.0	2008–2012

3.2. Entropy Estimation

The concept of entropy has been applied to several fields of study, for example, Jaynes [48] in statistical mechanics, Molgedey and Ebeling [49] in finance, Ulanowicz [50] in ecology, Mormarco, *et al.* [51] in hydraulics, Mogheir, *et al.* [52] in groundwater, and others. In hydrology, entropy has mostly been applied as a tool for modeling and decision-making (Singh [53,54]) including the evaluation of a sampling network. Yoo, *et al.* [55] evaluated the rain gauge network by comparing mixed and continuous distribution function applications. This study tried to apply the entropy method to find calibration sites for hydrological modeling. In this study, the number of class intervals was set to 500 for all sites. Mutual information was calculated using the same class interval number, though the class intervals' Δx are different from each site. First, the goodness-of-fit of the observed data for the log-normal distribution was tested. The Quantile-Quantile (QQ) plot, which is a very useful plot as one of several heuristics for assessing how closely a data set fits a particular distribution used to visually inspect the similarity between theoretical quantiles of log-normal distribution and quantiles of observation fit comparatively well in each site, as shown in Figure 3.

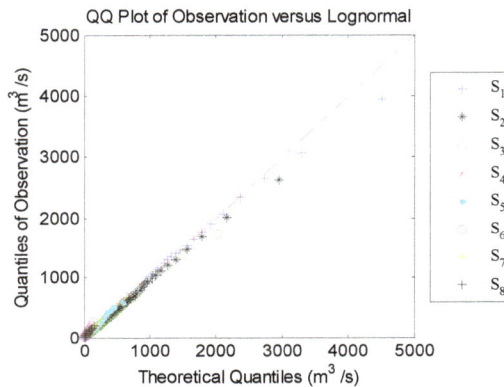

Figure 3. Quantile-Quantile (QQ) plot of observation *versus* log-normal distribution.

Table 2 shows the information matrices of the discharge-gauging sites from the entropy method. These matrices summarize the marginal entropy, transinformations between the sites, and the total information for a selected site, represented as the "sum". For example, if we select Discharge-Gauging Site 1 in Table 2, the total information from Gauging Site 1 is the marginal entropy (7.667) plus the sum of the transinformations.

Table 3 summarizes the optimal sites depending on the total number of sites. At the beginning of the selection of the discharge-gauging sites, the sum of the marginal entropy of the selected sites and the transinformations with the other sites is increasing. The increasing trend is valid until the threshold number of sites for a given basin. However, after the threshold number of discharge-gauging sites, the sum of transinformation between the selected site and the other unselected sites decreases more rapidly than the additional marginal entropy from a newly selected site. The total entropy thus decreases as the number of selected sites increases. In the study area, the highest number of maximum information is 66 when the five sites (Sites 1, 2, 3, 5, and 6) are selected.

Table 2. Information matrix.

Discharge-Gauging Sites	Discharge-Gauging Sites								
	1	2	3	4	5	6	7	8	Sum
1	7.667	2.708	2.643	2.543	2.353	1.745	2.123	1.609	23.396
2	2.708	7.079	2.599	2.530	2.337	1.452	2.070	1.641	22.415
3	2.643	2.599	6.783	2.505	2.771	1.867	2.354	1.857	23.378
4	2.543	2.530	2.505	6.007	2.755	2.049	2.462	1.948	22.798
5	2.353	2.337	2.771	2.755	6.457	1.938	2.353	1.808	22.772
6	1.745	1.452	1.867	2.049	1.938	4.288	3.075	2.474	18.888
7	2.128	2.070	2.354	2.462	2.353	3.075	5.124	2.187	21.755
8	1.609	1.641	1.857	1.948	1.808	2.474	2.187	4.140	17.665

Table 3. Changes in the total information depending on the selected sites.

Number of Sites	Selected Sites	Total Information	Change of Total Information
#1	1	23.4	
#2	1, 3	41.5	
#3	1, 3, 7	54.3	
#4	1, 2, 5, 7	62.4	
#5	**1, 2, 3, 5, 6**	**66.03**	
#6	1, 2, 3, 5, 6, 8	64.9	
#7	1, 2, 3, 4, 5, 6, 8	59.1	
#8	1, 2, 3, 4, 5, 6, 7, 8	47.5	

Sensitivity in each site was analyzed by calculating the losing information, which is the difference between the maximum information in each case and the maximum information from the eight sites. Here, each case means the combination of sites, with a specific site removed. For example, Case 1 estimates the maximum information using the other sites, without Site 1. Figure 4a shows the result of losing information, depending on the number of selecting sites in each case. Figure 4b shows the calculated sensitivity ranking in each site for each case. The ranking of the sites is: 1, 3, 2, 5, 7, 6 and 8.

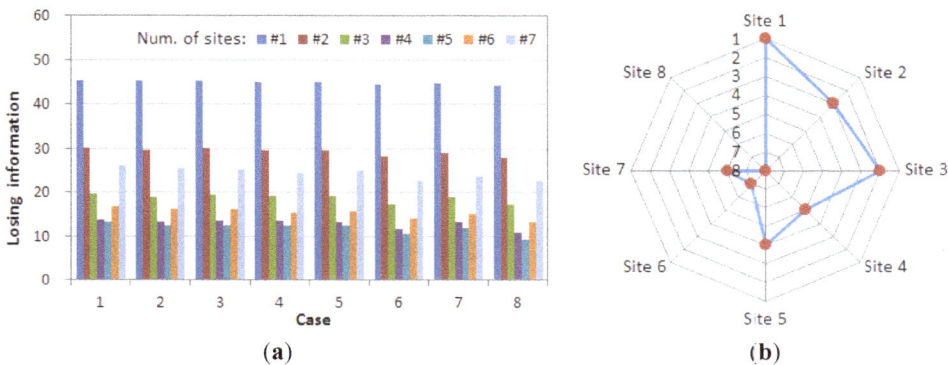

(a)

(b)

Figure 4. Sensitivity analysis. (a) Losing information in each case; (b) Sensitivity ranking.

3.3. Model Setup and Calibration

A rainfall-runoff model was built for the study basin using SWAT. Maps of 1:25,000 scale were collected to generate a 50×50 m^2 Digital Elevation Model (DEM) and a stream network. In addition, a land cover map (Figure 5b) and a soil map (Figure 5c) from the National Water Resources Management Information System (WAMIS; http://www.wamis.go.kr/) were used. The basin was classified into eight different land-use conditions, among which forests (82.2%) and rice paddies (10.3%) accounted for 92.5% of the land use. The soil map, which included classifications of 141 total types of soil, showed that apb (17.8%) and ana (15.5%) were the most prevalent soil types in the area. To build the model used for the study, GIS data were prepared to generate hydrological response units, based on the above data. Terrain analyses were conducted to delineate the channel network using the DEM of the Chungju Dam basin. The basin was divided into ten sub-basins, as shown in Figure 5a. The extract geomorphological characteristics in each sub-basin are shown in Table 4.

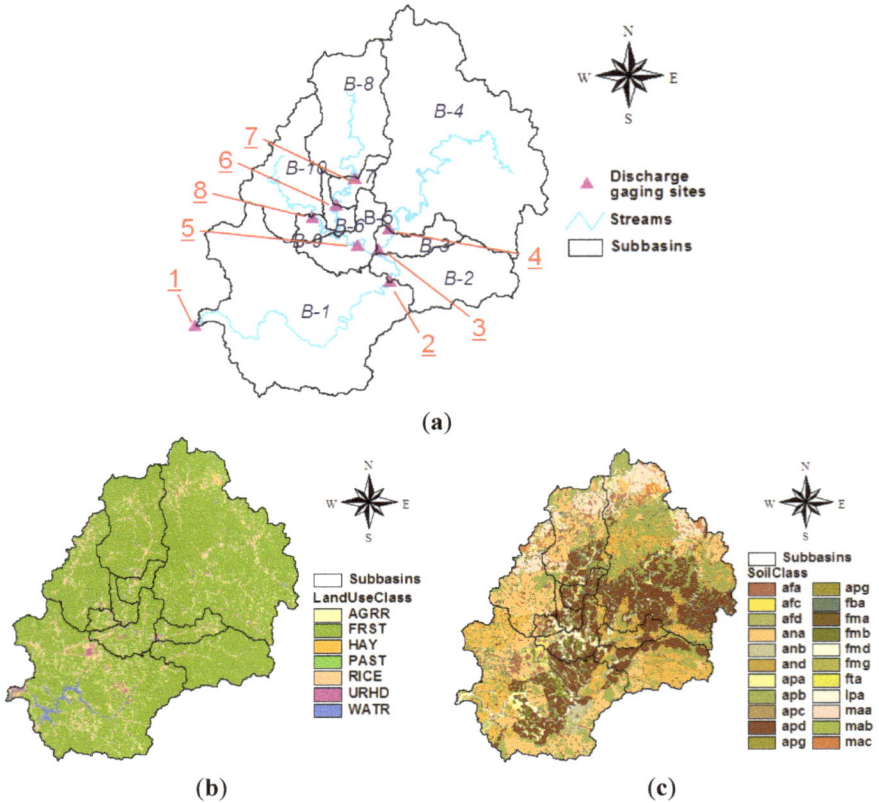

Figure 5. GIS data as SWAT input. (**a**) Stream network and sub-basins map; (**b**) Land use map; (**c**) Soil type map.

Table 4. Geomorphological characteristics in each sub-basin.

Sub-Basin	Basin				Stream				Remark
	Area (km²)	Slope (%)	Altitude (El. m)	Upstream Area (km²)	Length (km)	Slope (%)	Min. Alt. (El. m)	Max. Alt. (El. m)	
B-1	1905.1	27.2	391.0	6631.4	101.5	10.2	71.0	174.0	Site 1
B-2	553.6	35.0	487.0	4726.2	16.4	29.3	157.0	205.0	Site 2
B-3	164.6	33.7	243.0	2398.5	12.0	70.9	136.0	221.0	Site 3
B-4	2233.9	32.2	667.0	2233.9	128.9	30.2	216.0	605.0	Site 4
B-5	276.9	22.6	328.0	1774.2	26.8	17.9	193.0	241.0	Site 5
B-6	88.5	28.6	421.0	896.1	19.3	56.9	215.0	325.0	–
B-7	110.1	31.1	476.0	807.5	23.7	33.0	257.0	335.0	Site 6
B-8	697.4	28.5	636.0	697.4	52.4	47.0	291.0	537.0	Site 7
B-9	67.3	21.1	351.0	601.2	14.0	28.5	211.0	251.0	–
B-10	533.9	26.0	548.0	533.9	43.2	44.0	251.0	441.0	Site 8

In this study, surface runoff was estimated using the Soil Conservation Service Curve Number, which has an advantage to predict direct runoff or infiltration from excess rainfall using daily precipitation and GIS data like soil type and land-use maps in an ungagged area. Any water that does not become surface runoff enters the soil column, where it is removed through evapotranspiration or through deep percolation into the deep aquifer, or the runoff may move laterally in the soil column as a streamflow contribution. Groundwater contribution to streamflow is generated from both shallow and deep aquifers, and is based on groundwater balance. There are three methods for estimating evapotranspiration like Priestley-Taylor, Penman-Monteith, and Hargreaves in SWAT. The Penman-Monteith method [56] was used to estimate evapotranspiration using weather variables, such as mean temperature, wind speed, relative humidity, and solar radiation.

SWAT contains several parameters that are used to describe the spatially distributed movement of water through the watershed system. Some of these parameters, such as the Curve Number (CN), cannot be directly measured and must be estimated through calibration. SWAT is a distributed hydrological model and consequently there are potentially many (thousands) parameters. As it is impossible to calibrate all of them, a reduction of the number of parameters to estimate is inevitable. In this study, seven parameters that govern the surface water response and the subsurface water response of SWAT were used in the calibration. Table 5 shows a general description of the seven parameters [57]. The default parameters were determined by the methods introduced by Neitsch, *et al.* [58]. A more detailed presentation for primary parameters and sensitivity tests is referred in many studies [57–61].

There are several automatic calibration algorithms. Zhang, *et al.* [32] compared the efficacy of five global optimization algorithms, such as shuffled complex evolution method developed at The University of Arizona (SCE-UA), Genetic Algorithms (GA), Particle Swarm Optimization (PSO), Artificial Immune Systems (AIS), and Differential Evaluation (DE), for calibrating SWAT and found that GA is a promising single-objective optimization method. This study used GA to estimate the optimized parameters of SWAT. In GA, a roulette wheel algorithm is used to select chromosomes for the crossover and the mutation operations [62]. A two-point crossover method with a probability of 0.8 was selected for making the search shorter and more robust, and a mutation with a probability of 0.01 was selected. The RMSE fitness function (Fs) [25] was used in this study. This performance index was defined to minimize the RMSE, as shown in Equation (13):

$$Fs = \min(\text{RMSE}) = \min\left(\sqrt{\frac{1}{n} \sum (y_i - \widehat{y_l})} \right) \tag{13}$$

where y_i is simulated daily discharge, $\widehat{y_l}$ is observed daily discharge at the calibration site, and n is the number of days with observations.

Table 5. Parameters for the calibration of SWAT.

Num.	Parameter	Description	Range
Parameters governing surface water response			
1	CN2	Curve number 2	35–98
2	ESCO	Soil evaporation compensation factor	0–1
3	SOL_AWC	Available soil water capacity	0–1
Parameters governing subsurface water response			
4	GWQMN	Threshold depth of water in the shallow aquifer for return flow to occur (mm)	0–5000
5	REVAPMN	Threshold depth of water in the shallow aquifer for reevaporation to occur (mm)	0–500
6	GW_REVAP	Groundwater reevaporation coefficient	0.02–0.2
7	ALPHA_BF	Base flow recession constant	0–1

The size of the initial population was set to 50, and the number of generations was set to 1000. The sites were selected according to the entropy method. The algorithm was configured so that optimization was implemented sequentially, starting with the discharge-gauging site that was the furthest upstream. For example, if calibration is conducted for the case where there are three observation station sites (Sites 1, 3, and 7), then Site 7, which is the furthest upstream, would be the first to be calibrated, followed by Site 3 and Site 1.

The GA for the parameter optimization of the SWAT in this study was tested by comparing it to a simple Brute-force Search Algorithm (BSA) for checking the applicability of GA. The calibration was only performed at the outlet site of the whole basin. The optimized parameters in each algorithm are shown in Table 6. The parameters were remarkably similar and the RMSE between the results (from Figure 6) using these methods was about 0.07 m^3/s. This shows both the applicability of the GA and its usefulness in solving the problem of complex combinations in this study.

Table 6. Optimized parameters by GA and BSA.

Parameter	GA	BSA
CN2	48	48
ESCO	0.73	0.8
SOL_AWC	0.32	0.3
GWQMN	1694	1600
REVAPMN	132	150
GW_REVAP	0.08	0.1
ALPHA_BF	0.6	0.5

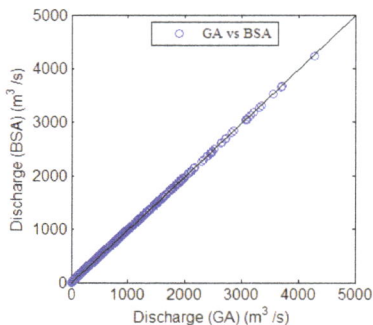

Figure 6. Discharge comparison of GA *vs.* BSA.

Using the above method, calibration was conducted at the respective sites. Table 3 was referenced for all of the cases where the number of sites selected was one to eight. After the respective cases were calibrated, the relation between observed daily discharge and simulated daily discharge at the eight discharge-gauging sites in the study basin was illustrated, as shown in Figure 7. Figure 7a shows the case where calibration was conducted at only one site (Case 1), whereas Figure 7b shows the case where calibration was performed at five different sites (Case 5). These cases were compared to the case where no calibration was conducted (no calibration; blue circle). Case 5 is included in the comparison because the maximum amount of information was indicated when five sites (Sites 1, 2, 3, 5, and 6) were selected in the study basin (see Table 3). It was determined that the simulated discharge in the case where no calibration was conducted had an underestimation issue (blue circles), and Case 5 (five sites selected) produced a better result than Case 1 (one site selected).

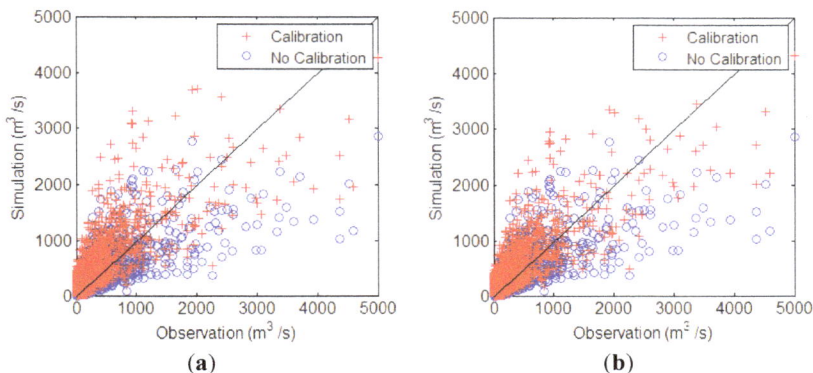

Figure 7. Scatter plot for the relation between observation and simulation. (**a**) Calibration at one site (Case 1); (**b**) Calibration at five sites (Case 5).

3.4. Calibration Results and Discussion

The calibration results, based on the respective results of Table 3 (from #1 to #8), were mutually compared. Three evaluation functions were applied for the observed and simulated discharges, coefficient of correlation (CC), RMSE, and Nash-Sutcliffe efficiency (NSE) [63]. The results of the case evaluations (with the selection of one to eight sites) using the evaluation functions are shown in Table 7 and Figure 8. The evaluation was conducted for all of the sites and for the outlet. First, the calibration results were applied to all of the sites for comparison. Even if only one site had been selected for calibration, it would have been compared with the respective observation discharge of eight sites after the simulated discharge of eight sites was extracted. Next, the outlet from the most important site (as determined in Table 3) was applied. The applicability of the SWAT model was outstanding in the study basin as the CC, RMSE, and NSE were 0.782, 147.4, and 0.482, respectively, even in the case where no calibration was conducted (#0); however, it was confirmed that the results were improved slightly when the model was calibrated. In particular, the result of the case with more sites selected was even better than the result of the case with only one site selected. Nevertheless, the calibration result did not improve any further when the number of sites selected exceeded a certain number. This characteristic is easily confirmed through Figure 8 and Case 5, where all of the sites were evaluated (five sites selected: CC, 0.813; RMSE, 138.8; NSE, 0.540), and Case 4, where the basin outlet point was evaluated (four sites selected: CC, 0.799; RMSE, 324.0; NSE, 0.575) and the best calibration result was produced. If the case evaluating all of the discharge-gauging sites in the basin is deemed to be more representative than the case evaluating only the outlet point of the basin, then Case 5, where five sites (Sites 1, 2, 3, 5, and 6) were selected for calibration, produces the best result.

Table 7. Calibration results at all sites and the outlet site.

Site Number	All Sites			Outlet Site		
	CC	RMSE (m³/s)	NSE	CC	RMSE (m³/s)	NSE
#0 (Non-C.)	0.782	147.4	0.482	0.763	351.3	0.501
#1	0.800	142.8	0.516	0.784	330.4	0.554
#2	0.805	141.1	0.530	0.798	325.2	0.568
#3	0.810	140.0	0.538	0.798	325.1	0.573
#4	0.812	139.7	0.539	0.799	324.0	0.575
#5	0.813	138.8	0.540	0.798	325.1	0.573
#6	0.809	140.3	0.536	0.797	325.5	0.572
#7	0.809	142.1	0.524	0.794	329.0	0.562
#8	0.809	142.1	0.524	0.794	329.2	0.562

The total information will increase if more sites are used. For example, the maximum information was about 66 when eight sites were used in this study (see Table 3). However, the maximum information was about 56.6 when seven sites were used in Case 8 (shown in Figure 9). Here, Case 8 means that Site 8 was removed from the eight sites and the maximum information is calculated using the other seven sites. There is a small difference between using seven sites among seven sites and using seven sites among eight sites. The maximum information was 59.1 when seven sites were selected among eight sites. However, the maximum information was shown when five sites (1, 2, 3, 5, and 6 sites) were selected among the eight sites. As a result, if in the future more observation sites are available, it will still be possible to get more information. However, the maximum information is not shown when all observation sites are used.

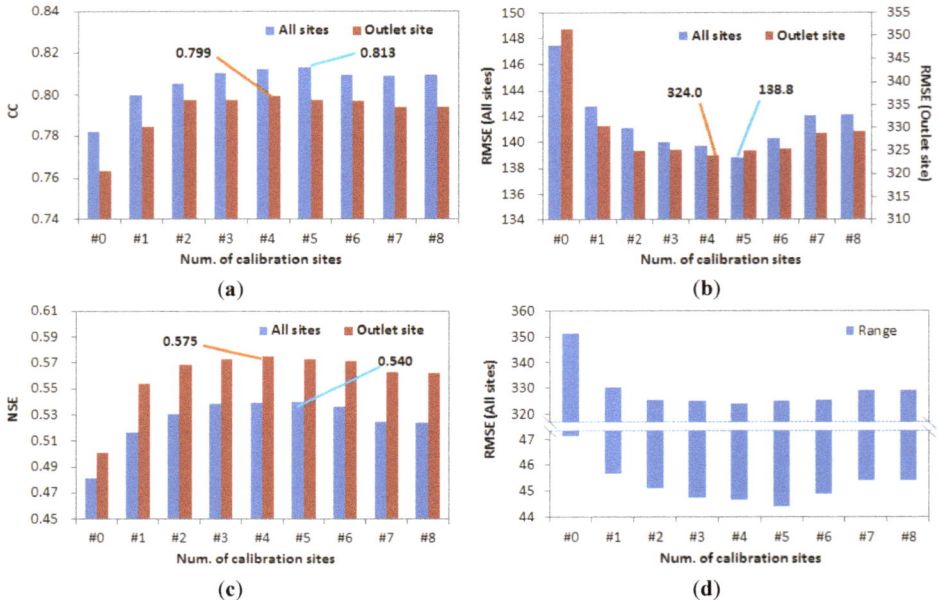

Figure 8. Calibration results using evaluation functions. (a) Coefficient of correlation; (b) RMSE; (c) NSE; (d) RMSE range in case of all sites.

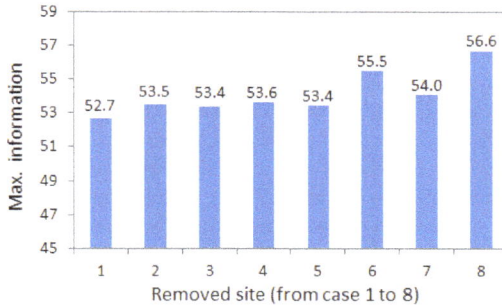

Figure 9. Maximum information using seven total sites.

The entropy method may identify the number of calibration sites after which the marginal increase in model efficiency to represent the observed runoff no longer significantly increases. Choi, *et al.* [31] stated that additional calibration sites can benefit model performance. However, the results of this study showed that model performance instead decreased if more four of five sites were selected (Table 7). There may be two reasons for this. First, the exclusion of one of the sites worsened the simulation result of the other sites. The sites that caused this response could be Site 4 and Site 8 because model performance with those sites is decreased. However, there is a limit to understanding the result of the model performance using only one problem in each site. This does not clearly explain the results in terms of Site 7. In fact, the model performance for Site 7 is positive in Case 3 and Case 4, and negative in Case 8 (as seen Tables 3 and 7). Here, error compensation is a very important point for multi-site calibration. In a case where many sites are considered for calibration, error compensation has an effect on model performance. In this study, error compensation can be prevented if all of the sites are used for calibration, and therefore decrease model performance. Model performance will increase due solely to the error compensation if fewer than the maximum number of sites is used for calibration. Therefore, the entropy method should not be preferred over an approach where all available sites are used for calibration, if time allows for it. The entropy method is useful in cases where computational requirements do not allow the use of all sites for calibration. In other words, the entropy method is only useful in reducing the time and effort of model calibration, but not in increasing model performance.

The growing importance of water resource management, along with the development of observation techniques, has recently resulted in the installation of significantly more water level observation stations in basins. Currently, there are 21 water level observation stations in the study basin, and it is expected that the observed discharge information will be continuously accumulated. Obviously, observation data obtained from more sites will be a great advantage to hydrological modeling. However, assuming that all 21 sites in the study basin can be utilized, the number of cases of the selection of sites for calibration is 2,097,151 ($\sum_{n=1}^{21} {}_{21}C_n = 2{,}097{,}151$). While this assumption does not consider the importance of the sites, the number of cases for the hydrological model calibration must still be high. If the brute-force search method is considered to select calibration sites in this area, we would waste too much time and effort. Sometimes, a modeling result does not improve any further, although we try to get a good result in model calibration. This study confirmed that the selection of more calibration sites did not lead to improved calibration results from the model. Therefore, the entropy method attempted in this study is expected to provide an excellent guideline to conduct the calibration of the hydrological model. In addition, the application of the theory will further increase when selecting a certain number of sites, depending on the purpose of the application of the model, because the theory also provides information as to which sites need to be selected.

4. Conclusions

The purpose of this study was to review the applicability of the entropy method in selecting the calibration sites for hydrological modeling. The entropy method was applied to the discharge data of eight different sites in the Chungju Dam Basin in Korea. Then, the selected sites were combined, case-by-case, so that the combination of sites can yield the maximum amount of information. In addition, the SWAT model was established for the study basin, and the model was calibrated by estimating the optimal parameters using a genetic algorithm at the discharge-gauging sites selected through the entropy method. As a result, we learned that the model calibration using the selected sites and the combined sites having maximum information based on the entropy method gave us excellent outcomes. Therefore, we confirmed the applicability of the entropy theory in the selection of calibration sites for hydrological modeling. In addition, the entropy method is only useful in reducing the time and effort spent on model calibration, but not in increasing model performance. The method needs to apply and evaluate its applicability through various hydrological models in the future.

In particular, selecting more sites does not always lead to a better model performance. The decrease in model performance when selecting more than the optimal number of sites indicated by the entropy method can be associated to error compensation. However, applying the entropy method can significantly reduce time and effort required for model calibration, and can therefore be a valuable tool if the computational requirements for parameter optimization against all available data exceed available resources. As more discharge-gauging stations are expected to be installed all over the world, the entropy method, which provides information on the preferential types of observation stations to consider for the calibration of the hydrological model, will have significantly more use in the future.

Acknowledgments: This research was supported by a grant (14AWMP-B082564-01) from Advanced Water Management Research Program funded by Ministry of Land, Infrastructure and Transport of Korean government. Moreover, this work was supported by the Inha University Research Grant.

Author Contributions: This research presented here was carried out in collaboration between all authors. Soojun Kim and Hung Soo Kim had the original idea for the study. Yonsoo Kim and Narae Kang conducted the research methods. All authors discussed the structure and comment on the manuscript at all stages.

Conflicts of Interest: The authors declare no conflict of interest.

References

1. Moriasi, D.N.; Wilson, B.N.; Douglas-Mankin, K.R.; Arnold, J.G.; Gowda, P.H. Hydrologic and water quality models: Use, calibration, and validation. *Trans. ASABE* **2012**, *55*, 1241–1247. [CrossRef]
2. Beven, K. Changing ideas in hydrology—The case of physically based models. *J. Hydrol.* **1989**, *105*, 157–172. [CrossRef]
3. Duan, Q.Y.; Sorooshian, S.; Gupta, V. Effective and efficient global optimization for conceptual rainfall-runoff models. *Water Resour. Res.* **1992**, *28*, 1015–1031. [CrossRef]
4. Beven, K.J.; Binley, A.M. The future of distributed models: Model calibration and uncertainty prediction. *Hydrol. Process.* **1992**, *6*, 279–298. [CrossRef]
5. Beven, K. Prophecy, reality, and uncertainty in distributed hydrological modeling. *Adv. Water Resour.* **1993**, *16*, 41–51. [CrossRef]
6. Oudin, L.; Perrin, C.; Mathevet, T.; Andréassian, V.; Michel, C. Impact of biased and randomly corrupted inputs on the efficiency and the parameters of watershed models. *J. Hydrol.* **2006**, *320*, 62–83. [CrossRef]
7. Tang, Y.; Reed, P.; van Werkhoven, K.; Wagener, T. Advancing the identification and evaluation of distributed rainfall-runoff models using global sensitivity analysis. *Water Resour. Res.* **2007**, *43*. [CrossRef]
8. Engel, B.; Storm, D.; White, M.; Arnold, J.; Arabi, M. A hydrologic/water quality model application protocol. *J. Am. Water Resour. Assoc.* **2007**, *43*, 1223–1236. [CrossRef]
9. Moriasi, D.N.; Arnold, J.G.; van Liew, M.W.; Bingner, R.L.; Harmel, R.D.; Veith, T.L. Model evaluation guidelines for systematic quantification of accuracy in watershed simulations. *Trans. ASABE* **2007**, *50*, 885–900. [CrossRef]

10. Harmel, R.D.; Smith, P.K.; Migliaccio, K.L. Modifying goodness-of-fit indicators to incorporate both measurement and model uncertainty in model calibration and validation. *Trans. ASABE* **2010**, *53*, 55–63. [CrossRef]

11. Pushpalatha, R.; Perrin, C.; le Moine, N.; Mathevet, T.; Andréassian, V. A downward structural sensitivity analysis of hydrological models to improve low-flow simulation. *J. Hydrol.* **2011**, *411*, 66–76. [CrossRef]

12. Beven, K.; O'Connell, P.E. *On the Role of a Physically Based Distributed Modeling in Hydrology*; Institute of Hydrology: Wallingford, UK, 1982.

13. Abbott, M.B.; Bathurst, J.C.; Cunge, J.A.; O'Connell, P.E.; Rasmussen, J. An introduction to the European hydrological system—Systeme hydrologique Europeen, "SHE," 1: History and philosophy of a physically based, distributed modelling system. *J. Hydrol.* **1986**, *87*, 45–59. [CrossRef]

14. Refsgaard, J.C.; Storm, B. Construction, Calibration and Validation of Hydrological Models. In *Distributed Hydrological Modeling*; Kluwer Academic: Dordrecht, The Netherlands, 1996; pp. 41–54.

15. Lee, H.; McIntyre, N.; Wheater, H.; Young, A. Selection of conceptual models for regionalization of the rainfall-runoff relationship. *J. Hydrol.* **2005**, *312*, 125–147. [CrossRef]

16. Sahoo, G.B.; Ray, C.; de Carlo, E.H. Calibration and validation of a physically distributed hydrological model, MIKE SHE, to predict streamflow at high frequency in a flashy mountainous Hawaii stream. *J. Hydrol.* **2006**, *327*, 94–109. [CrossRef]

17. Hu, W.; Shao, M.; Wang, Q.; She, D. Effects of measurement method, scale, and landscape features on variability of saturated hydraulic conductivity. *J. Hydrol. Eng.* **2013**, *18*, 378–386. [CrossRef]

18. Gholami, V.; Chau, K.W.; Fadaee, F.; Torkaman, J.; Ghaffari, A. Modeling of groundwater level fluctuations using dendrochronology in alluvial aquifers. *J. Hydrol.* **2015**, *529*, 1060–1069. [CrossRef]

19. Taormina, R.; Chau, K.W. ANN-based interval forecasting of streamflow discharges using the LUBE method and MOFIPS. *Eng. Appl. Artif. Intell.* **2015**, *45*, 429–440. [CrossRef]

20. Wu, C.L.; Chau, K.W.; Li, Y.S. Methods to improve neural network performance in daily flows prediction. *J. Hydrol.* **2009**, *372*, 80–93. [CrossRef]

21. Wang, W.C.; Chau, K.W.; Xu, D.M.; Chen, X.Y. Improving forecasting accuracy of annual runoff time series using ARIMA based on EEMD decomposition. *Water Resour. Manag.* **2015**, *29*, 2655–2675. [CrossRef]

22. Chen, X.Y.; Chau, K.W. A comparative study of population-based optimization algorithms for downstream river flow forecasting by a hybrid neural network model. *Eng. Appl. Artif. Intell.* **2015**, *46*, 258–268. [CrossRef]

23. Chau, K.W.; Wu, C.L. A hybrid model coupled with singular spectrum analysis for daily rainfall prediction. *J. Hydroinform.* **2010**, *12*, 458–473. [CrossRef]

24. Park, M.K.; Kim, D.G.; Kwak, J.W.; Kim, H.S. Evaluation of parameter characteristics of the storage function model. *J. Hydrol. Eng.* **2014**, *19*, 308–318. [CrossRef]

25. Hogue, T.S.; Sorooshian, S.; Gupta, H.V.; Holz, A.; Braatz, D. A multi-step automatic calibration scheme (MACS) for river forecasting models. *J. Hydrometeorol.* **2000**, *1*, 524–542. [CrossRef]

26. Nelder, J.A.; Mead, R. A simplex method for function minimization. *Comput. J.* **1965**, *7*, 308–313. [CrossRef]

27. Wang, Q.J. The genetic algorithm and its application to calibrating conceptual rainfall-runoff models. *Water Resour. Res.* **1991**, *27*, 2467–2471. [CrossRef]

28. Ajami, N.K.; Gupta, H.; Wagener, T.; Sorooshian, S. Calibration of a semidistributed hydrologic model for streamflow estimation along a river system. *J. Hydrol.* **2004**, *298*, 112–135. [CrossRef]

29. Merz, R; Blöschl, G. Regionalisation of catchment model parameters. *J. Hydrol.* **2004**, *287*, 95–123. [CrossRef]

30. Young, A. Streamflow simulation within UK ungauged catchments using a daily rainfall-runoff model. *J. Hydrol.* **2006**, *320*, 155–172. [CrossRef]

31. Choi, Y.S.; Choi, C.K.; Kim, H.S.; Kim, K.T.; Kim, S. Multi-site calibration using a grid-based event rainfall-runoff model: A case study of the upstream areas of the Nakdong River basin in Korea. *Hydrol. Process.* **2015**, *29*, 2089–2099. [CrossRef]

32. Zhang, X.; Srinivasan, R.; van Liew, M. Multi-site calibration of the SWAT model for hydrologic modeling. *Trans. ASABE* **2008**, *51*, 2039–2049. [CrossRef]

33. Shannon, C.E.; Weaver, W. *The Mathematical Theory of Communication*; University of Illinois Press: Urbana, IL, USA, 1949.

34. Yang, Y.; Burn, D.H. An entropy approach to data collection network design. *J. Hydrol.* **1994**, *157*, 307–324. [CrossRef]

35.   Amorocho, J.; Espildora, B. Entropy in the assessment of uncertainty in hydrologic systems and models. *Water Resour. Res.* **1973**, *9*, 1511–1522. [CrossRef]
36.   Chapman, T.G. Entropy as a measure of hydrologic data uncertainty and model performance. *J. Hydrol.* **1986**, *85*, 111–126. [CrossRef]
37.   Husain, T. Hydrologic uncertainty measure and network design. *Water Resour. Bull.* **1989**, *25*, 527–534. [CrossRef]
38.   Al-Zahrani, M.; Husain, T. An algorithm for designing a precipitation network in the southwestern region of Saudi Arabia. *J. Hydrol.* **1998**, *205*, 205–216. [CrossRef]
39.   Holland, J.H. *Adaptation in Natural and Artificial Systems*; University of Michigan Press: Ann Arbor, MI, USA, 1975.
40.   Ragab, R.; Austin, B.; Moidinis, D. The HYDROMED model and its application to semi-arid Mediterranean catchments with hill reservoirs 1: The rainfall-runoff model using a genetic algorithm for optimisation. *Hydrol. Earth Syst. Sci.* **2001**, *5*, 543–553.
41.   Bhattacharjya, R.K. Optimal design of unit hydrographs using probability distribution and genetic algorithms. *SADHANA Acad. Proc. Eng. Sci.* **2004**, *29*, 499–508. [CrossRef]
42.   Chang, C.L.; Lo, S.L.; Yu, S.L. The parameter optimization in the inverse distance method by genetic algorithm for estimating precipitation. *Environ. Monit. Assess.* **2006**, *117*, 145–155. [CrossRef] [PubMed]
43.   Refsgaard, J.C.; Storm, B. MIKE SHE. In *Computer Models of Watershed Hydrology*; Singh, V.P., Ed.; Water Resources Publications: Highland Ranch, CO, USA, 1995; pp. 809–846.
44.   Leavesley, G.H.; Stannard, L.G. The Precipitation Runoff Modeling System—PRMS. In *Computer Models of Watershed Hydrology*; Singh, V.P., Ed.; Water Resources Publications: Highland Ranch, CO, USA, 1995; pp. 281–310.
45.   Kite, G.W. The SLURP Model. In *Computer Models of Watershed Hydrology*; Singh, V.P., Ed.; Water Resources Publications: Highland Ranch, CO, USA, 1995; pp. 521–562.
46.   Arnold, J.G.; Srinivasan, R.; Muttiah, R.S.; Williams, J.R. Large area hydrologic modeling and assessment: Part I. model development. *J. Am. Water Resour. Assoc.* **1998**, *34*, 73–89. [CrossRef]
47.   Kim, N.W.; Chung, I.M.; Kim, C.; Lee, J.; Lee, J.E. Development and applications of SWAT-K (Korea). In *Soil and Water Assessment Tool (SWAT) Global Applications*; World Association of Soil and Water Conservation: Bangkok, Thailand, 2009.
48.   Jaynes, E.K. Information theory and statistical mechanics. *Phys. Rev.* **1957**, *106*, 620–630. [CrossRef]
49.   Molgedey, L.; Ebeling, W. Local order, entropy and predictability of financial time series. *Eur. Phys. J. B* **2000**, *15*, 733–737. [CrossRef]
50.   Ulaniwicz, R.E. Information theory in ecology. *Comput. Chem.* **2001**, *25*, 393–399. [CrossRef]
51.   Moramarco, T.; Saltalippi, C.; Singh, V.P. Estimation of mean velocity in natural channels based on Chiu's velocity distribution equation. *J. Hydrol. Eng.* **2004**, *9*, 42–50. [CrossRef]
52.   Mogheir, Y.; de Lima, J.L.M.P.; Singh, V.P. Characterizing the spatial variability of groundwater quality using the entropy theory: I. synthetic data. *Hydrol. Process.* **2004**, *18*, 2165–2178. [CrossRef]
53.   Singh, V.P. The use of entropy in hydrology and water resources. *Hydrol. Process.* **1997**, *11*, 587–626. [CrossRef]
54.   Singh, V.P. The entropy theory as a tool for modeling and decision making in environmental and water resources. *Water SA* **2000**, *26*, 1–12.
55.   Yoo, C.; Jung, K.; Lee, J. Evaluation of rain gauge network using entropy theory: Comparison of mixed and continuous distribution function applications. *J. Hydrol. Eng.* **2008**, *13*, 226–235. [CrossRef]
56.   Monteith, J.L. Evaporation and the environment. In the state and movement of water in living organisms. In *19th Symposia of the Society for Experimental Biology*; Cambridge University Press: London, UK, 1965; pp. 205–234.
57.   Van Liew, M.W.; Veith, T.L.; Bosch, D.D.; Arnold, J.G. Suitability of SWAT for the conservation effects assessment project: A comparison on USDA-ARS watersheds. *J. Hydrol. Eng.* **2007**, *12*, 173–189. [CrossRef]
58.   Neitsch, S.L.; Arnold, A.G.; Kiniry, J.R.; Srinivasan, J.R.; Williams, J.R. *Soil and Water Assessment Tool User's Manual*; Texas Water Resources Institute: College Station, TX, USA, 2005.
59.   Van Griensven, A.; Meixner, T.; Grunwald, S.; Bishop, T.; Diluzio, M.; Srinivasan, R. A global sensitivity analysis tool for the parameters of multi-variable catchment models. *J. Hydrol.* **2006**, *324*, 10–23. [CrossRef]

60. White, L.K.; Chaubey, I. Sensitivity analysis, calibration, and validations for a multisite and multivariable SWAT model. *J. Am. Water Resour. Assoc.* **2005**, *41*, 1077–1089. [CrossRef]
61. Malagò, A.; Pagliero, L.; Bouraoui, F.; Franchini, M. Comparing calibrated parameter sets of the SWAT model for the Scandinavian and Iberian peninsulas. *Hydrol. Sci. J.* **2015**, *60*, 949–967. [CrossRef]
62. Reca, J.; Martinez, J. Genetic algorithms for the design of looped irrigation water distribution networks. *Water Resour. Res.* **2006**, *42*. [CrossRef]
63. Nash, J.E.; Sutcliffe, J.V. River flow forecasting through conceptual models Part I—A discussion of principles. *J. Hydrol.* **1970**, *10*, 283–290. [CrossRef]

Article

Coupled Heuristic Prediction of Long Lead-Time Accumulated Total Inflow of a Reservoir during Typhoons Using Deterministic Recurrent and Fuzzy Inference-Based Neural Network

Chien-Lin Huang [1], Nien-Sheng Hsu [1],* and Chih-Chiang Wei [2]

[1] Department of Civil Engineering, National Taiwan University, No. 1, Sec. 4, Roosevelt Road, Taipei 10617, Taiwan; d98521008@ntu.edu.tw

[2] Department of Marine Environmental Informatics, National Taiwan Ocean University, No.2, Beining Rd.; Jhongjheng District, Keelung City 20224, Taiwan; d89521007@ntu.edu.tw

* Correspondence: nsshue@ntu.edu.tw; Tel.: +886-2-3366-2640; Fax: +886-2-3366-5866

Academic Editor: Athanasios Loukas

Received: 31 July 2015; Accepted: 9 November 2015; Published: 17 November 2015

Abstract: This study applies Real-Time Recurrent Learning Neural Network (RTRLNN) and Adaptive Network-based Fuzzy Inference System (ANFIS) with novel heuristic techniques to develop an advanced prediction model of accumulated total inflow of a reservoir in order to solve the difficulties of future long lead-time highly varied uncertainty during typhoon attacks while using a real-time forecast. For promoting the temporal-spatial forecasted precision, the following original specialized heuristic inputs were coupled: observed-predicted inflow increase/decrease (OPIID) rate, total precipitation, and duration from current time to the time of maximum precipitation and direct runoff ending (DRE). This study also investigated the temporal-spatial forecasted error feature to assess the feasibility of the developed models, and analyzed the output sensitivity of both single and combined heuristic inputs to determine whether the heuristic model is susceptible to the impact of future forecasted uncertainty/errors. Validation results showed that the long lead-time–predicted accuracy and stability of the RTRLNN-based accumulated total inflow model are better than that of the ANFIS-based model because of the real-time recurrent deterministic routing mechanism of RTRLNN. Simulations show that the RTRLNN-based model with coupled heuristic inputs (RTRLNN-CHI, average error percentage (*AEP*)/average forecast lead-time (*AFLT*): 6.3%/49 h) can achieve better prediction than the model with non-heuristic inputs (*AEP* of RTRLNN-NHI and ANFIS-NHI: 15.2%/31.8%) because of the full consideration of real-time hydrological initial/boundary conditions. Besides, the RTRLNN-CHI model can promote the forecasted lead-time above 49 h with less than 10% of *AEP* which can overcome the previous forecasted limits of 6-h *AFLT* with above 20%–40% of *AEP*.

Keywords: accumulated total reservoir inflow; long lead-time hydrograph prediction; coupled heuristic inputs; real-time recurrent learning neural network; adaptive network-based fuzzy inference system

1. Introduction

Taiwan is located in the path of typhoons as they move in from the Western Pacific, and as a result, three to five typhoons hit Taiwan annually [1,2]. As the basins of the reservoir in Taiwan are mostly steep-sided, the concentration time is especially short and the reservoir inflow is extremely high under typhoon-induced precipitation [3]. The frequency of typhoons that bring heavy rain has been growing due to climate change [4–6], and inflows are more frequently surpassing original design and construction standards. Therefore, effective methods of ameliorating typhoon-related disasters need to include non-engineered disaster prevention programs, such as effective disaster forewarning and associated response mechanisms, which include the ability to identify the disaster before it occurs. The optimal releasing strategies for flood control are to minimize the maximum release and maximize the final storage under the principles of avoiding dam failure and overflow from the upstream riverbank, and keeping the water level lower than the dead storage level. Hence, we can expect that an accurate accumulated total reservoir inflow forecast model plays a most important role in determining whether the releasing decision can achieve optimization for flood control.

However, previous research into real-time long lead-time accumulated total reservoir inflow forecast during typhoons has been scarce, and it has proved difficult to achieve effective and accurate results because of future meteorological-hydrological uncertainty. The traditional method to derive real-time forecasted reservoir inflow hydrographs and the corresponding accumulated total inflow is firstly to forecast the typhoon precipitation hyetograph, and then the reservoir inflow hydrograph of the entire typhoon event is derived from the rainfall-runoff model. This type of rainfall-runoff modeling has been examined in the fields of the hydrological approach [7–12] and statistical approach [13,14]. However, studies like those above, regarding the real-time precipitation hyetograph forecast of an entire typhoon event, are scarce, so efficient and accurate long lead-time accumulated total inflow forecast is still in urgent need of development.

The other method regarding inflow forecast is to directly predict short lead-time reservoir inflow, because the model inputs only consider the real-time observed meteorological-hydrological information. These related works have been categorized under both the hydrological approach [15–17] and the statistical approach which mostly applied artificial neural networks (ANNs) such as the back-propagation neural network (BPNN) [18–22], the state space neural network [23], the adaptive network-based fuzzy inference system (ANFIS) [24], the recurrent neural network (RNN) [21], support vector machine [1], and the radial basis function [2] as construction tools. The advantage of the short lead-time forecast is that it is fairly accurate in medium-low reservoir inflow, whereas the disadvantages are that (1) the effective forecasted lead-time is only 6 h; (2) the forecasted error in the high flow periods is high, within the range of 10% to 40% [1,2]; and (3) the time-lag circumstances of the forecasted flow rate of a longer forecasted lead-time are significant. The main reason is that the previous models do not consider future reliable meteorological-hydrological factors as inputs. The feasible inputs include the delays from the current moment to the various key moments on the rainfall-runoff hydrograph, the accumulated total precipitation, and the observed-predicted inflow increase/decrease rate (OPIID rate), *etc.* Besides, the above studies concluded that the forecasted ability of RNN and ANFIS is better than the traditional ANNs like BPNN, and they have the potential to simulate longer lead-time inflow with larger tolerance ability for input errors. Moreover, among various ANN models, Chang *et al.* (2002) [25] indicated that real-time recurrent learning neural networks (RTRLNN) possesses dynamic real-time recurrent routing mechanisms that can simulate time-varying systems effectively.

In summary, the previous models seldom can achieve a reservoir inflow forecast with a long lead-time of up to 48–72 h considering the future highly varied meteorology-hydrology uncertainty of a typhoon. Because of the powerful capability of ANNs to model any kind of nonlinear relationship between inputs and output through a series of transfer functions without the need to make assumptions in advance, in recent years, ANNs have been used increasingly in applications for modeling hydrological processes. The advantages of using ANNs include the ability to derive accurate and fast real-time short-term forecasts with low building costs. However, the development and application of accurate and effective ANN-based models that have the most potential for long lead-time real-time inflow forecast (e.g., RTRLNN and ANFIS) with the other advanced novel heuristic techniques in accumulated total inflow forecasts during typhoons is a subject that urgently requires development and scientific breakthrough.

The purpose of this study is to apply RTRLNN and ANFIS with specially devised novel heuristic inputs such as observed-predicted inflow increase/decrease rate (OPIID rate), total precipitation (TP), duration from current time to the time of maximum precipitation, and direct runoff ending (DRE) to develop heuristic-type long lead-time accumulated total reservoir inflow forecast models. This study also utilized temporal-spatial forecasted error feature analysis to assess the feasibility of the developed long lead-time RTRLNN- and ANFIS-based models, and conducted output sensitivity analysis of single/combined heuristic inputs to determine whether the developed heuristic model is superior to the non-heuristic model and whether it is vulnerable to the impact of future forecasted uncertainty and error on inputs.

2. Development of Methodology

2.1. Procedures

The procedures used in this study are divided into three steps as shown in Figure 1. The detailed procedures are thoroughly described as follows:

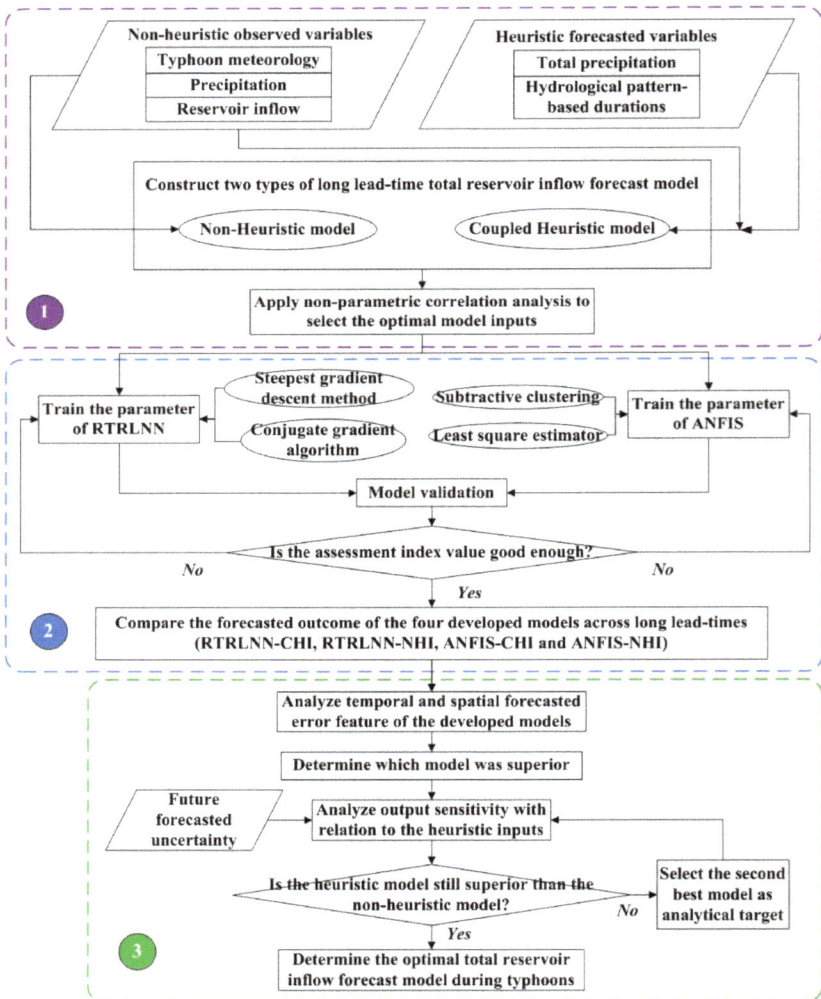

Figure 1. Flowchart of the methodology.

Step 1: First, observed short lead-time meteorological-, precipitation-, and pattern-based reservoir inflow factors during previous typhoons were specified as non-heuristic candidate inputs, and future long lead-time total precipitation- and pattern-based duration factors were specified as heuristic inputs. The optimal inputs for the non-heuristic and heuristic typhoon total inflow forecast model were selected by using non-parametric statistical correlation analysis.

Step 2: The steepest gradient descent (SGD) and conjugate gradient algorithm (CG) were used to train the parameter of RTRLNN, and subtractive clustering (SC) with the least square estimator (LSE) were applied to train the parameter of ANFIS. On obtaining the best model by comparing the assessment index value of the individually developed model type, the forecasted outcome for the RTRLNN-CHI (Coupled Heuristic Inputs) model, RTRLNN-NHI (No Heuristic Inputs) model, ANFIS-CHI model, and ANFIS-NHI model were compared across long lead-times.

Step 3-1: The temporal and spatial forecasted error feature of the four best types of long lead-time models developed were respectively analyzed, and a superior model determined.

Step 3-2: The output sensitivity of single or combined heuristic inputs due to future forecast uncertainty of the selected candidate optimal model among the four model types was analyzed under the impact of input forecasted error. Following the assessment, the optimal total reservoir inflow forecast model during typhoons was determined.

2.2. Developed Model Type of Accumulated Total Reservoir Inflow Forecast

This study designates the systematic operating mechanism of a reservoir of different stages as shown in Figure 2. To avoid dam failure and overflow from the upstream riverbank, the constraint can be expressed in Equation (1), and that to avoid a water level that is lower than dead storage is expressed in Equation (2).

$$A_2 - A_1 < S^{max}_{dam-safety} - x^S_0 \tag{1}$$

$$A_1 < x^S_0 - S^{dead} \tag{2}$$

where A_1, A_2, and A_3 are the increasing/reducing storage of Stage I, increasing storage of Stage II, and increasing/reducing storage of Stage III, respectively; $S^{max}_{dam-safety}$ is maximum safety storage for the dam; x^S_0 is the initial storage; and S^{dead} is the dead storage.

The releasing operating objectives of Stage I have to consider flood detention (expressed in Equation (3)) and final storage that at the same time (Equation (4)) are dominated by the future accumulated total inflow. Moreover, the constraint of Stage I involves avoiding the water level being lower than dead storage (Equation (2)). Hence, we can expect that the future accumulated total inflow is the key decision information of Stage I.

$$Max\{A_2\} \tag{3}$$

$$Min\left\{|A_1 + A_3 - A_2| - \left|S^{full} - x^S_0\right|\right\} \tag{4}$$

where $S^{max}_{dam-safety}$ is the maximum safety storage for the dam. In order to achieve optimal operation, the storage objective for the water supply is dominated primarily by Stage III and secondarily by Stage I, and the releasing operation of Stage II is used completely for flood detention (expressed in Equation (3)) that must subject to the safety constraint (Equation (1)). Hence, we can expect that the future total inflow is the key decision information of Stage II and Stage III.

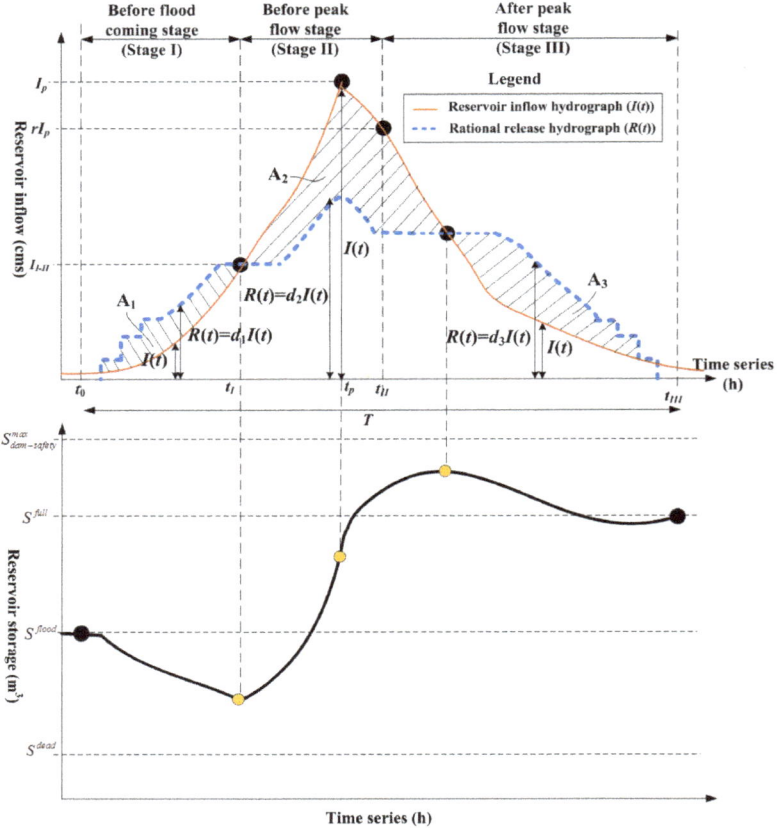

Figure 2. Schematic diagram of the flood operating mechanism of different stages in conjunction with the reservoir inflow.

The total reservoir inflow can be used as a criterion to determine the ideal amount of pre-discharge water and the benefit of flood detention under just filling the reservoir without overflowing the dam. Conventionally, the inflow can be calculated from the calculations of the rainfall-runoff simulation. The flow at the catchment outlet can be calculated using the unit hydrograph method, which is expressed as follows:

$$Q(t) = \int_A \int_0^t P(\tau) \cdot U(t - \tau) d\tau dA \qquad (5)$$

where $Q(t)$ is the inflow at time t; $P(\tau)$ is the effective rainfall; and $U(t - \tau)$ is the flow path unit response function. Liu *et al.* (2003) [26] estimated the travel time at an arbitrary point in the catchment area by combining the diffusive wave model with the flow path unit response function. Molnar and Ramirez (1998) [27] used Manning's equation and energy dissipation theory to solve the approximate solutions to the diffusion waves, which can be expressed as follows:

$$U(t) = \frac{1}{\sigma \sqrt{2\pi \cdot t^3/t_0^3}} \exp\left[-\frac{(t - t_0)^2}{2\pi \cdot t/t_0}\right] \qquad (6)$$

where t_0 is the average time of concentration for the water moving along the flow path from one point of the catchment area to the outlet; and σ is the standard deviation of the migration time. During the period of the typhoon, the effective rainfall in the future; $P(t+n)$, is related to the following atmospheric factors for the typhoon: distance between typhoon center and reservoir basin (h_{c-w}), grade 7/10 typhoon radius (R), typhoon movement speed (v_m), central wind speed (V_{max}), and central pressure (p_c). It can be expressed as the following:

$$P(t + \Delta t) = f(h_{c-w}, R, v_m, V_{max}, p_c) \tag{7}$$

where Δt is the forecasted lead-time. However, the uncertainty of the meteorology-hydrology relationship over a long lead-time is too high to make a determination as to the future typhoon atmospheric factors ahead of time. It is difficult to accurately forecast the rainfall hyetograph of the entire typhoon event in the future.

Hence, the rainfall-runoff model based on traditional hydrology was not used for real-time simulation and forecast of the reservoir inflow. A novel forecast method was developed and was found to be more reliable in forecasts. The new method adopted the total rainfall (P^{total}) method, and forecasted the various delays from the current moment to the key times along the rainfall-runoff hydrograph; for example, the delay from the current time to the maximum rainfall (T_{0-MP}), the delay to the end of the direct runoff (T_{0-DRE}), and the delay to the end of the water retreat (T_{0-EE}). The new method also used the observed-predicted inflow increase/decrease rate (OPIID rate) as the heuristic-type input. It is expected to be able to simulate the total reservoir inflow of the runoff hydrograph from the rainfall trend from a certain typhoon moving path in the future. A schematic diagram of hydrological key points within the rainfall-runoff hydrograph is shown in Figure 3. In this study, an original and innovative forecast model for the total reservoir inflow was developed with heuristic forecast inputs using ANFIS and RTRLNN. The model developed was analyzed and compared with the non-heuristic forecast model in which the input only included the real-time observed meteorology and hydrology information. The feasibility of the heuristic model for real-time forecast was also evaluated.

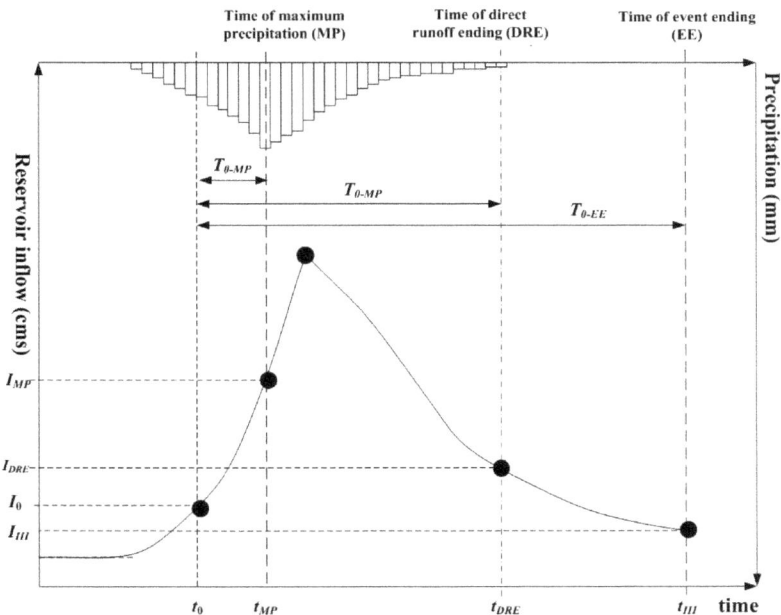

Figure 3. Schematic diagram of hydrological key points within the rainfall-runoff hydrograph.

2.2.1. Candidate Predictor

The choice of input candidates for the model is based on the theory of computation for the rainfall-runoff characteristics of the meteorology-hydrology relationship, such as the variables of reference Equations (5)–(7). In this study, four types of predictors which can be observed and predicted in real-time were used:

(1) Typhoon meteorological factor: longitude, latitude, central wind speed, central pressure, grade 7 typhoon radius, grade 10 typhoon radius, and typhoon movement speed, *etc.* The other feasible alternatives include relative humidity and temperature of the typhoon and basin, *etc.*, but the other feasible alternatives are relatively not highly related to inflow and were not selected as candidate inputs.

(2) Rainfall station factor: observed hourly rainfall and total precipitation at the ground station. The other feasible alternatives include radar reflective information and satellite image from the typhoon, but the accuracy and correlation toward surface rainfall is not as high as that of the ground station. Hence, the alternatives are not adopted as candidate inputs.

(3) The distance between the typhoon center and the forecasting basin center ($d(t)$): this distance can be obtained using a conversion formula from longitude/latitude to distance:

$$y(t) = 111.1 \times (lat_c(t) - lat_{fos}(t)) \tag{8}$$

$$x(t) = 111.1 \times (lon_c(t) - lon_{fos}(t)) \times \cos(\frac{lat_c(t) + lat_{fos}(t)}{2}) \tag{9}$$

$$d(t) = \sqrt{(x(t))^2 + (y(t))^2} \tag{10}$$

where $lat_c(t)$ and $lat_{fos}(t)$ are the latitudes of the typhoon center and the forecasting basin center at time t, and $lon_c(t)$ and $lon_{fos}(t)$ are longitudes of the typhoon center and the forecasting basin center at time t.

(4) Runoff factor:

I. The delays from the current moment to the various key moments on the rainfall-runoff hydrograph in hydrology. For example, these include the delay from the current moment to the moment the maximum rainfall occurs (T_{0-MP}), the delay to the end of the direct runoff (T_{0-DRE}), and the delay to the end of the water retreat (T_{0-EE}). The feasible alternative includes the delay to the inflection point after peak flow, which is equal to the delay to rainfall excess ending plus the time of concentration. However, it is difficult to predict the delay to rainfall excess ending in real-time across a long lead-time, leading to this alternative not being adopted.

II. The real-time observed hourly reservoir inflow and the observed-predicted inflow increase/decrease rate (OPIID rate).

The total precipitation could be obtained by constructing a forecast database from the historical samples of the relationship between the center position of the typhoon and the rainfall in the catchment area using data mining techniques. Similarly, the delay of the future typhoon invasion could be obtained by constructing a forecast database from the historical samples of the distribution of the center position of the typhoon when the maximum rainfall occurred, the time when the direct runoff ended, and the time when the water retreated using data mining techniques. The above-mentioned heuristic inputs (total precipitation and delays) are estimated by the path and direction of the typhoon and the characteristic database. Besides, the output of the model was the total reservoir inflow during the period from the current moment to the end of the event. In this research, a heuristic forecast model was studied. The inputs to this heuristic model simultaneously comprised the real-time observed meteorology and hydrology information (typhoon characteristic factors, basin hourly precipitation, basin reservoir hourly inflow) and future forecasted heuristic meteorology and hydrology information (the total rainfall from the current moment to the end of the event, $T_{0-MP}, T_{0-DRE}, T_{0-EE}$, and OPIID rate). The input for the non-heuristic forecast model only included the real-time observed meteorology and hydrology information. The structure of the developed heuristic-type and non-heuristic accumulated total inflow forecast model is shown in Figure 4.

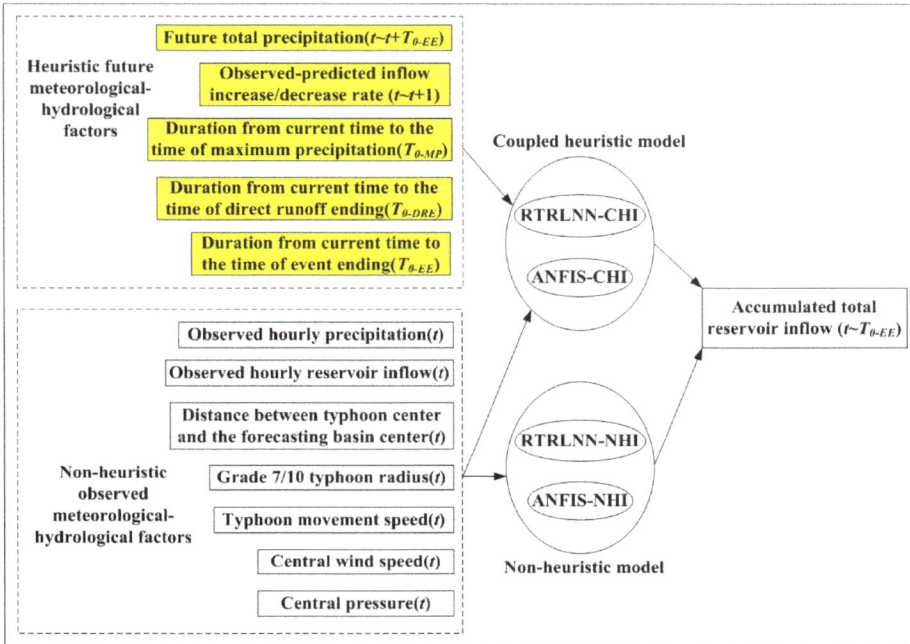

Figure 4. Structure of the developed coupled heuristic and non-heuristic accumulated total inflow forecast model.

2.2.2. Selection of Model Inputs

The feasible measures to select optimal model inputs include correlation analysis, principle component analysis, and the trial-and-error method. Among previous studies, the trial-and-error method is the most applied approach which is time-consuming. To effectively quantify the aptness for the large amount of candidate model inputs, this study uses correlation analysis for decision-making, and Spearman's rank correlation coefficient [28] is adopted as an analysis index. The analysis mechanism used for the correlation depends on the rank relationship of the time-series of two variables, and hence, this analysis can determine the correlation and suitability of input, regardless of the kind of relationship that exists between the candidate input and output, that is,

$$r_{rank} = 1 - \frac{6 \sum_{i=1}^{n} D_i^2}{n(n^2 - 1)} \tag{11}$$

$$D_i^2 = (Rank_{x_i} - Rank_{y_i})^2 \tag{12}$$

where r_{rank} is Spearman's rank correlation coefficient, n is the number of data, x is the candidate input of the forecast model (predictor), y is the model output also known as the predictant (accumulated total reservoir inflow during time $t + 1$ to $t + T_{0\text{-}EE}$), and $Rank_{x_i}$ and $Rank_{y_i}$ are the sort values of x_i and y_i in their individual time-series of the variable, respectively. The most correlated candidate predictors for forecasting accumulated total inflow will be selected as optimal inputs, and the selected inputs must subject to hydrological relationships and the r_{rank} must larger than the assigned threshold values.

2.2.3. Assessment Index of Forecast Models

The performance of the forecast models was evaluated using the mean absolute error (*MAE*) and correlation coefficient (*CC*) criterion in the present study. The other feasible alternatives are root mean square error (*RMSE*), R^2, and coefficient of efficiency (*CE*). However, *RMSE* and R^2 are respectively similar to *MAE* and *CC*, and *CE* cannot assess the time delay effect of the forecast. Hence, the other alternatives are not adopted. The computational equations of *MAE* and *CC* are expressed as follows:

$$MAE = \frac{\sum\limits_{t=1}^{n} |\hat{Y}(t) - Y(t)|}{n} \tag{13}$$

$$CC = \frac{N\sum \hat{Y}(t)Y(t) - \sum \hat{Y}(t)\sum Y(t)}{\sqrt{\sum \hat{Y}^2(t) - \frac{(\sum \hat{Y}(t))^2}{n}}\sqrt{\sum Y^2(t) - \frac{(\sum Y(t))^2}{n}}} \tag{14}$$

where $\hat{Y}(t)$ is the forecasted value at time t; $Y(t)$ is the actual value at time t; and n is the number of data. Smaller values of *MAE* imply a higher accuracy of the forecast model, and larger *CC* values indicate a closer coupling between the forecasted and measured series.

2.3. Heuristic Construction of RTRLNN

RTRLNN is a dynamic neural network with a stable routing mechanism and algorithm. The dynamic characteristics of a RTRLNN could be illustrated by the outputs of time-series based on an instantaneous impulse to the RTRLNN. The network structure is different from the traditional static and feed-forward neural networks in that it allows recurrence between neurons and offers the function of local and temporal memory in the network, so the RTRLNN can simulate complex and time-varying systems that previous static neural networks could not handle effectively [25,29]. RTRLNN generally contains one or several recurrent loops. The RTRLNN network structure that we adopt in this study is shown in Figure 5. It is a multilayer perceptron and is composed of a concatenated input-output layer, a processing layer, and an output layer. The recurrent loops are recurrent from the output vector of the processing layer to the concatenated input-output layer. Hence, the concatenated input-output layer not only includes the input factor of the outer environment, but also stores the processed information from the processing layer before the current time. This allows the network to establish a temporal mutual connection and a dependent relationship between input variables because of the inner recurrent connection relationship, so the structure and mechanism can effectively learn the connection of the time-series (Elman, 1990 [30]).

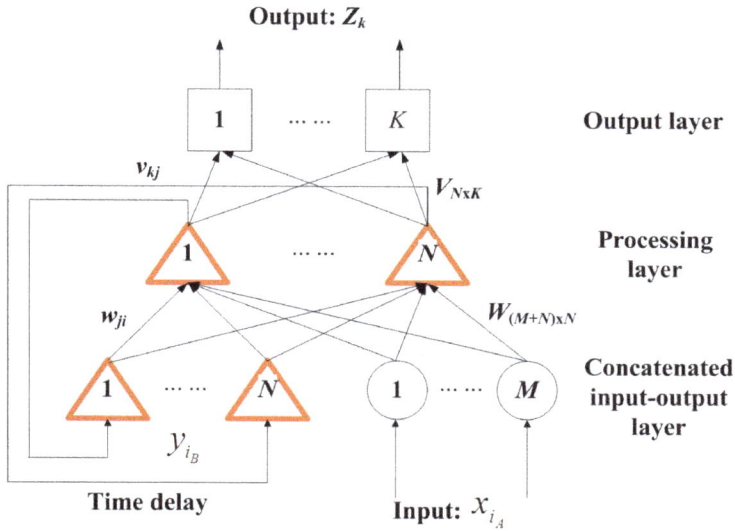

Figure 5. Structure of a RTRLNN.

The input vector of the concatenated input-output layer contains actual input variables x_{i_A} and recurrent input variables y_{i_B} (i_A and i_B are the number of actual and recurrent inputs, respectively):

$$u_i = [x_{i_A}, y_{i_B}] \quad for \quad i_A = 1, \ldots, M \quad i_B = 1, \ldots, N \tag{15}$$

where M and N are the total numbers of actual and recurrent inputs, respectively. The feed-forward propagation of the network first multiplies the input vector (u_i) with the corresponding weights (w_{ji}) to obtain net_j, then transfers net_j by a transfer function ($f(\cdot)$) to obtain the output of the processing layer (y_j):

$$net_j = \sum_{i \in i_A \cup i_B} w_{ji} u_i \tag{16}$$

$$y_j = f(net_j) \tag{17}$$

where i, j, and k are the neuron numbers of the concatenated input-output layer, the processing layer, and the output layer, respectively. Multiplying y_j with the corresponding weights (v_{kj}) and summing them gives net_k, and transfer net_k by a transfer function ($f(\cdot)$) gives the output of the output layer (z_k):

$$net_k = \sum v_{kj} y_j \tag{18}$$

$$z_k = f(net_k) \tag{19}$$

In this study, the feasible transfer functions of the processing layer include tan-sigmoid (expressed in Equation (20)), linear, log-sigmoid, radial basis function, and symmetric saturating linear function, while the output layer is linear. The best suitable transfer function for the forecast model is extracted fully by trail results.

$$y_j = \frac{e^{net_j} - e^{-net_j}}{e^{net_j} + e^{-net_j}} \tag{20}$$

During RTRLNN training, the network not only continuously executes the message handling, but also revises each connected weighted vector in real-time according to the simulated error that belongs to the learning algorithm. Set $d_k(t)$ as the target value of neuron k at time t. Then we define a time-varying $K \times 1$ error vector $e_k(t)$, whose kth element is:

$$e_k(t) = d_k(t) - z_k(t) \tag{21}$$

Then we define the instantaneous overall network error $(E(t))$ at time t as

$$E(t) = \frac{1}{2} \sum_{k=1}^{K} e_k^2(t) \tag{22}$$

The total cost function (E_{total}) is obtained by summing $E(t)$ over all time T

$$E_{total} = \sum_{t=1}^{T} E(t) \tag{23}$$

To minimize the cost function, this study applies the recursive steepest gradient descent method and the conjugate gradient algorithm to adjust the weights ($\mathbf{V}$ and $\mathbf{W}$) along the negative of ∇E_{total}. The other feasible alternative is the Quasi-Newton method which is more time-consuming than the others, so the method is not adopted. Because the total error is the sum of the errors at the individual time-steps, we compute this gradient by accumulating the value of ∇E for each time-step along the trajectory. The weight change for any particular weight $(\Delta v_{kj}(t))$ can thus be written as

$$\Delta v_{kj}(t) = -\eta_1 \frac{\partial E(t)}{\partial v_{kj}(t)} \tag{24}$$

where η_1 is the learning-rate parameter. In Equation (24), $\frac{\partial E(t)}{\partial v_{kj}(t)}$ can be written as

$$\frac{\partial E(t)}{\partial v_{kj}(t)} = -e_k(t) f\prime(net_k(t)) y_j(t) \tag{25}$$

The same method can also be implemented for the specific weight w_{mn}, that is

$$\Delta w_{mn}(t-1) = -\eta_2 \frac{\partial E(t)}{\partial w_{mn}(t-1)} \tag{26}$$

where η_2 is the learning-rate parameter. The partial derivative $\frac{\partial E(t)}{\partial w_{mn}(t-1)}$ can be obtained by the chain rule for differentiation as follows:

$$\frac{\partial E(t)}{\partial w_{mn}(t-1)} = \left[\sum_{k=1}^{K} -e_k(t) f\prime(net_k(t)) v_{kj}(t) \right] \frac{\partial y_j(t)}{\partial w_{mn}(t-1)} \tag{27}$$

$$\Rightarrow \frac{\partial y_j(t)}{\partial w_{mn}(t-1)} = f\prime(net_j(t)) \frac{\partial net_j(t)}{\partial w_{mn}(t-1)} \tag{28}$$

$$\Rightarrow \frac{\partial net_j(t)}{\partial w_{mn}(t-1)} = \sum_{i \in (i_A \cup i_B)} \frac{\partial (w_{ji}(t-1) u_i(t-1))}{\partial w_{mn}(t-1)} \tag{29}$$

$$\Rightarrow \frac{\partial net_j(t)}{\partial w_{mn}(t-1)} = \sum_{i \in (i_A \cup i_B)} \left[w_{ji}(t-1) \frac{\partial u_i(t-1)}{\partial w_{mn}(t-1)} + \frac{\partial w_{ji}(t-1)}{\partial w_{mn}(t-1)} u_i(t-1) \right] \tag{30}$$

$$subject \quad to$$

$$\frac{\partial w_{ji}(t-1)}{\partial w_{mn}(t-1)} = \begin{cases} 1, & when \quad (j=m) \cap (i=n) \\ 0, & else \end{cases} \tag{31}$$

Equation (30) can be rewritten as

$$\frac{\partial net_j(t)}{\partial w_{mn}(t-1)} = \sum_{i \in (i_A \cup i_B)} w_{ji}(t-1)\frac{\partial u_i(t-1)}{\partial w_{mn}(t-1)} + \delta_{mj}u_n(t-1) \tag{32}$$

$$subject \quad to$$

$$\delta_{mj} = \begin{cases} 1, & if \quad j = m \\ 0, & else \end{cases} \tag{33}$$

where δ_{mj} is the Kronecker delta. From the definition of $u_i(t)$, we also note that

$$\frac{\partial u_i(t-1)}{\partial w_{mn}(t-1)} = \begin{cases} 0, & when \quad i \in i_A \\ \frac{\partial y_i(t-1)}{\partial w_{mn}(t-1)}, & when \quad i \in i_B \end{cases} \tag{34}$$

According to the propagation mechanism of RTRLNN, the initial state of the network at time $t = 0$ has no functional dependence on the synaptic weights, that is

$$\frac{\partial y_j(0)}{\partial w_{mn}(0)} = 0 \tag{35}$$

$$\frac{\partial y_j(t)}{\partial w_{mn}(t-1)} = f\prime(net_j(t)) \left[\sum_{i \in i_B} w_{ji}(t-1)\frac{\partial y_i(t-1)}{\partial w_{mn}(t-1)} + \delta_{mj}u_n(t-1) \right] \tag{36}$$

Let

$$\frac{\partial y_j(t)}{\partial w_{mn}(t)} = \left\{ \pi_{mn}^j(t) | (\forall j \in i_B) \cap (\forall m \in i_B) \cap [\forall n \in (i_A \cup i_B)] \right\} \approx \frac{\partial y_j(t)}{\partial w_{mn}(t-1)} \tag{37}$$

where $\pi_{mn}^j(t)$ are the triple indexed sets of variables which describe a dynamic system. For each time step t and all appropriate m, n, and j, the dynamics of the system are governed by

$$\pi_{mn}^j(t) = f\prime(net_j) \left[\sum_{i \in i_B} w_{ji}(t-1)\pi_{mn}^i(t-1) + \delta_{mj}u_n(t-1) \right] \tag{38}$$

$$I.C.: \quad \pi_{mn}^j(0) = 0$$

Then the weight changes can be computed as

$$\Delta w_{mn}(t-1) = \eta_2 \left[\sum e_k(t)f\prime(net_k(t))v_{kj}(t) \right] \pi_{mn}^j(t) \tag{39}$$

$$\Delta v_{kj}(t) = \eta_1 e_k(t)f\prime(net_k(t))y_j(t) \tag{40}$$

2.4. Heuristic Construction of ANFIS

ANFIS was proposed by Jang (1993) [31], and is based on a fuzzy inference system constructed by combining the self-organization characteristics of a neural network. Hence, ANFIS integrates two algorithms to improve its accuracy, and solves for the best parameters by employing capabilities of learning and self-adaption. ANFIS is composed of an input layer, a rule layer, a normalization layer, a consequent layer, and an output layer, as shown in Figure 6. The modeling tool can transform the fuzzy-complex process and phenomenon into an artificial logic language that is therefore a potential approach for typhoon precipitation forecasting. The computation and transmission of each layer is described as follows.

69

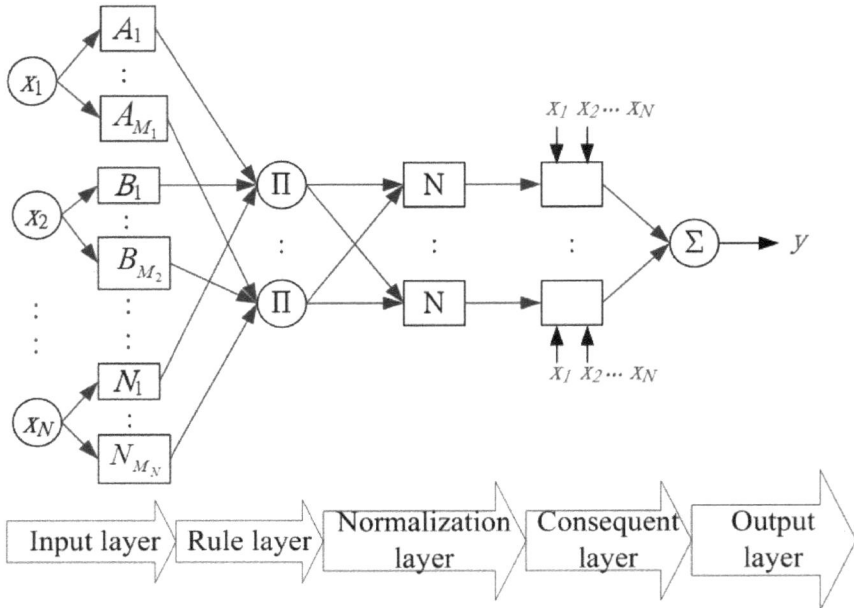

Figure 6. Structure of an ANFIS.

(1) Input layer

This layer projects input to a group of fuzzy sets and estimates the values of a group of membership functions. The most common types of membership functions are triangular, trapezoidal, Gaussian, generalized bell-shaped, and sigmoid functions. To retrieve the parameters of the input layer efficiently, this study adopts a group of Gaussian functions as the membership functions with subtractive clustering (SC), which can be expressed as follows:

$$O_{1,ji} = u_{ji}(x_i) = \exp\left(-\frac{\|x_i - c_{ji}\|^2}{2\sigma_{ji}^2}\right) \quad i=1,2,\ldots,N \quad j=1,2,\ldots,M_i \tag{41}$$

where $u_{ji}(x_i)$ is the membership function; c_{ji} and σ_{ji} are the antecedent parameters; N is the number of inputs; and M_i is the number of the fuzzy membership functions of input i.

(2) Rule layer

This layer precedes the antecedent match of the fuzzy logic rule between variables, and then applies a T-norm product operation to obtain the weighted value of each rule, that is,

$$O_{2,p} = w_p = \prod_{i=1}^{N} u_{pi}(x_i) \quad p=1,\ldots,P \tag{42}$$

where w_p is the weighted value; and P is the number of rules.

(3) Normalization layer

The node of this layer computes the output ratio between the node and all other nodes, that is,

$$O_{3,p} = \overline{w}_p = \frac{w_p}{\sum_{p=1}^{P} w_p} \tag{43}$$

(4) Consequent layer

The output of the consequent layer node is the product of the outputs of the normalization layer and the Sugeno fuzzy model (Takagi and Sugeno, 1983 [32]), that is,

$$O_{4,p} = \overline{w}_p f_p = \overline{w}_p (\sum_{i=0}^{N} r_{pi} x_i) \tag{44}$$

where r_{pi} represents the consequent parameters; and x_0 is equal to 1.

(5) Output layer

This layer sums the outputs of the previous layer to compute the model output, that is,

$$O_{5,p} = \sum_{p=1}^{P} \overline{w}_p f_p = \frac{\sum\limits_{p=1}^{P} w_p f_p}{\sum\limits_{p=1}^{P} w_p} \tag{45}$$

ANFIS is a feed-forward neural network and is constructed by supervised learning. The network parameters can be divided into antecedent parameters (nonlinear parameters: c_{ji}, σ_{ji}) and consequent parameters (linear parameters: r_{pi}), and the model structure is determined by setting the number of membership functions in the input layer and the number of nodes in the rule layer. The parameters can be solved by the steepest gradient descent method and Newton's method, for example. However, the methods would be slow and would produce a worse convergence and drop-in local optimum if the searching problem was more complex. To decrease the time for model construction in obtaining the best network structures and parameters, this study constructs ANFIS using hybrid algorithms including subtractive clustering (SC) and a least square estimator (LSE). The input and output vectors were first classified by subtractive clustering before training the model. The number of clusters obtained from the classification was set as the number of membership functions for node fuzzification at the various input layers and the number of nodes at the rule layers. After determining the network structures, the center point and standard deviation of each cluster were taken as the initial parameters of the input layer membership functions (Gaussian function). The training data were then fed into the network with the consequent linear parameter set and the antecedent nonlinear parameter set solved by the least squares estimator and the gradient steepest descent method, respectively. The corresponding algorithm flowchart of the model construction is shown in Figure 7. The network structure significantly reduces the time required to retrieve the optimal number of fuzzy membership functions, number of rules, and network parameters; the optimal network structure and parameters can be obtained after simply setting the adjacent radius in subtractive clustering between 0 and 1 (Jang, 1993 [31]).

Subtractive clustering was employed in the present study to construct fuzzy if-then rules in order to reduce the number of parameters of the fuzzy membership function in the ANFIS model. This was performed to establish a suitable rule base in the fuzzy inference system. Subtractive clustering was proposed by Chiu (1994) [33], in which every data point is treated as the candidate of the cluster center. Subtractive clustering is a fast and independent clustering method: the computational complexity is proportional to the number of data and is independent of the system dimension. For example, $x_i (i = 1, 2, \ldots, n)$ are n sets of data in an M-dimensional space and the corresponding density measures D are defined as

$$D_i = \sum_{j=1}^{n} \exp \left(-\frac{\|x_i - x_j\|^2}{(r_a/2)^2} \right) \tag{46}$$

where the adjacent radius r_a is a positive number representing the distance near the center, and the data points outside the radius have minimum impact on the density measure. The density measure is calculated for each data point (x_i), and the one with the highest density (D_{c1}) is selected as the first cluster center (x_{c1}). The definition of the density measure is then modified to select the next cluster center. Setting that x_{ck} is the cluster center selected at the kth round, and the corresponding density measure is D_{ck}, the modified formula is as follows:

$$D_i = D_i - D_{ck} \exp\left(-\frac{\|x_i - x_{ck}\|^2}{(r_b/2)^2}\right) \tag{47}$$

where radius r_b has the same definition as r_a and is usually set as $1.5r_a$ so that the selected center will not be too close to that of the previous one. The above procedure of cluster center selection is repeated until a termination condition is reached, or there is a sufficient number of cluster centers.

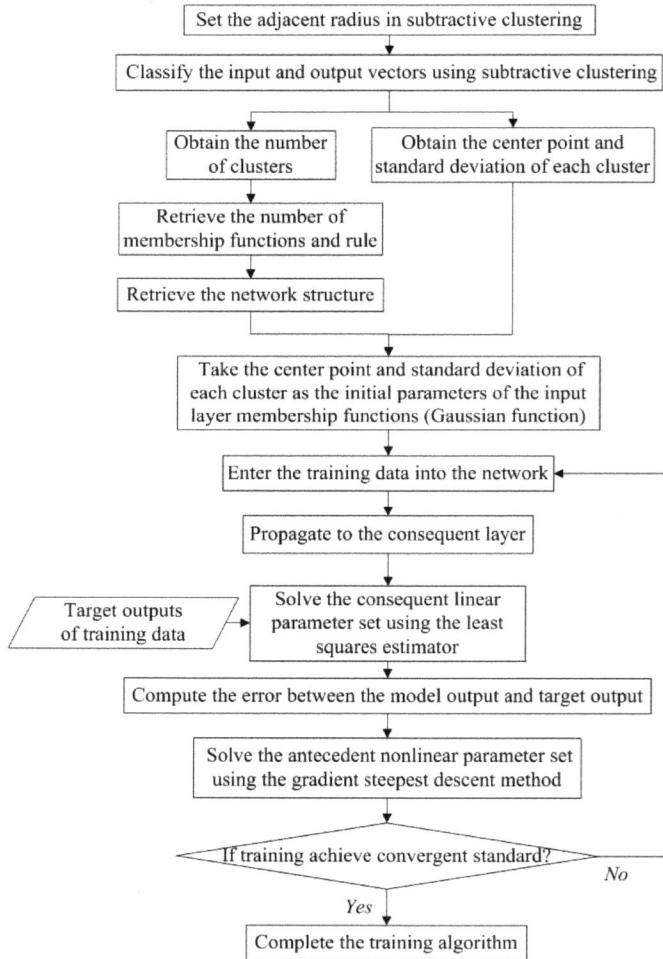

Figure 7. Flowchart of training the parameter and structure of ANFIS.

2.5. Analysis of Temporal and Spatial Forecasted Error Feature of the Developed Long Lead-Time Models

In this research, RTRLNN and ANFIS were used to study four types of coupled heuristic and non-heuristic forecast models (RTRLNN-CHI, RTRLNN-NHI, ANFIS-CHI and ANFIS-NHI) for long lead-time forecast of the total reservoir inflow. To evaluate the forecast accuracy and applicability of the four models on typhoon invasion, analyses were conducted on the characteristics of the temporal and spatial forecast errors for the most optimal forecast case of the four models. Assessments were made as to which model had the best forecast performance. For the analysis of the temporal forecast error, calculations were made for each forecast model for the absolute error between the forecasted time and the forecasted total reservoir inflow during the verification phase of the typhoon event at each field. The errors were then used to assess the capability and limits of the model for the long lead-time forecasting of the total reservoir inflow, which could be calculated as follows:

$$AEP(\Delta t) = \frac{\sum\limits_{p=1}^{P} \frac{\left|\hat{Y}_p(\Delta t) - Y_p(\Delta t)\right|}{Y_p(\Delta t)}}{P} \times 100\% \tag{48}$$

where $AEP(\Delta t)$ is average error percentage for forecasted lead-time Δt, $\hat{Y}_p(\Delta t)$ and $Y_p(\Delta t)$ are the forecasted and actual accumulated total reservoir inflow on typhoon event number p for forecasted lead-time Δt, respectively; and P is the total number of typhoon events.

For each forecast model, the analysis of the spatial forecast error included calculation of the absolute error on the forecasted total reservoir inflow at the spatial position of the typhoon center during the verification phase of the typhoon event at each field. These errors were used to discuss the capability and limits of the long lead-time forecasting of the total reservoir inflow for each model when the typhoon center moved to each of the spatial grids, which could be expressed as

$$AEP(x, y) = \frac{\sum\limits_{p=1}^{P} \frac{\left|\hat{Y}_p(x,y) - Y_p(x,y)\right|}{Y_p(x,y)}}{P} \times 100\% \tag{49}$$

where $AEP(x, y)$ is the average error percentage while the typhoon center is located at longitude x and latitude y, $\hat{Y}_p(x, y)$ and $Y_p(x, y)$ are the forecasted and actual accumulated total reservoir inflow on typhoon event number p while the typhoon center is located at longitude x and latitude y, respectively, and P is the total number of typhoon events.

2.6. Output Sensitivity Analysis of Single or Combined Heuristic Inputs Due to Future Forecasted Uncertainty

The coupled heuristic model in this research can forecast the rainfall-runoff hydrology under a specific movement path for the future typhoon, which increases the long lead-time forecast accuracy of the accumulated total reservoir inflow. However, if this model was applied to real-time forecasting, the uncertainty of the meteorology and hydrology for the long lead-time typhoon in the future would be unacceptably high. There would be cases with unavoidable forecast errors on quantities such as the long lead-time total rainfall in the future, the delay from the current time to the maximum rainfall (T_{0-MP}), the delay to the end of the direct runoff (T_{0-DRE}), and the delay to the end of the water retreat in the typhoon event (T_{0-EE}). When such heuristic information is coupled with the input of the heuristic model, it is possible that unexpected errors will be generated on the forecast output of the model. Thus, in order to evaluate the feasibility, applicability, and accuracy of the heuristic model for real-time forecasting, sensitivity analysis was conducted on the effects on the output when forecast errors exist in the heuristic input of the most optimal heuristic model. The above analysis was used to judge whether the forecast accuracy of the heuristic model was better than that of the non-heuristic model for real-time forecasting when errors exist in the input. The expression for the analysis is as shown below:

$$\hat{Y}_i^H(t) = f_{\substack{RTRLNN-CHI \\ ANFIS-CHI}}(x_i^H(t) \pm EP \cdot x_i^H(t), X^{NH}(t)) \tag{50}$$

$$AEP(i, \pm EP) = \frac{\sum\limits_{t=1}^{n} \frac{\left|\hat{Y}_i^H(t) - Y(t)\right|}{Y(t)}}{n} \times 100\% \tag{51}$$

where $\hat{Y}_i^H(t)$ is the forecasted value at time t under entering error into heuristic input number i; $f_{\left[\begin{smallmatrix} RTRLNN-CHI \\ ANFIS-CHI \end{smallmatrix}\right]}$ is the developed coupled heuristic forecast model; $x_i^H(t)$ is the input value of heuristic input number i at time t; $\pm EP$ is the average error percentage based on previous studies; $X^{NH}(t)$ is the value of non-heuristic input at time t; $Y(t)$ is the actual value at time t; and n is the number of data.

3. Application

3.1. Study Area

The methodology proposed in the present study was applied to the Shihmen Reservoir catchment area, which measures approximately 763.4 km². The main stream within this area is the Dahan Creek, which is the upper stream of the Tamsui River. The effective capacity is approximately 2.098×10^8 cubic meters. The annual average rainfall in the catchment area is approximately 2350 mm, with 80% of the annual rainfall concentrated in the period between May and October. Most of the rainfall is from typhoon precipitation. The annual inflow of the Shihmen Reservoir is approximately 1.510 billion tons. The study area is shown in Figure 8.

3.2. Data Used in Model Construction

This study used instantaneous observed non-heuristic and coupled heuristic information to forecast accumulated total inflow during current time to the event recessional ending. The output variable was taken as the future accumulated total inflow forecast in the Shihmen Reservoir catchment area. In this study, the end of the typhoon flood event was defined as the moment that simultaneously satisfied the following conditions: (1) the Meteorology Bureau lifted the alarm for typhoon on land and over the sea; (2) rainfall completely stopped in the catchment areas; (3) the reservoir inflow decreased below 300 cms. The model construction included two stages, namely the training and validation stages. The adopted typhoon events for training are Aere, Matsa, Talim, Long-Wang, Wipha, Fung-Wong, Sinlaku, Morakot, Megi, and Meari, and for validation they are Haitang, Sepat, Krosa, Jangmi, and Parma. The total data number for training is 459, and for validation it is 211. The adopted typhoon events for model construction among the training and validation stages are shown in Table 1, and the moving paths of the typhoons used in model construction are shown in Figure 9.

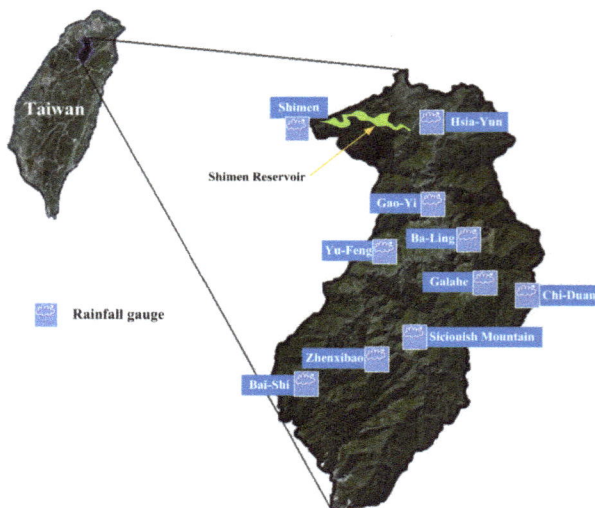

Figure 8. Study area.

Table 1. The adopted typhoon events for model construction among the training and validation stages.

Construction Stage	Typhoon Name	Time Period	Total Reservoir Inflow (m³)	Data Number	Total Data Number
Training	Aere	23–26 August 2004	748, 936, 728	58	459
	Matsa	4–6 August 2005	541, 872, 324	61	
	Talim	31 August 2005–2 September 2005	201, 308, 580	33	
	Long-Wang	2–3 October 2005	68, 596, 704	24	
	Wipha	18–20 September 2007	186, 601, 752	48	
	Fung-Wong	28–29 July 2008	103, 422, 564	33	
	Sinlaku	13–16 September 2008	554, 322, 600	75	
	Morakot	7–10 August 2009	205, 435, 980	71	
	Megi	21–22 October 2010	54, 991, 728	37	
	Meari	25 June 2011	44, 826, 012	19	
Validation	Haitang	17–20 July 2005	237, 416, 256	53	211
	Sepat	18 August 2007	128, 935, 224	20	
	Krosa	6–8 October 2007	409, 855, 824	53	
	Jangmi	28–30 September 2008	220, 301, 136	53	
	Parma	6 October 2009	40, 997, 340	18	
	Fanapi	19 September 2010	33, 694, 956	14	

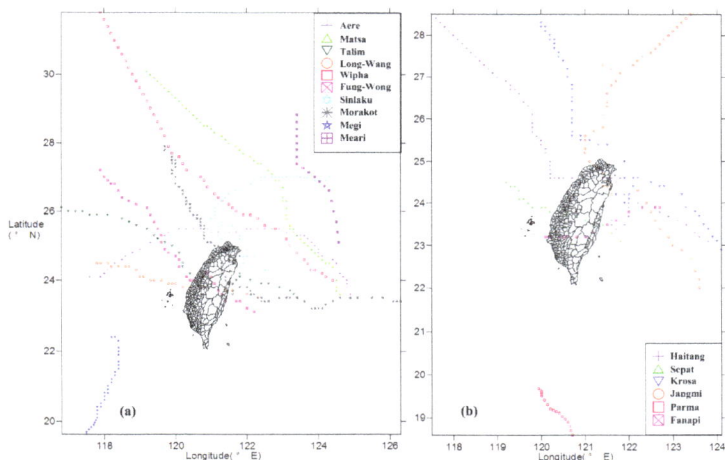

Figure 9. Moving paths of typhoons used in model construction: (**a**) training; (**b**) validation.

3.3. Results and Discussion

3.3.1. Model Inputs Selection

Correlation analysis was applied in the present study to assess the correlation coefficient between each input factor and the future accumulated total inflow for the Shihmen Reservoir. The selected heuristic model inputs and corresponding correlation coefficients are the future accumulated total basin precipitation (r_{rank}: 0.926), duration from current time to the end of the flood event (r_{rank}: 0.960), duration from current time to the time of DRE (r_{rank}: 0.751), duration from current time to the time of maximum precipitation (r_{rank}: 0.548), and observed-predicted inflow increase/decrease rate (r_{rank}: 0.401). These selected variables are the most correlated inputs among all heuristic candidate predictors and the r_{rank} value of all the selected inputs must be larger than 0.4. Furthermore, the selected non-heuristic model inputs and corresponding correlation coefficients are the observed hourly basin precipitation at the current time (r_{rank}: 0.672), hourly reservoir inflow (r_{rank}: 0.509), typhoon central longitude (r_{rank}: 0.610), central wind speed (r_{rank}: 0.650), and central pressure (r_{rank}: 0.639); these selected variables are the most correlated inputs among all non-heuristic candidate predictors and the r_{rank} values must all be larger than 0.5. Research conducted by Lin and Chen (2005) [34] revealed that excessive model inputs could introduce additional noise into the model, therefore 10 input factors were selected as a maximum based on the correlation coefficients. Based on the above analytical results, the developed heuristic forecast model includes 10 inputs including both heuristic and non-heuristic inputs, and the non-heuristic model only includes five non-heuristic inputs. The heuristic parameters are considered to be essential for use in eliminating the forecasting uncertainty, and for characterizing future long lead-time accumulated total inflow.

3.3.2. Results of Model Construction

In this study, RTRLNN and ANFIS were used to construct coupled heuristic and non-heuristic forecast models for long lead-time forecasting of the future accumulated total inflow for the Shihmen Reservoir. The choice of the particular set of parameters of the optimal model is retrieved by applying an intelligent heuristic searching strategy on the setting structure parameters (*i.e.*, neuron numbers of the processing layer for RTRLNN and the adjacent radius for ANFIS), and the values of the connected parameters corresponding to the setting structure are calibrated by using the heuristic algorithm described in Sections 2.3 and 2.4. The searching strategy first constructs models by setting a series of neuron numbers (1–15) and adjacent radius (0–1) equally from the feasible domain with the reliable representative amount (10 per neuron number and 100 for adjacent radius), and then the structure parameter of the best model among the equally distributed sampling process was strengthened by construction with more experimental frequency to retrieve the optimal model efficiently. The forecasted outcomes of the most optimal model of the four types of forecast architecture (RTRLNN-CHI, RTRLNN-NHI, ANFIS-CHI, and ANFIS-NHI) are shown in Table 2. The best training and verification results for the RTRLNN-CHI model, ANFIS-CHI model, and RTRLNN-NHI model are shown in Figures 10–12, respectively. The *MAE* values for the verification stage of the RTRLNN-CHI model, RTRLNN-NHI model, ANFIS-CHI model, and ANFIS-NHI model were respectively 11,721,556 m³, 30,475,270 m³, 14,429,374 m³, and 53,236,429 m³, while the *CC* values for the verification were 0.979, 0.876, 0.975, and 0.658, respectively. The results indicate that the respective forecast accuracy and stability of the RTRLNN-CHI and ANFIS-CHI models are significantly higher than those of the RTRLNN-NHI and ANFIS-NHI models. This shows that the proposed heuristic forecast model may be highly accurate in its forecast of the total reservoir inflow under the following conditions: (1) when the input includes key inputs such as the future accumulated total precipitation and the delays from the current moment to the key hydrology points of the hydrograph (maximum precipitation, direct runoff ending, and event recessional ending); (2) with assistance of the comprehensive simulation of the real-time observed atmospheric factors and rainfall-runoff factors of the typhoon.

Table 2. Best assessment indexes values of the four kinds of constructed models.

Structure Parameters/Assessment Indexes	RTRLNN-CHI Model	RTRLNN-NHI Model	Structure Parameters/Assessment Indexes	ANFIS-CHI Model	ANFIS-NHI Model
Best node number of hidden layer	3	9	Best adjacent radius/rule number	0.922/2	0.836/3
MAE of training (m³)	4587459	22430139	*MAE* of training (m³)	7249160	59066261
MAE of validation (m³)	11721556	30475271	*MAE* of validation (m³)	14429375	53236429
CC of training	0.999	0.980	*CC* of training	0.998	0.867
CC of validation	0.980	0.876	*CC* of validation	0.976	0.659

The input information for the RTRLNN-NHI and ANFIS-NHI models only included the current real-time observed conditions of the typhoon atmosphere and rainfall-runoff status. The average forecasted accuracy of the RTRLNN-NHI and ANFIS-NHI models is respectively worse than that of the RTRLNN-CHI/ANFIS-CHI models by 1.6/1.11 times and 3.54/2.68 times, and average forecasted stability is worse by 10.5%/10.2% and 32.8%/32.5%. Hence, these two non-heuristic models could not be used to accurately and physically simulate the accumulated total reservoir inflow after long lead-time changes in the meteorology and hydrology. The reason is that the model inputs only have initial conditions (observed rainfall-runoff variables) but do not have boundary conditions for future periods to simulate the shape and duration of future inflow hydrographs. This obviously caused the forecasting accuracy and stability of the accumulated total inflow at the moment of maximum rainfall in the early stage of the event to be inferior to that at the later stages after the flood peaked. Moreover, the activation function in the hidden layer of the most optimal RTRLNN-based forecast model for the total reservoir inflow was a tan-sigmoid transfer function, while the activation function in the output layer was a linear activation function. The reason is that the shape of the tan-sigmoid function is similar to the cumulative distribution function (CDF) of the inflow hydrograph, and the shape of the CDF is exactly the inverse of the accumulated total inflow hydrograph. Hence, the tan-sigmoid function can simulate future accumulated total inflow better than the other shapes of functions. Furthermore, the numbers of neurons for the processing layer of the most optimal models in the RTRLNN-CHI and RTRLNN-NHI models were three and nine, respectively, and the rule numbers for the most optimal ANFIS-CHI and ANFIS-NHI models were two and three, respectively. This indicates that there was insufficient input information to represent future boundary conditions of the typhoon rainfall-runoff relationship over a long lead-time in the non-heuristic model. Therefore, a more complicated and time-consuming model is required to simulate the accumulated total reservoir inflow in the future.

In addition, from the evaluation-index point of view, for the two heuristic models, the overall forecast accuracy and stability of the RTRLNN-CHI model for forecasting the total reservoir inflow was slightly better than that of the ANFIS-CHI model by 0.23 times of *MAE* and 0.41% of *CC*. The reason is that there is a fixed-ratio real-time feedback calculation mechanism in the structure of the RTRLNN model. When the simulation mechanism and characteristics of the model were applied to forecasting time-varying output targets with a long lead-time and high uncertainty, better forecasting results were obtained than with the ANFIS model, which lacks flexibility in the input and rule layers that were used.

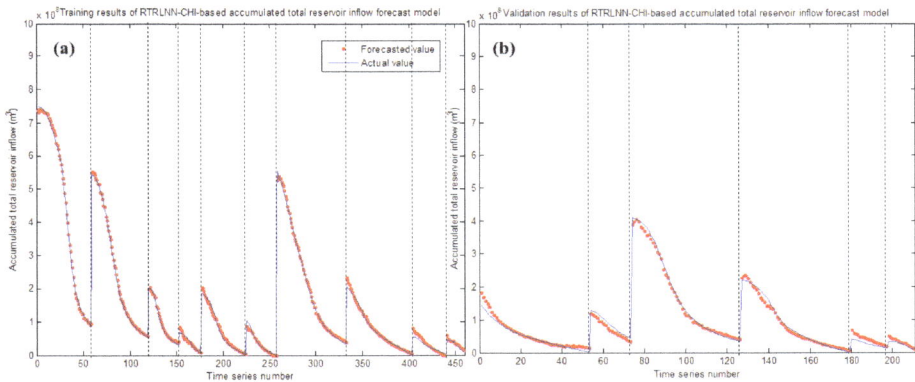

Figure 10. Training and validation results of RTRLNN-CHI-based accumulated total reservoir inflow forecast model: (**a**) training stage; (**b**) validation stage.

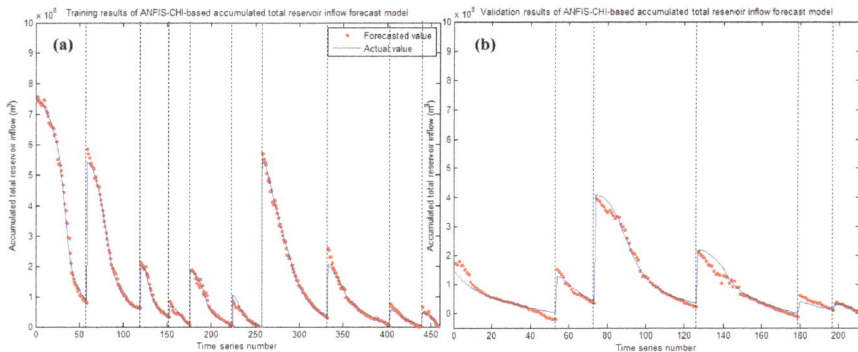

Figure 11. Training and validation results of ANFIS-CHI-based accumulated total reservoir inflow forecast model: (**a**) training stage; (**b**) validation stage.

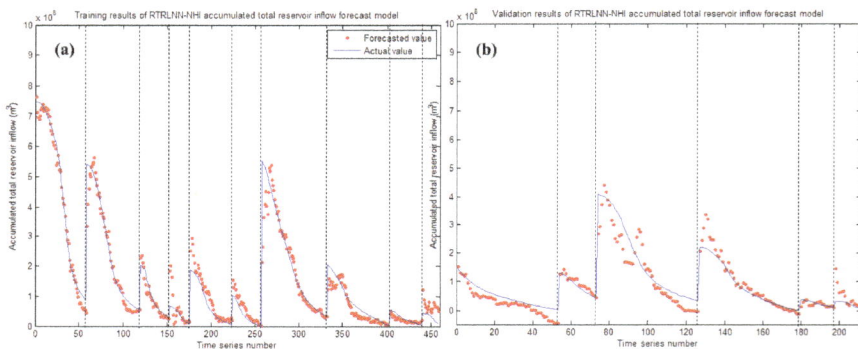

Figure 12. Training and validation results of RTRLNN-NHI-based accumulated total reservoir inflow forecast model: (**a**) training stage; (**b**) validation stage.

3.3.3. Analytical Results of Temporal and Spatial Forecasted Error Feature of the Developed Models

In this research, characteristic analyses were made on the temporal and spatial forecast errors of the four forecast models (RTRLNN-CHI, RTRLNN-NHI, ANFIS-CHI, and ANFIS-NHI) for long lead-time and total reservoir inflow. The analysis targets were six typhoon events for verification, which were used to evaluate the limits and applicability of the four models for long lead-time forecasting. Judgments were also made on the range of the typhoon center where the future total reservoir inflow may be accurately and appropriately forecasted. The average error percentages of the four developed accumulated total inflow forecast models across long lead-times are shown in Table 3, and a comparison of the temporal forecasted error features of the developed models across long lead-times is given in Figure 13. The percentages of the average forecast errors in the forecast time range of 24 to 48 h for the four models (RTRLNN-CHI, RTRLNN-NHI, ANFIS-CHI, and ANFIS-NHI), ($\frac{\sum_{\Delta t=24}^{48} AEP(\Delta t)}{24}$), were 4.6%, 16.7%, 7.7%, and 27.1%, respectively. The average error percentages (AEP) for the period of 48 to 72 h, ($\frac{\sum_{\Delta t=48}^{72} AEP(\Delta t)}{24}$), were 9.3%, 16.1%, 12.1%, and 39.3%, respectively. The AEP in the period of 20 to 79 h, ($\frac{\sum_{\Delta t=20}^{79} AEP(\Delta t)}{60}$), were 6.3%, 15.2%, 9.2%, and 31.8%, respectively. The results indicate that the long lead-time forecast accuracy of the heuristic model is obviously better than that of the non-heuristic model by 9%–23% for a lead-time of 24–48 h and 4%–30% for a lead-time of 48–72 h. The forecast error of the heuristic model did not significantly increase along with the increasing of the forecasted lead-time. The hydrograph patterns of the reservoir inflow for the meteorology and hydrology of the future typhoon can be appropriately simulated ahead of time with heuristic inputs. Therefore, the accumulated total inflow can be accurately forecasted for the long lead-time future. Furthermore, there was a highly complicated nonlinear relationship between the rainfall from the typhoon meteorology and the runoff in the catchment area from hydrology. There was better flexibility in the calculation mechanism of the RTRLNN model than in the ANFIS model. RTRLNN had detailed linkage between various types of inputs and outputs. It also calculated feedback information in real-time. Moreover, the accuracies of the various forecasted time intervals using the RTRLNN-CHI model were better than those obtained using the ANFIS-CHI model. The forecast error was less than 10% when the forecasted lead-time reached three days. The *AEP* for a forecasted lead-time of an average 49 h, ($\frac{\sum_{\Delta t=20}^{79} AEP(\Delta t)}{60}$), was only 6.3% for the RTRLNN-CHI model. Hence, a long lead-time forecast model for the accumulated total reservoir inflow was successfully developed using the heuristic technique in this study.

Table 3. Average error percentage of the four developed models across long lead-times.

Forecasted Lead-Time	RTRLNN-CHI Model	RTRLNN-NHI Model	ANFIS-CHI Model	ANFIS-NHI Model
During 24 to 48 h	4.6%	16.7%	7.7%	27.1%
During 48 to 72 h	9.3%	16.1%	12.1%	39.3%
During 20 to 79 h	6.3%	15.2%	9.2%	31.8%

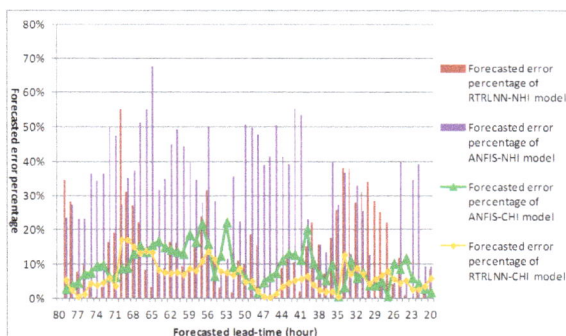

Figure 13. Comparison of temporal forecasted error features of the four developed accumulated total inflow forecast models across long lead-times.

The comparison of the spatial forecasted error feature of the four developed accumulated total inflow forecast models for the Shihmen Reservoir with relation to the central location of the typhoon is shown in Figure 14. This figure represents the absolute error percentage ($AEP(x, y)$) on the forecasted total reservoir inflow in the catchment area of the Shihmen Reservoir when the typhoon center was moving in the vicinity of any region in Taiwan (in the range of longitude 118–124 degrees, latitude 22–28 degrees). It can be seen from the spatial distributions of the forecast errors of the four models that the overall error space and range of the heuristic models (e.g., Figure 14a for the RTRLNN-CHI model, and Figure 14c for the ANFIS-CHI model) are much smaller than those of the non-heuristic models (e.g., Figure 14b for the RTRLNN-NHI model, and Figure 14d for the ANFIS-NHI model). In the error spatial distribution map of the RTRLNN-CHI model, the range where the $AEP(x, y)$ was less than 10% (which was about 61% of the researched range) was much bigger than that of the ANFIS-CHI model (which was about 47% of the researched range). The range where the $AEP(x,y)$ was greater than 20% (which was about 13% of the researched range) was much smaller than that of the ANFIS-CHI model (which was about 32% of the researched range). Figure 14 confirms that the forecast accuracy and stability of the RTRLNN-CHI model were better than those of other models when typhoon invasion was at the basin of the Shihmen Reservoir. When the typhoon center was in the southeast of Taiwan, the structure and meteorology field after the typhoon passed Taiwan was destroyed by the terrain. There was also the co-existing effects of the monsoon. Therefore, there was a significant difference between the future typhoon meteorology and rainfall-runoff conditions and the observed data when the typhoon center was in the southeast of Taiwan. As a result, the forecast error on the total reservoir inflow of the typhoon when it is located in the southeast of Taiwan is greater than that when the typhoon center is located elsewhere. However, after the typhoon center passed Taiwan, the circulation structure was not affected by the terrain. Hence, the forecast error on the total reservoir inflow was relatively small.

3.3.4. Sensitivity Analysis Results of Output with Relation to Heuristic Inputs Due to Future Forecasted Uncertainty

In order to evaluate the feasibility, applicability, and accuracy of the heuristic model when applied to real-time forecasting, a sensitivity analysis was conducted on the forecasted error effects of the outputs with relation to single or combined heuristic inputs for the most optimal heuristic model (RTRLNN-CHI). According to the previously developed short lead-time hydrological forecast models [35,36], an average forecast error ($\pm EP$) of 10% was assumed on each heuristic input, which was inputted into the model to simulate the absolute error percentage ($AEP(i, \pm EP)$) of the forecast. The results from the analysis are shown in Figure 15, where Heuristic input 1 (HI1) is the future accumulated total precipitation, HI2 is the duration from the current time to the flood recessional ending time, HI3 is the duration from the current time to the DRE time, and HI4 is the duration from the current time to the maximum precipitation time. The results displayed show that when $\pm 10\%$ error was inputted with HI2, the maximum output error would appear regardless of whether the case was that of a single input or combinations of multiple inputs. This indicates that the flood duration is the most important factor in forecasting the future accumulated total reservoir inflow, which is also the most sensitive input for the output of the model. Among all the combinations of heuristic input errors, the average forecast error was 9.98% for a 10% overestimation on the input, with a maximum of 13.6% (when there are 10% errors on all of HI1, HI2, HI3, and HI4). For the case of underestimation with a 10% error on the input, the average forecast error was 11.01%, with a maximum of 13.6%. There was an additional 1.03% error on the output for the 10% underestimation error on the heuristic inputs when compared to the case of 10% overestimation on the input. These results indicate that the absolute error percentage (13.6%) of the heuristic model with a 10% error on all the heuristic inputs was still lower than that of the most optimal non-heuristic model (RTRLNN-NHI), $AEP = 15.2\%$. This shows that the real-time forecast accuracy of the RTRLNN-CHI model is still better than that of the non-heuristic models (RTRLNN-NHI and ANFIS-NHI) even when there are errors on the heuristic inputs.

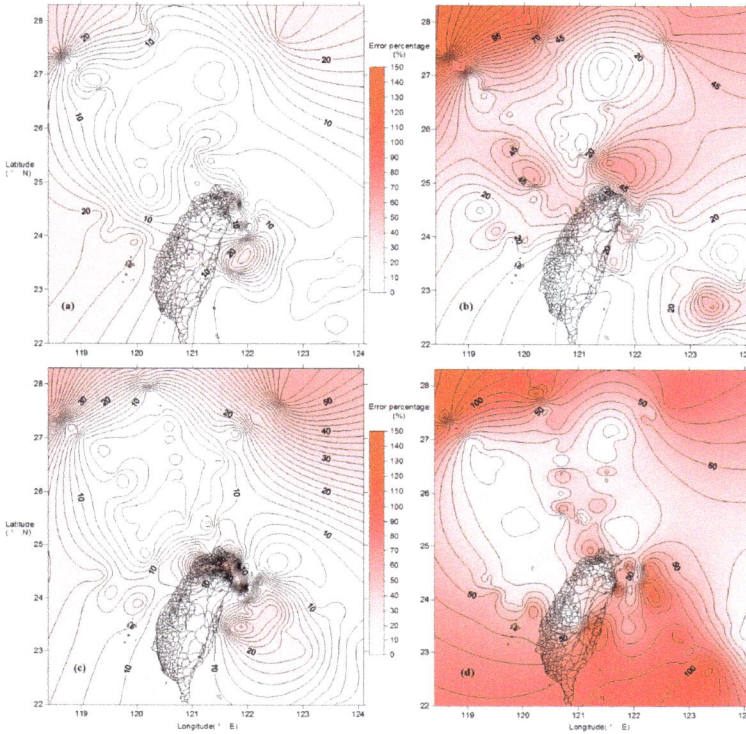

Figure 14. Comparison of spatial forecasted error feature of the four developed accumulated total inflow forecast models for the Shihmen Reservoir with relation to the typhoon central location: (**a**) RTRLNN-CHI model; (**b**) RTRLNN-NHI model; (**c**) ANFIS-CHI model; and (**d**) ANFIS-NHI model.

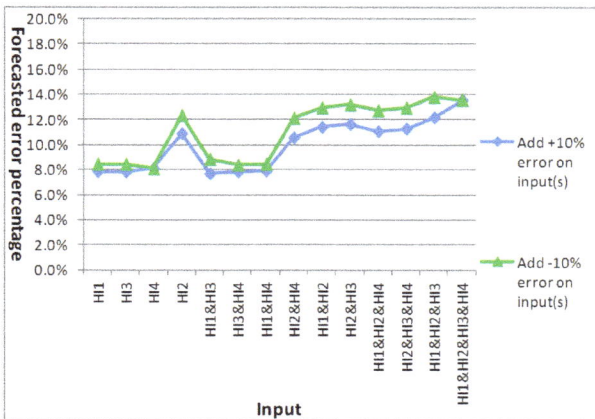

Figure 15. Sensitivity analysis results of model output with relation to single or combined heuristic inputs due to future forecasted uncertainty.

3.3.5. Construction Results of Heuristic Forecast Database for Heuristic Inputs

In this study, heuristic data mining techniques were used to construct a forecast database for the relationship between the position of the typhoon center, the rainfall hyetograph, and the inflow hydrograph in the catchment area from historical samples. The database was constructed to facilitate forecasting of the future accumulated total precipitation. Similarly, heuristic data mining techniques can also be applied on the delay of the future typhoon invasion by constructing a forecast database from relationships on the spatial position distribution of the typhoon center when the water has completely retreated, the moment of maximum rainfall, and the end time of direct runoff in historical samples. The characteristic map of the typhoon center position *vs.* the rainfall in the Shihmen Reservoir basin is as shown in Figure 16, which is the contour map after Kriging interpolation of the spatial sample information (X axis (typhoon central longitude), Y axis (typhoon central latitude), Z axis (basin precipitation of Shihmen Reservoir)). In this figure, strong rainfalls occurred when the typhoon center was at the southeast of Taiwan because the typhoon was under the influence of the Coriolis Effect. The air exhibits counterclockwise rotation in the Northern Hemisphere. When the typhoon was in the southeast of Taiwan, the typhoon rain belt entrained by the wind field under counterclockwise rotation was not blocked by the terrain of the mostly flat lands before entering the catchment area of the Shihmen Reservoir. After the rain belt entered the catchment area of the Shihmen Reservoir from the northwest to the southeast, it was blocked by the Snow-Capped mountain range. The catchment area of the Shihmen Reservoir belonged to the upwind side and heavy rain would happen then. In contrast, when the typhoon was not in the southeast of Taiwan, the rain belt entrained by the wind field was blocked by the Snow-Capped mountain range, the Central mountain range, and the Yusan mountain range before entering the catchment area of the Shihmen Reservoir. The catchment area of the Shihmen Reservoir was at leeward and there were no heavy rains in the Shihmen Reservoir at this time. With the assistance of this figure, the rainfall hyetograph in the catchment area of the Shihmen Reservoir during the future whole typhoon flood event can be obtained from the combined information of the hourly forecasted positions of the future typhoon center, the real-time estimated amount of rainfall, and the correction from the observed amount. The desired forecast of the total rainfall for the total reservoir inflow was obtained by summing over the rainfall hyetograph.

In this study, derivations on the spatial characteristics of the position distribution of the typhoon center were made for the moment when the maximum rainfall occurred, the direct runoff ended, and the water retreat ended in the typhoon flood events. First, the basin of the Shihmen Reservoir was located as the ellipse E_b in Figure 16, and then the terrain factors that might affect the rainfall in the reservoir basin were identified. Then, an axis (Line M_1–M_2) was marked along the direction of the Snow-Capped mountain range. The second axis (Line P_1–P_2), was defined as being perpendicular to Line M_1–M_2. Using these two axes as the reference, a contour map was created of the spatial distribution of the positions of the typhoon center when the water retreated below 300 cm of the reservoir inflow for the periods when a typhoon alarm is historically issued on land until the alarm is lifted. This resulted in the elliptical distribution line (E_E), from which the starting time of the forecast and the ending time of the water retreat could be determined. Regarding the model construction event, a contour map could be made for the spatial distribution of the positions of the typhoon center between the start of the rainfall and the end of the direct runoff for historical typhoon flood events. This resulted in the elliptical distribution line E_{DRE}. Further, the elliptical distribution line E_{MP} could be obtained from the contour map of the spatial distribution of the typhoon center when the maximum rainfall occurred in the historical typhoon flood events. The time of the maximum rainfall may be determined from this distribution line (E_{MP}) and the contour lines of rainfall.

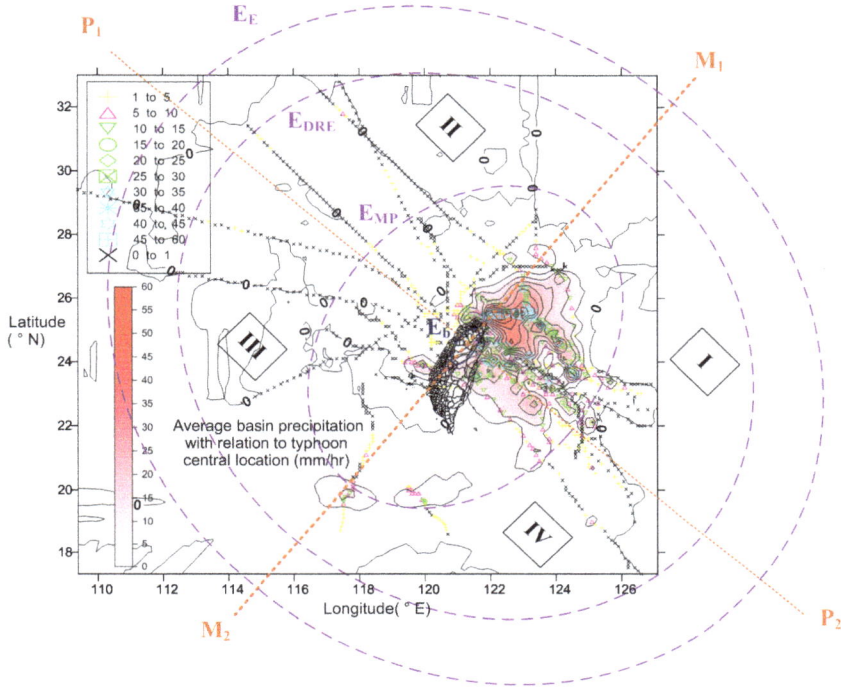

Figure 16. Construction results of heuristic forecast database for the Shihmen basin precipitation and duration characteristics curves with relation to the typhoon central location.

In Figure 16, the distribution lines were mainly elliptical, which was due to the Coriolis effect and the Terrain effect during the movements of the typhoon. When the path and direction of typhoon movement and the spatial distribution of terrain height are non-uniform, the distribution lines are elliptical instead of circular. The main axis of the ellipse was related to the direction of the terrains and mountains, so the elliptical distribution was a rotation of the main axis. Besides, the delay of the hydrograph pattern of rainfall was mainly dominated by the moving path of the typhoon. Because the Coriolis effect acted on the typhoon, it moved toward the direction of 270° to 360°, while the synthetic moving direction coincided with Line P_1–P_2, *i.e.*, the perpendicular line of the Snow-Capped mountain range. Therefore, the long axes of E_E and E_{DRE} are along Line P_1–P_2, while the long axis of E_{MP} was in the direction of the Snow-Capped mountain range (Line M_1–M_2) because whether or not strong rainfall occurred was mainly related to the angle and position between the direction from which the rain belt of typhoon entered the reservoir basin and the direction of the Snow-Capped mountain range. In addition, from a monsoon climatology point of view, Taiwan is mainly affected by southwest monsoons from mid-March to mid-September, and is predominantly under the effects of the northeast monsoon at other times. When the typhoon center was located in quadrants I and II in Figure 16, the wind field with counterclockwise rotation easily accompanied the northeast monsoon in the basin direction of the Shihmen Reservoir; when it was located in quadrants III and IV, the wind field was easily accompanied by the southwest monsoon. For typhoon invasion in quadrants I and II after mid-September and in quadrants III and IV during mid-March and mid-September, the typhoon was easily accompanied by co-existing effects of the monsoon to increase rainfall duration and precipitation. The contour lines of E_E, E_{DRE}, and E_{MP} can be expressed with the following equations:

$$\frac{\left[(x\cos 49° + y\sin 49°)\Delta d_{lon.} - 13481.3_{(E,km)}\right]^2}{\left[1113.92_{(km)}\right]^2} + \frac{\left[(-x\sin 49° + y\cos 49°)\Delta d_{lat.} - 2758.7_{(N,km)}\right]^2}{\left[1179.209_{(km)}\right]^2} = 1 \tag{52}$$

$$\frac{\left[(x\cos 49° + y\sin 49°)\Delta d_{lon.} - 13481.3_{(E,km)}\right]^2}{\left[885.2_{(km)}\right]^2} + \frac{\left[(-x\sin 49° + y\cos 49°)\Delta d_{lat.} - 2758.7_{(N,km)}\right]^2}{\left[942.7_{(km)}\right]^2} = 1 \tag{53}$$

$$\frac{\left[(x\cos 49° + y\sin 49°)\Delta d_{lon.} - 13481.3_{(E,km)}\right]^2}{\left[587.4_{(km)}\right]^2} + \frac{\left[(-x\sin 49° + y\cos 49°)\Delta d_{lat.} - 2758.7_{(N,km)}\right]^2}{\left[425.6_{(km)}\right]^2} = 1 \tag{54}$$

where $\Delta d_{lon.}$ and $\Delta d_{lat.}$ are the representative distance of each longitude and latitude, respectively.

4. Conclusions

Typhoon long lead-time rainfall-runoff is characterized as a chaotic, fuzzy, highly uncertain, and nonlinear system. The routing mechanism and characteristics of the real-time recurrent learning neural network (RTRLNN) and the adaptive network-based fuzzy inference system (ANFIS) have the potential ability to reason and learn using deterministic real-time recurrent routing and fuzzy logic. Therefore, the present study applied RTRLNN and ANFIS combined with multiple artificial intelligence-based heuristic techniques to develop coupled heuristic long lead-time accumulated total reservoir inflow forecast models (RTRLNN-CHI and ANFIS-CHI), in order to improve the accuracy and stability of long-term accumulated total inflow forecasting. The proposed system was evaluated by a comparison with the RTRLNN- and ANFIS-based non-heuristic models (RTRLNN-NHI and ANFIS-NHI). The inputs of the heuristic models are composed of coupled observed non-heuristic inputs (typhoon characteristics factors, hourly basin precipitation, hourly reservoir inflow) and forecasted heuristic inputs (future accumulated total precipitation, duration from the current time to the time of maximum precipitation, direct runoff ending and event recessional ending, and observed-predicted inflow increase/decrease rate). The present study first employed non-parametric correlation analysis to assess the most appropriate input variables for long lead-time non-heuristic and heuristic models. This study also analyzed temporal and spatial forecasted error features to assess the goodness and applicability of the developed four long lead-time models, and we also analyzed the output sensitivity of single or combined heuristic inputs to determine whether the developed heuristic model can suffer the impact of future forecasted uncertainty and error on inputs.

The proposed method was applied to Taiwan's Shihmen Reservoir catchment area with a study period from 2004 to 2012. The results showed lead us to the following conclusions. (1) The accuracy and stability of the RTRLNN-based long lead-time accumulated total reservoir inflow prediction model are better than that of the ANFIS-based model. This is because RTRLNN incorporates a real-time recurrent deterministic routing mechanism with a more elastic and fine connection than ANFIS. (2) Under the synthesized simulation using key heuristic inputs of future total precipitation, flooding duration, and OPIID rate with other real-time observed hydrometeorological factors, the coupled heuristic RTRLNN-based model (RTRLNN-CHI, average error percentage (*AEP*): 6.3%, average forecasted lead-time: 49 h) and ANFIS-based model (ANFIS-CHI, *AEP*: 9.2%) could achieve a better prediction than the non-heuristic model (RTRLNN-NHI, *AEP*: 15.2%; ANFIS-NHI, *AEP*: 31.8%) because of the full consideration of different runoff/infiltration scenarios and initial/boundary conditions in each time step. (3) The hydrograph pattern of the reservoir inflow for the future typhoon meteorology and hydrology could be appropriately simulated ahead of time by using heuristic inputs. The accuracy of the long lead-time (24–72 h) total inflow forecast at the typhoon center during the invasion period in Taiwan (longitude 118–124 degrees, latitude 22–28 degrees) of the heuristic model was obviously better than that of the non-heuristic model. (4) When there were 10% errors on all the heuristic inputs, the *AEP* (13.6%) of the heuristic model was still lower than that of the most optimal non-heuristic model (RTRLNN-NHI, 15.2%). This indicates that the real-time forecast accuracy of the RTRLNN-CHI model even with errors on the heuristic inputs is still higher than that of the non-heuristic models (RTRLNN-NHI and ANFIS-NHI).

The key factors to effectively forecast long lead-time accumulated total reservoir inflow under a complex typhoon effect in real-time rely on the predicted accuracy of the meteorological-hydrological heuristic inputs and the associated data-preprocessing process. Future study can focus on improving the predicted accuracy of the heuristic inputs by coupling with novel numerical weather forecast models as a basis to provide future rainfall-runoff boundary conditions for a soft-computing model.

Acknowledgments: This research was partially supported by the Ministry of Science and Technology, Taiwan (Grant Nos. MOST103-2221-E-002-246 and MOST104-2111-M-464-001). In addition, the authors are indebted to the reviewers for their valuable comments and suggestions.

Author Contributions: Chien-Lin Huang performed the model construction and experiments, analyzed the data and wrote the paper; Nien-Sheng Hsu and Chih-Chiang Wei conceived and designed the models and experiments.

References

1. Lin, G.F.; Chen, G.R.; Huang, P.Y.; Chou, Y.C. Support vector machine-based models for hourly reservoir inflow forecasting during typhoon-warning periods. *J. Hydrol.* **2009**, *372*, 17–29. [CrossRef]
2. Lin, G.F.; Wu, M.C.; Chen, G.R.; Tsai, F.Y. An RBF-based model with an information processor for forecasting hourly reservoir inflow during typhoons. *Hydrol. Process.* **2009**, *23*, 3598–3609. [CrossRef]
3. Hsu, N.S.; Huang, C.L.; Wei, C.C. Real-time forecast of reservoir inflow hydrographs incorporating terrain and monsoon effects during typhoon invasion by novel intelligent numerical-statistic impulse techniques. *J. Hydrol. Eng.* **2015**, *20*. [CrossRef]
4. Webster, P.J.; Holland, G.J.; Curry, J.A.; Chang, H.R. Changes in tropical cyclone number, duration, and intensity in a warming environment. *Science* **2005**, *309*, 1844–1846. [CrossRef] [PubMed]
5. Wu, L.; Wang, B.; Geng, S. Growing typhoon influence on East Asia. *Geophys. Res. Lett.* **2005**, *32*. [CrossRef]
6. Knutson, T.R.; McBride, J.L.; Chan, J.; Emanuel, K.; Holland, G.; Landsea, C.; Held, I.; Kossin, J.P.; Srivastava, A.K.; Sugi, M. Tropical cyclones and climate change. *Nat. Geosci.* **2010**, *3*, 157–163. [CrossRef]
7. Bertoni, J.C.; Tucci, C.E.; Clarke, R.T. Rainfall-based real-time flood forecasting. *J. Hydrol.* **1992**, *131*, 313–339. [CrossRef]
8. Lardet, P.; Obled, C. Real-time flood forecasting using a stochastic rainfall generator. *J. Hydrol.* **1994**, *162*, 391–408. [CrossRef]
9. Toth, E.; Brath, A.; Montanari, A. Comparison of short-term rainfall prediction models for real-time flood forecasting. *J. Hydrol.* **2000**, *239*, 132–147. [CrossRef]
10. Anderson, M.; Chen, Z.; Kavvas, M.; Feldman, A. Coupling HEC-HMS with atmospheric models for prediction of watershed runoff. *J. Hydrol. Engine* **2002**, *7*, 312–318. [CrossRef]
11. Collischonn, W.; Haas, R.; Andreolli, I.; Tucci, C.E.M. Forecasting river uruguay flow using rainfall forecasts from a regional weather-prediction model. *J. Hydrol.* **2005**, *305*, 87–98. [CrossRef]
12. Dahlke, H.E.; Easton, Z.M.; Fuka, D.R.; Walter, M.T.; Steenhuis, T.S. Real-time forecast of hydrologically sensitive areas in the salmon creek watershed, New York state, using an online prediction tool. *Water* **2013**, *5*, 917–944. [CrossRef]
13. Brath, A.; Montanari, A.; Toth, E. Neural networks and non-parametric methods for improving real-time flood forecasting through conceptual hydrological models. *Hydrol. Earth Syst. Sci.* **2002**, *6*, 627–639. [CrossRef]
14. Hsu, N.S.; Wei, C.C. A multipurpose reservoir real-time operation model for flood control during typhoon invasion. *J. Hydrol.* **2007**, *336*, 282–293. [CrossRef]
15. Kitanidis, P.K.; Bras, R.L. Real-time forecasting with a conceptual hydrologic model: 1. Analysis of uncertainty. *Water Resour. Res.* **1980**, *16*, 1025–1033. [CrossRef]

16. Georgakakos, K.P.; Bras, R.L. Real-time, statistically linearized, adaptive flood routing. *Water Resour. Res.* **1982**, *18*, 513–524. [CrossRef]

17. Ho, J.-Y.; Lee, K.T. Grey forecast rainfall with flow updating algorithm for real-time flood forecasting. *Water* **2015**, *7*, 1840–1865. [CrossRef]

18. Thirumalaiah, K.; Deo, M. Hydrological forecasting using neural networks. *J. Hydrol. Engine* **2000**, *5*, 180–189. [CrossRef]

19. Xu, Z.X.; Li, J.Y. Short-term inflow forecasting using an artificial neural network model. *Hydrol. Process.* **2002**, *16*, 2423–2439. [CrossRef]

20. Wu, J.; Han, J.; Annambhotla, S.; Bryant, S. Artificial neural networks for forecasting watershed runoff and stream flows. *J. Hydrol. Engine* **2005**, *10*, 216–222. [CrossRef]

21. Aqil, M.; Kita, I.; Yano, A.; Nishiyama, S. Neural networks for real time catchment flow modeling and prediction. *Water Resour. Manag.* **2007**, *21*, 1781–1796. [CrossRef]

22. Wu, C.L.; Chau, K.W.; Li, Y.S. Methods to improve neural network performance in daily flows prediction. *J. Hydrol.* **2009**, *372*, 80–93. [CrossRef]

23. Pan, T.Y.; Wang, R.Y. State space neural networks for short term rainfall-runoff forecasting. *J. Hydrol.* **2004**, *297*, 34–50. [CrossRef]

24. Chau, K.; Wu, C.; Li, Y. Comparison of several flood forecasting models in Yangtze river. *J. Hydrol. Eng.* **2005**, *10*, 485–491. [CrossRef]

25. Chang, F.J.; Chang, L.C.; Huang, H.L. Real-time recurrent learning neural network for stream-flow forecasting. *Hydrol. Process.* **2002**, *16*, 2577–2588. [CrossRef]

26. Liu, Y.B.; Gebremeskel, S.; de Smedt, F.; Hoffman, L.; Pfister, L. A diffusive approach for flow routing in GIS based flood modeling. *J. Hydrol.* **2003**, *283*, 91–106. [CrossRef]

27. Molnar, P.; Ramirez, J.A. Energy dissipation theories and optimal channel characteristics of river networks. *Water Resour. Res.* **1998**, *34*, 1809–1818. [CrossRef]

28. Spearman, C. The proof and measurement of association between two things. *Amer. J. Psychol.* **1904**, *15*, 72–101. [CrossRef]

29. Haykin, S. *Neural Networks: A Comprehensive Foundation*, 2nd ed.; Prentice Hall: Upper Saddle River, NJ, USA, 1999.

30. Elman, J.L. Finding structure in time. *Cogn. Sci.* **1990**, *14*, 179–211. [CrossRef]

31. Jang, J.S.R. ANFIS: Adaptive Network-based Fuzzy Inference System. *IEEE Trans. Syst. Man Cybern.* **1993**, *23*, 665–685. [CrossRef]

32. Takagi, T.; Sugeno, M. Derivation of Fuzzy Control Rules from Human Operator's Control Actions. In Proceedings of the IFAC Conference on Fuzzy Information, Marseille, France, 19–21 July 1983; pp. 55–60.

33. Chiu, S.L. Fuzzy model identification based on cluster estimation. *J. Intell. Fuzzy Syst.* **1994**, *2*, 267–278.

34. Lin, G.F.; Chen, L.H. Application of an artificial neural network to typhoon rainfall forecasting. *Hydrol. Process.* **2005**, *19*, 1825–1837. [CrossRef]

35. Chau, K.W.; Wu, C.L. A hybrid model coupled with singular spectrum analysis for daily rainfall prediction. *J. Hydroinform.* **2010**, *12*, 458–473. [CrossRef]

36. Wang, W.C.; Chau, K.W.; Xu, D.M.; Chen, X.Y. Improving forecasting accuracy of annual runoff time-series using ARIMA based on EEMD decomposition. *Water Resour. Manag.* **2015**, *29*, 2655–2675. [CrossRef]

water

MDPI

Article

Estimation of Rainfall Associated with Typhoons over the Ocean Using TRMM/TMI and Numerical Models

Nan-Ching Yeh [1], Chung-Chih Liu [2,*] and Wann-Jin Chen [3]

[1] Department of Aircraft Engineering, Air Force Institute of Technology, Kaohsiung 82047, Taiwan; jim912104@gmail.com

[2] Natural Sciences Teaching Center, Minghsin University of Science and Technology, Hsinchu 30401, Taiwan

[3] Department of Electronic Engineering, Ta Hwa University of Science and Technology, Hsinchu 30740, Taiwan; wannjin@gmail.com

* Author to whom correspondence should be addressed; ccliu@must.edu.tw; Tel.: +886-7-6250743; Fax: +886-7-3801663.

Academic Editor: Kwok-wing Chau

Received: 31 July 2015; Accepted: 23 October 2015; Published: 3 November 2015

Abstract: This study quantitatively estimated the precipitation associated with a typhoon in the northwestern Pacific Ocean by using a physical algorithm which included the Weather Research and Forecasting model, Radiative Transfer for TIROS Operational Vertical Sounder model, and data from the Tropical Rainfall Measuring Mission (TRMM)/TRMM Microwave Imager (TMI) and TRMM/Precipitation Radar (PR). First, a prior probability distribution function (PDF) was constructed using over three million rain rate retrievals from the TRMM/PR data for the period 2002–2010 over the northwestern Pacific Ocean. Subsequently, brightness temperatures for 15 typhoons that occurred over the northwestern Pacific Ocean were simulated using a microwave radiative transfer model and a conditional PDF was obtained for these typhoons. The aforementioned physical algorithm involved using a posterior PDF. A posterior PDF was obtained by combining the prior and conditional PDFs. Finally, the rain rate associated with a typhoon was estimated by inputting the observations of the TMI (attenuation indices at 10, 19, 37 GHz) into the posterior PDF (lookup table). Results based on rain rate retrievals indicated that rainband locations with the heaviest rainfall showed qualitatively similar horizontal distributions. The correlation coefficient and root-mean-square error of the rain rate estimation were 0.63 and 4.45 mm·h^{-1}, respectively. Furthermore, the correlation coefficient and root-mean-square error for convective rainfall were 0.78 and 7.25 mm·h^{-1}, respectively, and those for stratiform rainfall were 0.58 and 9.60 mm·h^{-1}, respectively. The main contribution of this study is introducing an approach to quickly and accurately estimate the typhoon precipitation, and remove the need for complex calculations.

Keywords: quantitative precipitation estimate; WRF model; RTTOV model; prior probability distribution function; conditional PDF; posterior PDF

1. Introduction

The precipitation of typhoons at the early stages can be estimated by satellites by using visible (VIS) and infrared (IR) channels. VIS channels are used only during daytime. Furthermore, IR channels are affected by cloud layers and, therefore, data for the region below the cloud top cannot be collected. Unlike IR channels, passive microwave channels enable observing precipitation conditions below clouds.

Scientists have established the regression relation between the passive microwave brightness temperature (TB) and the actual rain rate (rain rate, RR); thus, an observed TB can be input into the regression relation to estimate the RR [1,2]. However, the disadvantage of regression relations is that they are restricted to specific periods, areas, and weather systems. Past studies have mentioned various methods in which passive microwave channels are used to estimate the precipitation intensity after 1990 [3–8].

Many studies have indicated that a major method for estimating the RR over the ocean involves using multi-satellite passive microwave channels. Satellite passive microwave data can provide estimates of precipitation over the vast ocean, where there is a lack of observed data, and the estimates are unot influenced by cloud layers [9]. In the presence of the emission and scattering effects of raindrops, the relationship between the TB and the RR is non-monotonic [10].

Since 2000, many scholars have used satellite passive microwave channels to estimate the RR. Chen and Li [11] utilized the passive microwave channel of the Tropical Rainfall Measuring Mission (TRMM) along with synchronous satellite data to research precipitation estimation. Kidd *et al.*, [8] developed a precipitation estimation method by combining passive microwave and IR channels, and the time resolution of the method is 30 min. Different microwave channels have different physical features and limitations related to precipitation retrieval. Therefore, some researchers have used multiple channels to estimate the RR and to increase the dynamic range of precipitation retrieval [12,13]. Kummerow *et al.*, [14] presented the Goddard profiling algorithm for passive-microwave-data-based RR estimation.

Although the passive microwave sensor has become the preferred choice for estimating precipitation associated with typhoons over the ocean, an IR sensor is superior for estimating long-period precipitation since the passive microwave sensor has extremely low time resolution [15–17]. Clearly, the use of RR estimation algorithms is restricted to the ocean [18–20]. Since the ocean has low emissivity (approximately 0.5) and a low (cold) radiation background, regions where precipitation occurs show a high (warm) radiation rate (emissivity close to 1.0). Therefore, precipitation locations over the vast ocean can be easily identified.

Information on the type of land feature, such as whether an area is snow covered, a desert, or semi-arid [18,21–23], is necessary when estimating precipitation on land. Thus, it is difficult to conduct a study of land precipitation by using emission data. Studies on land precipitation retrieval typically focus on scattering data [24,25]. High-frequency microwave channels can be used to estimate land precipitation [4,5,18,21,23].

Overall, although satellite precipitation data are quantitative and provide spatiotemporal coverage over the ocean [26], they contain uncertainties and have limitations [27]. Therefore, many studies have evaluated, improved, and used satellite-based rainfall data for different areas [28–30]. Moreover, the accuracy of satellite-based rainfall data for different locations, seasons, and weather systems has been evaluated [31,32].

Moreover, a strong relationship exists between the rainfall intensity and water resources management. Water resources management involves the activity of planning, developing, distributing, and managing the optimum use of water resources, such as reservoir operation, rainfall runoff, water supply planning, irrigation system, and so on.

For example, Chau *et al.*, [33] illustrated that the provision of an accurate and timely rainfall forecast is a key factor in reservoir operation. Meanwhile, Wang *et al.*, [34] tried to improve the forecasting accuracy of annual runoff time series using numerical models and empirical models. Although a physical method has shortcomings such as requiring complex computations and being time consuming, regression relations used in a physical method do not change with time and place, similar to statistical methods. The time required to establish a relationship between the RR and attenuation index is longer than the time needed to establish a relationship between the RR and multi channels' TB. Furthermore, a Bayesian method is a complex and time-consuming physical method in advance. This study simulated the TB of typhoons before their occurrence by using the Weather Research and Forecasting (WRF) and Radiative Transfer for TIROS Operational Vertical Sounder (RTTOV) models. The TB was then transferred to the attenuation index. Finally, a lookup table for the attenuation index and RR was constructed using a Bayesian approach. The following step merely involves transferring the observed TB to the attenuation index and then estimating the RR of typhoons by using the lookup table. Consequently, the use of time-consuming physical methods can be avoided. The main contribution of this study is providing a method that can quickly and accurately estimate the typhoon rain rate.

This paper is organized as follows. In Section 2, we briefly review a theory used in this study; the theory presents the relationship between microwave observations (transferred to the attenuation index) and RR. In Section 3, we detail the basis of our methodology, including the physical algorithm, established rainfall threshold, and Bayesian approach. In Section 4, case validation and the results of this study are discussed. Finally, conclusions are presented in Section 5.

2. Theory

During rainfall, rain droplets over the ocean absorb and emit radiation. Therefore, the TB increases with the RR, implying that the TB can be used for precipitation estimation. The relationship between the TB and RR is shown in Figure 1 [35]. The text in the right side of Figure 1 describes the frequency and polarization of TMI which correspond to each line. For example, TB10V is the 10 GHz vertical polarization. Figure 1 was simulated as the standard atmosphere. For example, the standard atmospheric pressure was 1013.250 hPa.

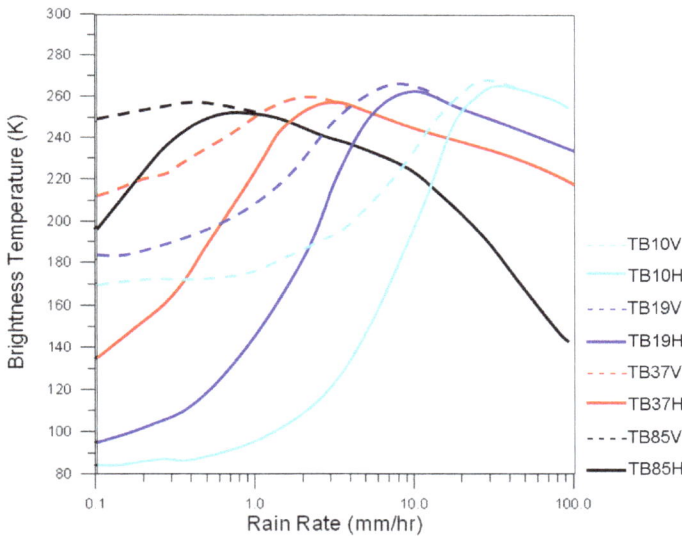

Figure 1. Ideal plot of brightness temperature (TB) *versus* rain rate (RR) over the ocean for the Tropical Rainfall Measuring Mission Microwave Imager (TMI) channels [35]. The text in the right side of Figure 1 describes the frequency and polarization of TMI which correspond to each line.

The microwave TB and RR do not have a one-to-one relationship [36]. If an equation relating them is developed directly, it would not be applicable to precipitation estimation. The attenuation index developed by Petty [12] is determined according to the difference between vertical polarization and horizontal polarization, and it is referred to as the P value. It is used to obtain the relationship between the TB and RR. The definition of the P value is as follows:

$$P \equiv \frac{TB_V - TB_H}{TB_{V,O} - TB_{H,O}} \tag{1}$$

where TB_V and TB_H denote the vertical polarization TB and horizontal polarization TB, respectively, and $TB_{V,O}$ and $TB_{H,O}$ represent the values of TB_V and TB_H under identical atmospheric conditions after the removal of the effect of rain clouds. The p value ranges from 0 to 1. The value 1 indicates that clouds and rain are absent from the field of view (FOV) of the satellite, whereas 0 indicates that the optical thickness in the FOV becomes extremely opaque because of clouds and rain [37]. Figure 2 shows the inverse relation between precipitation intensity and the attenuation index [35]. The results of Figure 2 were calculated by Equation (1) using the data of Figure 1. The P10, P19, P37, and P85 in the Figure 2 indicate the attenuation index at 10, 19, 37, and 85 GHz of TMI. Figure 1 was simulated using typhoon cases. Therefore, they are more suitable for estimating the rain rate of the typhoon. In Figure 2, it was found that the attenuation index at 85 GHz approaches zero for RR just above 1 mm/h and, thus, the error of RR estimation from P would be significant at a higher rainfall rate, especially for typhoon cases. Therefore, the 85 GHz data are not used in this study.

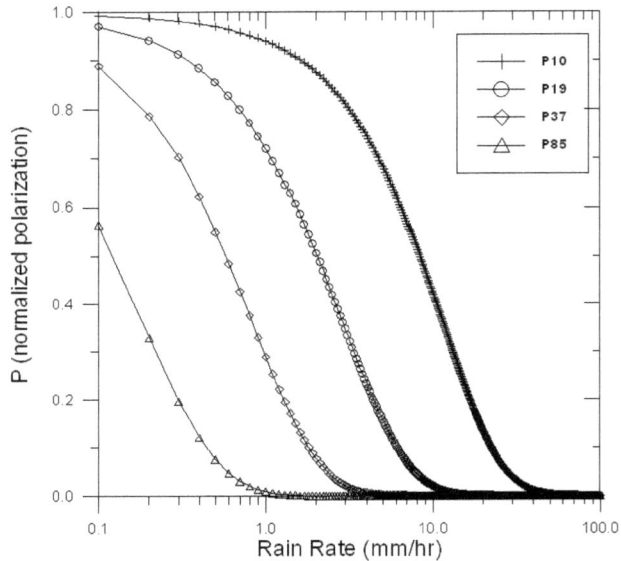

Figure 2. Relationship between attenuation index and RR for TMI channels [35]. The P10, P19, P37, and P85 in Figure 2 indicate the attenuation index at 10, 19, 37, and 85 GHz of TMI.

3. Methodology

3.1. Physical Algorithm

In the precipitation estimation method proposed in this study, the WRF model is used to simulate the vertical hydrometeor distribution of a typhoon over the western Pacific. The vertical hydrometeor distribution is the standard output products of WRF. The hydrometeor distribution is then inputted into the RTTOV model to simulate the TBs of the TMI channels, and a conditional probability distribution function (PDF) is constructed using the output of the WRF and RTTOV models. Moreover, a prior PDF is constructed using 3,115,544 PR precipitation data over the ocean. Finally, the posterior PDF is obtained on the basis of Bayesian theory. Therefore, a lookup table of the probability of occurrence of various RR corresponding to the attenuation index of TMI channels can be constructed. In other words, a rain rate can be estimated when the satellite observations are converted to the attenuation index.

The complete flowchart for precipitation estimation is shown in Figure 3. The dotted square represents the processing procedure of the model, which includes the WRF and RTTOV models, and the dashed square represents the processing method of the satellite.

3.2. Establishing a Threshold for Rain

To obtain the precipitation threshold of each TMI channel over the northwestern Pacific during summer, TRMM swaths that were within the range of the northwestern Pacific from June to October of 2009 and 2010 were obtained. There were a total of 2242 TRMM swaths, which included observed values of the TMI and PR. Within the 2242 TRMM swaths contains 127,382 PR data points corresponding to the absence of rain. Histograms of the TB for each TMI channel in the absence of rain were drawn (Figures 4–8). Samples that were within ±1 of the standard deviation were reanalyzed excluding outlier and possibly noisy data. The average TB values of each channel represented the precipitation threshold (Table 1).

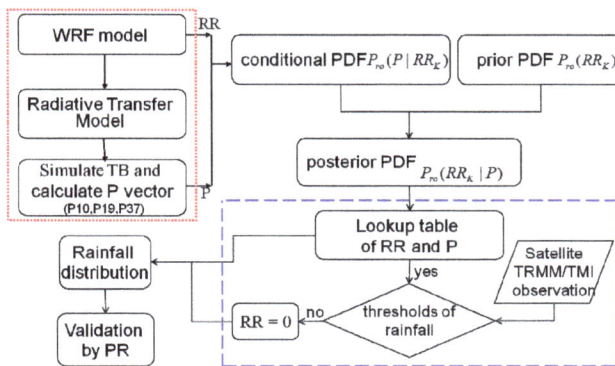

Figure 3. Flowchart for precipitation estimation proposed in this study.

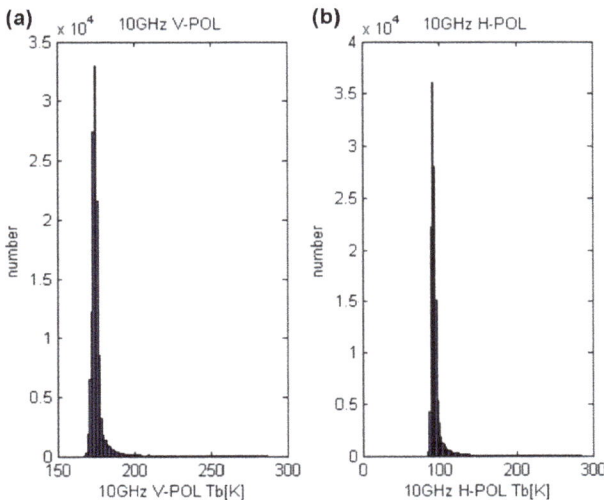

Figure 4. Histograms of the TB for the TMI in the absence of rain: (**a**) TB10V and (**b**) TB10H.

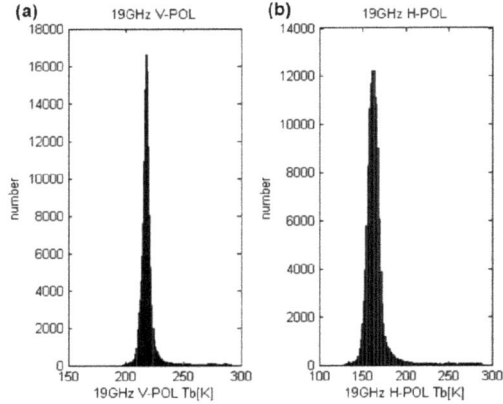

Figure 5. Histograms of the TB for the TMI in the absence of rain at 19 GHz: (**a**) TB10V and (**b**) TB10H.

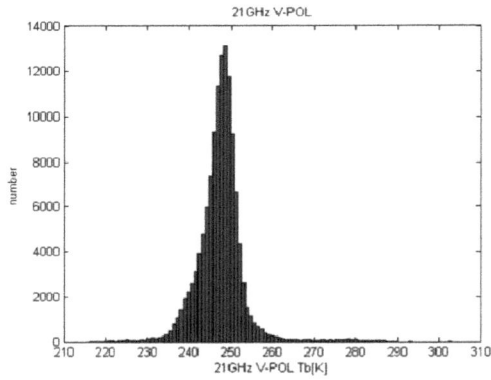

Figure 6. Histogram of the TB for the TMI in the absence of rain at 21 GHz.

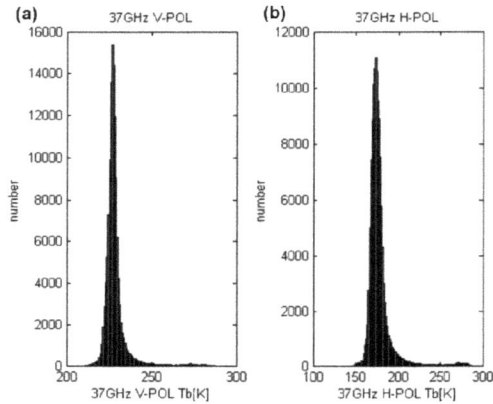

Figure 7. Histograms of the TB for the TMI in the absence of rain at 37 GHz: (**a**) TB10V and (**b**) TB10H.

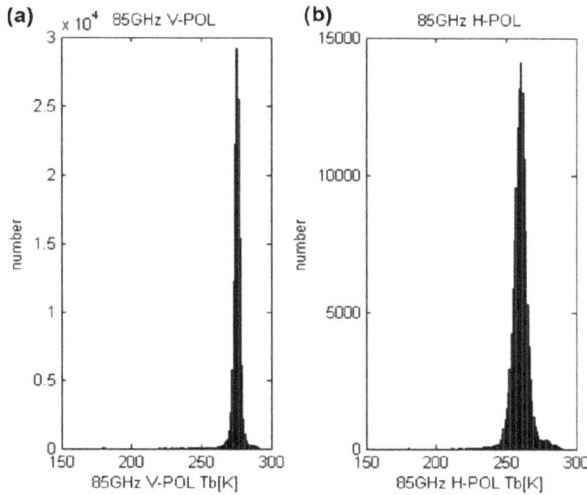

Figure 8. Histograms of the TB for the TMI in the absence of rain at 85 GHz: (**a**) TB10V and (**b**) TB10H.

Table 1. Precipitation thresholds and standard deviations for TMI channels.

Frequencies	Threshold (Mean)	Standard Deviation
10-V GHz	175.78 K	1.27 K
10-H GHz	93.78 K	2.39 K
19-V GHz	218.77 K	2.73 K
19-H GHz	163.46 K	5.05 K
21-V GHz	248.21 K	3.41 K
37-V GHz	228.09 K	2.39 K
37-H GHz	175.74 K	5.05 K
85-V GHz	276.17 K	1.63 K
85-H GHz	260.77 K	3.76 K

3.3. Prior PDF

The main difficulties are constructing the prior and conditional PDFs [38] and obtaining numerous and distinct samples to extend the distribution range of the P value and RR. The objective of this study was to estimate the RR associated with typhoons that may impact Taiwan. Therefore, near-surface RR data were collected by using the PR for a nine-year period (2002–2010), from June to November, over the northwestern Pacific and South China Sea regions (longitude 110°–155° E, latitude 5°–35° N), and the data were used to construct the prior PDF.

The minimum measurable echo intensity was 17 dBZ, which is equal to an RR of 0.7 mm·h^{-1} [39]. A total of 15,480 swaths and over 60 million observation data were obtained over the South China Sea and northwestern Pacific in the nine-year period. The number of RR data used in this study to construct the prior PDF was 3,115,544.

The symbol "+" in Figure 9 is used to represent the RRs near the nadir of the curve. The x coordinate represents the RR, and the y coordinate represents the prior PDF. The solid line represents the probability distribution obtained by fitting a logarithmic normal distribution to the portion of the curve marked by "+" symbols.

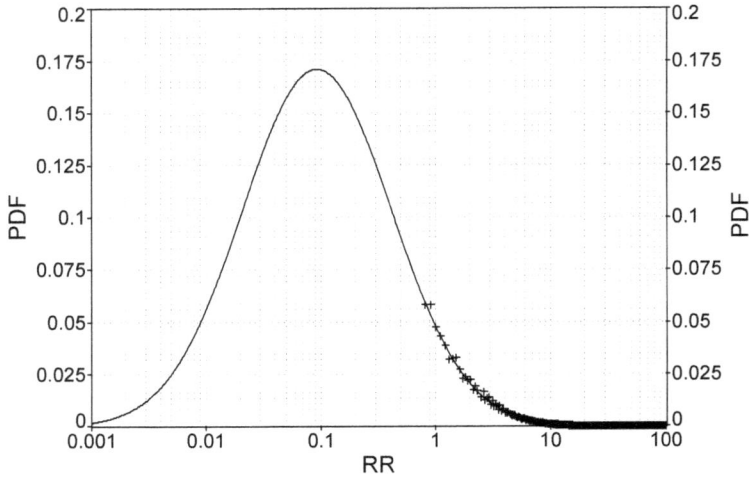

Figure 9. Rain rate distribution-PR (near nadir). Points marked by "+" represent the RRs near the nadir of the curve, and the solid line denotes the probability distribution.

3.4. Conditional PDF

Calculating the conditional PDF mainly involved calculating the probability distribution of the p value at different RRs. Numerous samples are required to obtain the relevant statistics and increase the dynamic range of the P value and RR. For this purpose, most of the chosen typhoons were moderate or strong when conducting the simulation.

The conditional PDF was calculated by WRF model to simulate various vertical hydrometeor distributions such as rain, snow, hail, and *graupel*, that is the standard output products of WRF. The results of hydrometeor sensitivity can be found in Yeh *et al.*, [40]. According to Chien *et al.*, [41], an analysis was made on the respective advantages and disadvantages for various combinations of different model parameters. The study used WSM6 (WRF Single-Moment) scheme in the microphysics option, YSU (Yonsei University) scheme in the boundary layer option, and KF (Kain-Fritsch) scheme in the cumulus option. These vertical hydrometeor distributions were inputted into the RTTOV model to obtain the TB of the TMI channels. RTTOV stands for Radiative Transfer for TOVS and is a very fast radiative transfer model for nadir-viewing passive visible, infrared, and microwave satellite radiometers, spectrometers, and interferometers. Fifteen typhoons occurring over the northwestern Pacific (Table 2) were simulated.

Table 2. Fifteen typhoons considered for constructing the conditional probability density function.

Number	Typhoon Nane	Typhoon Strength	Simulation Time (UTC)
1	BOLAVEN	Strong	2012/8/25 1800–2012/8/26 1800
2	GUCHOL	Strong	2012/6/17 0600–2012/6/17 0600
3	NANMADOL	Strong	2011/8/25 1800–2011/8/26 1800
4	SONGDA	Strong	2011/5/26 1200–2011/5/27 1200
5	SINLAKU	Strong	2008/9/12 0600–2008/9/13 0600
6	PRAPIROON	Medium	2012/10/11 1800–2012/10/12 1800
7	JELAWAT	Medium	2012/9/28 0000–2012/9/29 0000
8	SANBA	Medium	2012/9/14 1200–2012/9/15 1200
9	HAIKUI	Medium	2012/8/6 0000–2012/8/7 0000
10	MUIFA	Medium	2011/8/3 0600–2011/8/4 0600
11	CHABA	Medium	2010/10/27 1800–2010/10/28 1800
12	MEGI	Medium	2010/10/21 0000–2010/10/22 0000
13	FANAPI	Medium	2010/9/17 1200–2010/9/18 1200
14	LUPIT	Medium	2009/10/18 0000–2009/10/19 0000
15	PARMA	Weak	2009/10/4 0600–2009/10/5 0600

3.5. Posterior PDF

Nine years of near-surface RR data were used to construct the prior PDF, and the WRF model was used to simulate the vertical hydrometeor distribution and surface RR for 15 typhoons and to calculate the P value, which was then simulated using the RTTOV model; subsequently, the conditional PDF was constructed. Finally, According to Bayesian theory, the posterior PDF derived from the prior and conditional PDF, and the posterior PDF could be used along with satellite observations to estimate the RR associated with a typhoon. In other words, the rain rate of typhoon was estimated by inputting the vector $\vec{P} = (P_{10}, P_{19}, P_{37})$ into the lookup table (posterior PDF). The physical meaning is that the probability distribution of the RR is estimated using a certain known observation vector $\vec{P} = (P_{10}, P_{19}, P_{37})$.

There are two advantages of using the model when the Bayesian approach is used to estimate precipitation. First, the model can simulate a massive amount of data and a wide range of RRs. In the statistical point of view, a large amount of data can improve its reliability. Additionally, a large amount of data can also expand the range of RR estimation and its accuracy. Second, the RR can be estimated instantly without any calculations. The advantage of the Bayesian approach can be found in Chiu and Petty [38]. In addition to the Bayesian approach, the relationship of P and RR, as shown in Figure 2, can also be used to estimate the RR. The result of the RR estimation can be seen in Section 4.2. Meanwhile, additional descriptions have been added to Section 4.2.

4. Validation and Discussion

4.1. Analysis of TB

To clearly understand the differences between the simulated TB and the observed TB, a quantitative analysis of the TB was performed by considering typhoons in only a selected region. The region considered for quantitative analysis and the corresponding number of data for each typhoon are listed in Table 3.

Table 3. Information on the simulated typhoons.

No.	Typhoon Name	Scan Time (UTC)		The Range of Quantitative Analysis				Data Number	Correlation Coefficient
				North Latitude		East Longitude			
1	BOLAVEN	2012/8/26	759	23	29	125	133	3437	0.74
2	GUCHOL	2012/6/17	1848	19.5	24	125	130	1846	0.87
3	NANMADOL	2011/8/26	842	15.5	19	122	126	1020	0.64
4	SONGDA	2011/5/27	609	17	22.5	121.5	126	1921	0.73
5	SINLAKU	2008/9/12	1912	22	26.5	121.5	125.5	1297	0.79
6	PRAPIROON	2012/10/12	709	17	23	126	132	3117	0.78
7	JELAWAT	2012/9/28	1508	23	28	123	128	1960	0.83
8	SANBA	2012/9/15	347	21.5	26	126	131	1840	0.8
9	HAIKUI	2012/8/6	1820	24	30	121.5	128	2589	0.7
10	MUIFA	2011/8/3	1841	21.5	27	128	134	2682	0.77
11	CHABA	2010/10/28	1016	23	28	127	131	1553	0.88
12	MEGI	2010/10/21	1330	21.5	27	128	134	2156	0.84
13	FANAPI	2010/9/18	620	21.5	25.5	123	128	1575	0.84
14	LUPIT	2009/10/18	1434	15	21	131	137	2307	0.82
15	PARMA	2009/10/4	2232	17	22	117	122	1691	0.72

The precipitation lookup table was constructed by using frequencies of 10, 19, and 37 GHz to estimate the precipitation. Therefore, the quantitative analysis involved these three frequencies for the vertical and horizontal polarization. The correlation coefficient of the TB of each channel was calculated, and the average correlation coefficient of six channels was obtained. The average correlation coefficients of the observed TB and simulated TB were obtained. The correlation coefficients of the 15 typhoons are listed in Table 3. The conditional PDF was constructed using the TB and RR of the 15 typhoons, and the average correlation coefficient between the simulation and observation is 0.78.

Validation of TB Simulation

The conditional PDF was constructed by considering the 15 typhoons. The 10 GHz vertical polarization for the typhoons is discussed in this section.

Typhoon Nanmadol occurred on 26 August 2011 at 0842 UTC, and its track number is 78483. Figure 10 shows the satellite IR image at 0830 UTC. Clearly, the center of typhoon Nanmadol was approximately located to the east of the Philippines (latitude 17.5° N, Longitude 123.5° E). The cloud rainband shows a symmetrical and complete structure, indicating that Nanmadol was a strong typhoon.

Figure 11a shows the TB observations of the TMI, Figure 11b shows the TB simulated by the RTTOV model, and Figure 11c shows the histogram of the TB for the region within the dashed square. The blue bar represents TB observations, and the yellow bar denotes the simulated TB.

A qualitative analysis of Figures 11 and 12 shows that the center of the simulation of the typhoon is approximately identical in both figures and the entire simulation pattern is similar to the observed pattern of the typhoon. The TB of the clear sky simulated by the model shows a value that is consistent with the observation. The TB of the simulated typhoon rainband is overestimated.

Figure 10. Infrared (IR) image recorded at 0830 UTC on 26 August 2011.

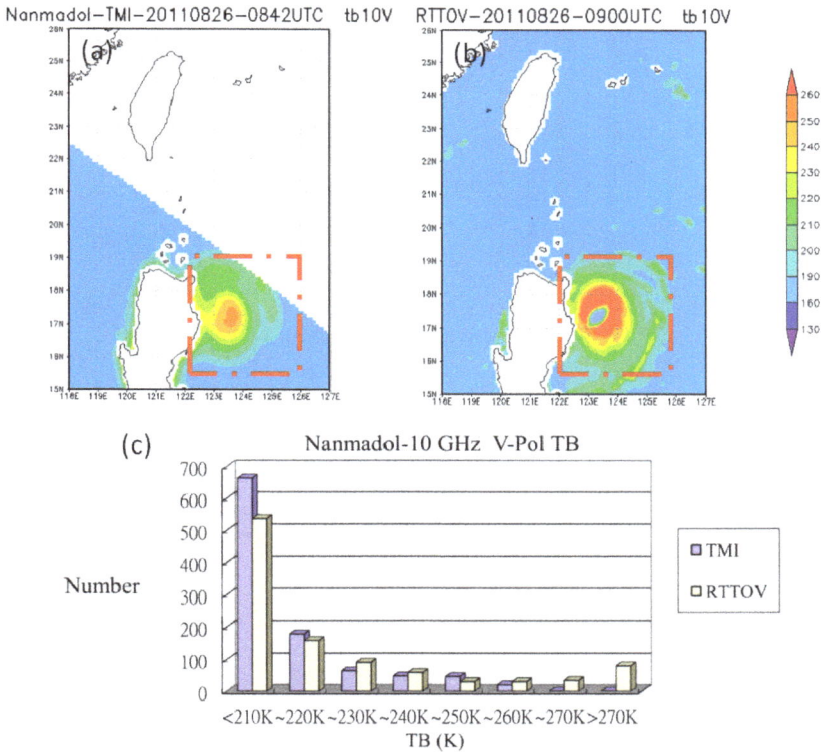

Figure 11. TB10V of Typhoon Nanmadol: (**a**) TMI observation; (**b**) Radiative Transfer for TIROS Operational Vertical Sounder (RTTOV) simulation; and (**c**) histogram for the region within the dashed square in the preceding panels.

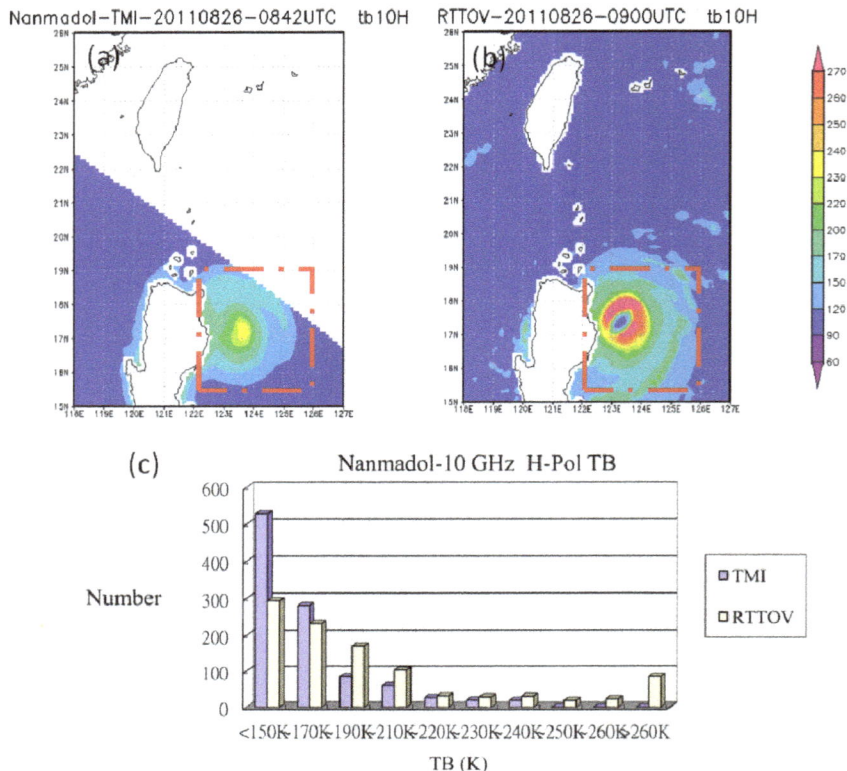

Figure 12. TB10H of Typhoon Nanmadol: (**a**) TMI observation; (**b**) RTTOV simulation; and (**c**) histogram for the region within the dashed square in the preceding panels.

The TB of the clear sky is identical in the simulation and observation (Figure 11c). The sizes of simulated and observed typhoons are similar. Therefore, the TB values of the clear sky within the dashed squares of the simulated and observed patterns are roughly identical. The highest TB of the rainband in Figure 11a is 230–240 K, and in Figure 11b, it is greater than 270 K. Therefore, the histogram of Figure 11c pertains to simulated TB values above 270 K. Figure 12 shows a similar situation. In other words, the simulation overestimated the TB in the rainband, because the WRF-model simulation of the precipitation associated with the typhoon was overestimated. The simulated RR was overestimated by the WRF model, and emissions dominated the 10 GHz frequency. Therefore, the simulated TB was overestimated because of emissions from raindrops, regardless of whether polarization was vertical or horizontal.

The difference between the simulation time and observation time is 18 min. Overall, the intensity and the structure of the typhoon are similar in the TMI observation and simulation, and only the scale of the typhoon differs slightly between the simulation and the observation. Therefore, the correlation coefficient between the simulation and observation is only 0.64.

4.2. Validation of RR Estimation

In this study, five complete typhoons, including 10 swaths scanned by the TMI in 2011 and 2012, were examined to verify the estimated precipitation. Information on the name, scanning time, and track number of the typhoons is presented in Table 4. Because there were few *in situ* observations (on islands and buoys), the verification was performed by considering the near-surface RR data recorded by the PR as the true value. RR verification was divided into quantitative analysis and qualitative analysis.

Numbers 1 to 10 in Table 4 represent 10 cases. However, for some typhoons, nadir scanning by the PR did not encompass the full rainband of the typhoons. Therefore, quantitative analysis was not performed for case numbers 1 and 3. The average correlation coefficient for the other eight cases is 0.62, and the average root-mean-square for the other eight cases error is 4.45. The results of the average root-mean-square and RMSE showed that the proposed method can accurately estimate the typhoon rain rate. Overall, the position of the typhoon heavy rainfall could be displayed, but the heaviest rainfall intensity was underestimated. One of the key sources of the error is that this method does not use the high-frequency channel. One case in Table 4 is discussed in this section, and the quantitative analysis results of the other cases are presented in the Table 4.

Table 4. RR validation cases.

Number	Typhoon Name	Scan Time (UTC)	Orbital Number	Correlation Coefficient	RMSE
1	MUIFA	2011/08/03 1307	78127	–	–
2	MUIFA	2011/08/03 1940	78131	0.52	3.48
3	MUIFA	2011/08/04 1732	78146	–	–
4	NANMADOL	2011/08/29 0025	78524	0.78	2.67
5	TEMBIN	2012/08/23 0943	84141	0.7	4.63
6	TEMBIN	2012/08/26 0832	84187	0.58	4.27
7	TEMBIN	2012/08/27 0736	84202	0.54	2.36
8	SANBA	2012/09/12 0733	84451	0.44	6.05
9	SANBA	2012/09/14 0540	84481	0.66	5.97
10	JELAWAT	2012/09/28 1544	84706	0.72	6.14

Case Study

Figure 13 shows the estimated precipitation for typhoon Nanmadol. Figure 13a shows the RR estimated by the PR (hereinafter referred to as PR-RR), Figure 13b shows the RR estimated using the Bayesian method developed in this study (hereinafter referred to as TMI-RR), and Figure 13c shows a scatter plot of both types of estimates. In Figure 13a, typhoon Nanmadol consists of two regions with heavy precipitation. Region A is the southwestern sea area of Taiwan, and region B extends from the Bashi Channel to the southern part of the Taiwan Strait. In Figure 13b, the regions with heavier precipitation are located in regions A' and B', which match the locations of regions A and B in Figure 13a. Further analysis of Figure 13a,b regarding the intensity and range of heavy precipitation shows that the maximum PR-RR is higher than the maximum TMI-RR and that the range of the second greatest precipitation (yellow parts, 10–25 mm·h^{-1}) of the TMI-RR is greater than that of the PR-RR.

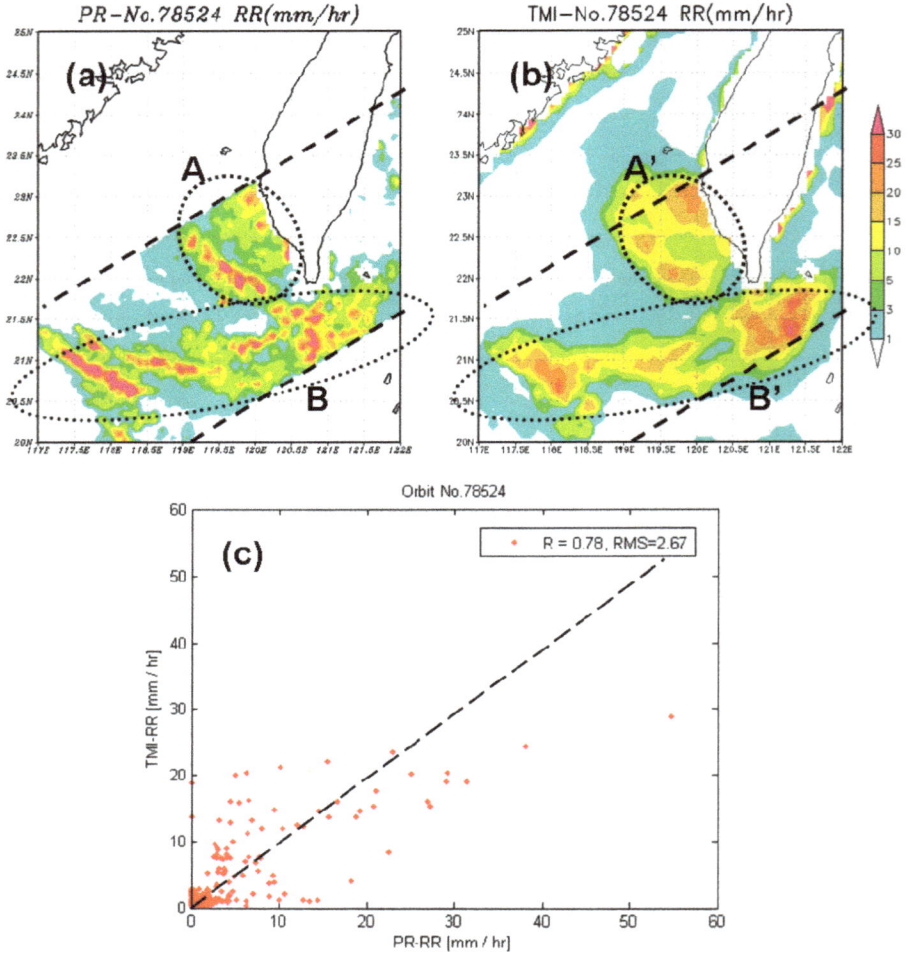

Figure 13. RR estimation for Typhoon Nanmadol: (**a**) near-surface RR estimated by the PR (PR-RR); (**b**) RR estimated using the Bayesian method and the TMI data (TMI-RR); and (**c**) scatter plot of the PR-RR and TMI-RR.

There is a possible reason for the discrepancy between Figure 13a,b regarding the intensity and range: the space resolution and accuracy of the PR-RR. The horizontal resolution (10 km) of the TMI is twice that of the PR (5 km), and the TMI-RR is the result of averaging smaller RR values and the maximum RR in the FOV. Another possible reason was the physics in models do not reproduce the typhoon environment well. The correlation coefficient between the PR-RR and TMI-RR is 0.78, and the root-mean-square error is 2.67 mm·h^{-1}.

The TMI-RR for this typhoon did not exceed 30 mm·h^{-1}, possibly because the heavy precipitation consists of individual short-range convective cells that average light precipitation in their vicinity. Finally, the maximum RR of the TMI-RR is smaller than that of the PR-RR, and the range of the second largest RR of the TMI-RR is greater than that of the PR-RR.

For the case being discussed, the space resolution of the PR-RR is 5 km, which is suitable for observing a shorter range of convective precipitation. Therefore, a single grid point of RR can show a high precipitation value. By contrast, the space resolution of the TMI-RR is 10 km, and partial heavier precipitation and partial smaller precipitation in the FOV is easier to appear. These factors may cause the maximum RR of the TMI-RR to be smaller than that of the PR-RR, the RR range to be smooth, and the range of the TMI-RR to be greater than that of the PR-RR after averaging the precipitation distribution, as shown in Figure 13a,b. These are the differences in the precipitation features between the PR-RR and the TMI-RR.

Although the space resolution of the PR-RR is superior to that of the TMI-RR, the precipitation estimation of the PR is based on using the radar reflectivity to retrieve the RR. Furthermore, comparing Figure 13a,b reveals that the swath of the TMI-RR is three times that of the PR-RR, and its utilization is superior to that of the PR-RR.

Figure 14 shows the RR estimated by combining RR estimations from the 10, 19, and 37 GHz attenuation indices for Typhoon Nanmadol (hereinafter referred to as P-RR). In Figure 14, Typhoon Nanmadol consists of two regions where the areas that have the heaviest rain. Moreover, the locations of the two regions match the locations of regions A and B in Figure 13a.

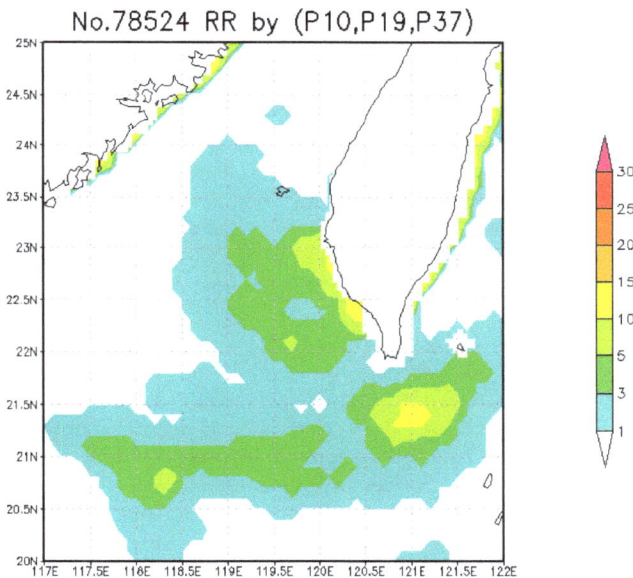

Figure 14. RR estimated using the 10, 19, and 37 GHz attenuation indice.

Further analysis of Figure 14 regarding the intensity of the heavy precipitation shows that the maximum P-RR is lower than 15 mm·h^{-1}. By comparing the TMI-RR and P-RR, the heavy rainfall locations are similar and match the locations of the PR-RR, and the intensity of P-RR is significantly lower than the PR-RR. The possible season for the low P-RR values less than 15 mm·h^{-1} at high PR-RR above 25 mm·h^{-1} is that the Figure 2 is not a production for typhoons near Taiwan. Therefore, the proposed method provides better results than the approach in directly estimating the rain rate from the attenuation index.

4.3. Precipitation Type Analysis

Figure 15 shows all convective and stratiform precipitation of the eight swaths considered in this study and verified using the PR-RR. The type of rain was taken from PR data. The horizontal coordinate represents the PR-RR, and the vertical coordinate denotes the TMI-RR. Figure 15a represents convective precipitation and Figure 15b represents stratiform precipitation. The black dashed line is the straight line $x = y$. The purpose of classification verification is to determine the performance of different types of precipitation.

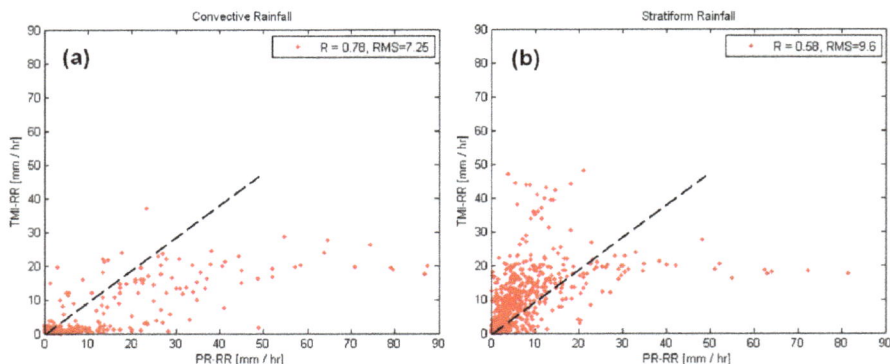

Figure 15. Scatterplot of TMI-RR and PR-RR for (**a**) convective rainfall and (**b**) stratiform rainfall.

An analysis of Figure 15a shows that some rainfall intensity values of the PR are greater than 30 mm·h^{-1}, and the corresponding rainfall of the TMI is less than 10 mm·h^{-1}. The probability of heavy precipitation on a small scale is higher for convective precipitation. Regions A and B in Figure 13a,b are examples. The area which has the maximum RR is smaller than the FOV, and the RR of this area will be averaged. The PR-RR is averaged to the same horizontal resolution as the TMI. The maximum PR-RR can also be obtained by averaging it to the TMI resolution. The correlation coefficient between the TMI-RR and PR-RR is 0.78, and the root-mean-square error is 7.25 mm·h^{-1}.

Compared with Figure 15a,b shows that the points of the TMI-RR are below 5 mm·h^{-1}, but the number of points of the PR-RR that reach 10–50 mm·h^{-1} is considerably smaller. The TMI-RR data are mostly located on the left side of $x = y$, whereas the PR-RR values are less than 20 mm·h^{-1}. The right side of $x = y$ contains PR-RR values greater than 30 mm·h^{-1}, implying that the TMI-RR values are overestimating when the PR-RR values are less than 20 mm·h^{-1}. The TMI-RR values are underestimating when the PR-RR values are greater than 30 mm·h^{-1}. Iguchi *et al.*, (2000) [42] showed that there are differences in the coefficients in the reflectivity-rainfall rate relationship between different precipitation types as a result of larger raindrops in convective rain. Thus, an error in classification of convective actual type as stratiform type would lead to lower (by about 40%) estimated rainfall rate PR-RR than the actual value (and 2.5 times higher values for the opposite classification error). A possible reason for the high TMI-RR values above 20 mm·h^{-1} at low PR-RR less than 10 mm·h^{-1} values under stratiform rainfall is that they are errors in TRMM precipitation classification as the stratiform type while it is actually the convective type of rain, which leads to lower PR-RR values than actual RR. The correlation coefficient between the TMI-RR and the PR-RR is 0.58, and the root-mean-square error is 9.6 mm·h^{-1}.

Further analysis shows that the distribution of convective precipitation is different from stratiform precipitation. There are two possible reasons for this. First, the reliability of stratiform precipitation reaching 30 mm·h^{-1} is questionable because such high RR values do not occur in stratiform precipitation. However, if there is a TRMM classification error for these points, the results of the proposed method will underestimate even more significantly if they correspond to classification errors; second, the conditional PDF of Bayesian theory was constructed by considering 15 typhoons (heavy precipitation), and therefore, it is more suitable for heavy precipitation. In theory, high RR values are typical of convective precipitation. The most likely reason of the RR estimation error is that the physics in the models do not reproduce the typhoon environment well.

There are two discussions from Figure 15a,b. First, the convection points are less than the stratiform points and for stratiform retrievals TMI-RR and PR-RR seem to compare better than for convective retrievals. Second, PR-RR greater than 30 mm·h^{-1} are underestimated by TMI-RR, which could be explained partially by possible rainfall classification errors (actual stratiform rainfall classified as the convective type). The conclusion from Figure 15 is that stratiform rainfall (excluding possible bad classification points) is overestimated by the proposed method and convective rainfall is underestimated (including high convective PR-RR rainfall classified as stratiform from TRMM algorithms in Figure 15b).

5. Conclusions

This study simulated the TB for various atmospheric conditions by using the WRF and RTM models and then compared the simulated TB with the TB observed by the TRMM/TMI. The result showed that the simulated TB was virtually identical to the observed TB at 10 GHz under clear sky conditions, but the rainband was overestimated in the simulation. This discrepancy might originate from the difference between the simulation time and observation time. Another concern was the difference between actual weather conditions and the weather conditions corresponding to the initial data used in the simulation. In other words, the physics in the models do not reproduce the typhoon environment well. For future research, further improvement in the model physics is absolutely needed to better simulate the typhoon environment.

A qualitative comparison of the TB simulated by the RTM, the TB observed by the TMI, and the simulated TB of clear sky showed that the rainband of the typhoons considered and the typhoon patterns were similar to the observed rainband and patterns. A quantitative analysis of 15 typhoons yielded an average correlation coefficient of 0.78. However, a key point is that the conditional PDF was as extensive as possible and could simulate all rainfall intensities and confirm the simulation accuracy. Therefore, the posterior PDF can be used for a variety of rainfall intensities.

The attenuation index can reduce the impact caused by the environment background, and it has the advantage of decreasing with an increase in the RR; both these parameters have a one-to-one relationship. Therefore, the attenuation index is extremely suitable for use in precipitation estimation research. A Bayesian method was used to estimate the RR of 10 satellite swaths, and the estimated values were verified by comparing them with PR-RR. A qualitative analysis of the RR pattern, intensity, and location showed that the TMI-RR was underestimated in short-range heavy precipitation, and the location and range of the TMI-RR were similar to those of the PR-RR. Eight typhoon events were quantitatively analyzed, and the average correlation coefficient between the TMI-RR and the PR-RR is 0.63; the root-mean-square error is 4.45 mm·h^{-1}. Furthermore, the correlation coefficient of the convective RR is 0.78, and the root-mean-square error is 7.25 mm·h^{-1} with a systematic underestimation of RR compared to PR. The correlation coefficient of the stratiform RR is 0.58, and the root-mean-square error is 9.6 mm·h^{-1} with a systematic overestimation of RR compared to PR. The results show that the Bayesian method can be effective in estimating the RR associated with typhoons over the ocean.

Acknowledgments: This research was supported by Ministry of Science and Technology of Taiwan under contract MOST 104-2111-M-344-001. In addition the authors would like to thank Wallace Academic Editing and Charlie C.K. Liang for their professionalism in reviewing and editing the English writing.

Author Contributions: Nan-Ching Yeh and and Wann-Jin Chen conceived and designed the study. Nan-Ching Yeh and Chung-Chih Liu collected the data, analyzed the results. Nan-Ching Yeh wrote the paper.

Conflicts of Interest: The authors declare no conflict of interest.

References

1. Adler, R.F.; Rodgers, E.B. Satellite-observed latent heat release in tropical cyclones. *Mon. Weather Rev.* **1997**, *105*, 956–963. [CrossRef]

2. Spencer, R.W.; Hinton, B.B.; Olson, W.S. Nimbus-7 37 GHz radiances correlated with radar rain rates over the Gulf of Mexico. *J. Climate Appl. Meteorol.* **1983**, *22*, 2095–2099. [CrossRef]

3. Wilheit, T.T. Algorithm for the retrieval of rainfall from passive microwave measurements. *Remote Sens. Rev.* **1994**, *11*, 163–194. [CrossRef]

4. Barrett, E.C. The first WetNet precipitation intercomparison project (PIP-1): Interpretation of results. *Remote Sens. Rev.* **1994**, *11*, 303–373. [CrossRef]

5. Petty, G.W. The status of satellite-based rainfall estimation over land. *Remote Sens. Environ.* **1995**, *51*, 125–137. [CrossRef]

6. Smith, E.A.; Lamm, J.E.; Adler, R.; Alishouse, J.; Aonashi, K.; Barrett, E.; Bauer, P.; Berg, W.; Chang, A.; Ferraro, R.; *et al.* Results of WetNet PIP-2 project. *J. Atmos. Sci.* **1998**, *55*, 1483–1536. [CrossRef]

7. Levizzani, V.; Amorati, R.; Meneguzzo, F. *A Review of Satellite-based Rainfall Estimation Methods*; European Commission Project Music Report: Brussels, Belgium, 2002; pp. 1–66.

8. Kidd, C.; Kniveton, D.R.; Todd, M.C.; Bellerby, T.J. Satellite Rainfall Estimation Using a Combined Passive Microwave and Infrared Algorithm. *J. Hydrometeorol.* **2003**, *4*, 1088–1104. [CrossRef]

9. Adler, R.F.; Kidd, C.; Petty, G.; Morissey, M.; Goodman, H.M. Intercomparison of global precipitation products: The third precipitation interconparison project (PIP-3). *Bull. Am. Meteorol. Soc.* **2001**, *82*, 1377–1396. [CrossRef]

10. Petty, G.W. Physical Retrievals of Over-Ocean Rain Rate from Multichannel Microwave Imagery. Part I: Theoretical Characteristics of Normalized Polarization and Scattering Indices. *Meteorol. Atmos. Phys.* **1994**, *54*, 79–100. [CrossRef]

11. Chen, W.J.; Li, C.C. Rain Retrievals Using Tropical Rainfall Measuring Mission and Geostationary Meteorological Satellite 5 Data Obtained during the SCSMEX. *Int. J. Remote Sens.* **2002**, *23*, 2425–2448. [CrossRef]

12. Liu, G.R.; Liu, C.C.; Kuo, T.H. A Satellite-Derived Objective Potential Index for MCS Development during the Mei-Yu Period. *J. Meteorol. Soc. Jpn.* **2002**, *80*, 503–517. [CrossRef]

13. Joyce, R.J.; Janowiak, J.E.; Arkin, P.A.; Xie, P. CMORPH: A Method that Produces Global Precipitation Estimates from Passive Microwave and Infrared Data at High Spatial and Temporal Resolution. *J. Hydrometeorol.* **2004**, *5*, 487–503. [CrossRef]

14. Kummerow, C.; Shin, D.B.; Hong, Y.; Olson, W.S.; Yang, S.; Adler, R.F.; McCollum, J.; Ferraro, R.; Petty, G.; Wilheit, T.T. The Evolution of the Goddard Profiling Algorithm (GPROF) for Rainfall Estimation from Passive Microwave Sensors. *J. Appl. Meteorol.* **2001**, *40*, 1801–1820. [CrossRef]

15. Arkin, P.A.; Meisner, B. The Relationship between Large-Scale Convective Rainfall and Cold Cloud over the Western Hemisphere during 1982–1984. *Mon. Weather Rev.* **1987**, *115*, 51–74. [CrossRef]

16. Chiu, L.S.; North, G.R.; Short, D.A.; McConnell, A. Rain Estimation from Satellites: Effect of Finite Field of View. *J. Geophys. Res.* **1990**, *95*, 2177–2185. [CrossRef]

17. Adler, R.F.; Negri, A.J.; Keehn, P.R.; Hakkarinen, I.M. Estimation of Monthly Rainfall over Japan and Surrounding Waters from a Combination of Low-Orbit Microwave and Geosynchronous IR Data. *J. Appl. Meteorol.* **1993**, *32*, 335–356. [CrossRef]

18. Ferraro, R.R. SSM/I Derived Global Rainfall Estimates for Climatological Applications. *J. Geophys. Res.* **1997**, *102*, 16715–16735. [CrossRef]

19. Wilheit, T.T.; Chang, A.T.C.; Chiu, L.S. Retrieval of Monthly Rainfall Indices from Microwave Radiometric Measurements Using Probability Distribution Functions. *J. Atmos. Ocean. Technol.* **1991**, *8*, 118–136. [CrossRef]

20. Janowiak, J.E. Tropical Rainfall: A Comparison of Satellite-Derived Rainfall Estimates with Model Precipitation Forecasts, Climatologies, and Observations. *Mon. Weather Rev.* **1992**, *120*, 448–462. [CrossRef]

21. Grody, N.C. Classification of Snow Cover and Precipitation Using the Special Sensor Microwave Imager. *J. Geophys. Res.* **1991**, *96*, 7423–7435. [CrossRef]

22. Ferraro, R.R.; Grody, N.C.; Marks, G.F. Effects of Surface Conditions on Rain Identification Using the SSM/I. *Remote Sens. Rev.* **1994**, *11*, 195–209. [CrossRef]

23. Ferraro, R.R.; Weng, F.; Grody, N.C.; Basist, A. An Eight-Year (1987–1994) Time Series of Rainfall, Clouds, Water Vapor, Snow Cover, and Sea Ice Derived from SSM/I Measurements. *Bull. Am. Meteorol. Soc.* **1996**, *77*, 891–905. [CrossRef]

24. Kidder, S.Q.; VonderHaar, T.H. *Satellite Meteorology: An Introduction*; Academic Press: San Diego, CA, USA, 1995; pp. 1–339.

25. Wilheit, T.; Kummerow, C.; Ferraro, R. Rainfall Algorithms for AMSR-E. *IEEE Trans. Geosci. Remote Sens.* **2003**, *41*, 204–214. [CrossRef]

26. Kidd, C.; Huffman, G. Global precipitation measurement. *Meteorol. Appl.* **2011**, *18*, 334–353. [CrossRef]

27. Tapiador, F.J.; Turk, J.; Petersen, W.; Hou, A.Y.; García-Ortega, E.; Machado, L.A.T.; Angelis, C.F.; Salio, P.; Kidd, C.; Huffman, G.J. Global precipitation measurement: Methods, datasets and applications. *Atmos. Res.* **2012**, *104–105*, 70–97. [CrossRef]

28. Chen, S.; Hong, Y.; Gourley, J.J.; Kirstette, P.E.; Yong, B.; Tian, Y.; Zhang, Z.; Hardy, J. Similarity and difference of the two successive V6 and V7 TRMM multi-satellite precipitation analysis (TMPA) performance over China. *J. Geophys. Res.* **2013**, *118*, 13060–13074.

29. Chen, S.; Hong, Y.; Gourley, J.J.; Huffman, G.J.; Tian, Y.; Cao, Q.; Kirstetter, P.E.; Hu, J.; Hardy, J.; Xue, X. Evaluation of the successive V6 and V7 TRMM multi-satellite precipitation analysis over the continental United States. *Water Resour. Res.* **2013**, *49*, 8174–8186. [CrossRef]

30. Kirstetter, P.E.; Hong, Y.; Gourley, J.; Schwaller, M.; Petersen, W.; Zhang, J. Comparison of TRMM 2A25 products, version 6 and version 7, with NOAA/NSSL ground radar-based national mosaic QPE. *J. Hydrometeorol.* **2013**, *14*, 661–669. [CrossRef]

31. Huang, Y.; Chen, S.; Cao, Q.; Hong, Y.; Wu, B.; Huang, M.; Qiao, L.; Zhang, Z.; Li, Z.; Li, W.; Yang, X. Evaluation of Version-7 TRMM Multi-Satellite Precipitation Analysis Product during the Beijing Extreme Heavy Rainfall Event of 21 July 2012. *Water* **2014**, *6*, 32–44. [CrossRef]

32. Rana, S.; McGregor, J.; Renwick, J.A. Precipitation seasonality over the Indian Subcontinent: An evaluation of gauge, reanalyses and satellite retrievals. *J. Hydrometeorol.* **2015**, *16*, 631–651. [CrossRef]

33. Chau, K.W.; Wu, C.L. A Hybrid Model Coupled with Singular Spectrum Analysis for Daily Rainfall Prediction. *J. Hydroinform.* **2010**, *12*, 458–473. [CrossRef]

34. Wang, W.C.; Chau, K.W.; Xu, D.M.; Chen, X.Y. Improving forecasting accuracy of annual runoff time series using ARIMA based on EEMD decomposition. *Water Resour. Manag.* **2015**, *29*, 2655–2675. [CrossRef]

35. Hu, J.C.; Chen, W.J.; Chiu, J.C.; Wang, J.L.; Liu, G.R. Quantitative Precipitation Estimation over Ocean Using Bayesian Approach from Microwave Observations during the Typhoon Season. *Terr. Atmos. Ocean. Sci.* **2009**, *20*, 817–832. [CrossRef]

36. Petty, G.W.; Boukabara, S.A.; Snell, N.; Moncet, J.L. *Algorithm Theoretical Basis Document (ATBD) for the Conical-Scanning Microwave Imager/Sounder (CMIS) Environmental Data Records (EDRs), Volume 5: Precipitation Type and Rate EDR*; Atmospheric and Environmental Research: Lexington, MA, USA, 2001; pp. 1–112.

37. Chiu, J.C. Bayesian Retrieval of Complete Posterior PDFs of Rain Rate from Satellite Passive Microwave Observations. Ph.D. Thesis, Purdue University, West Lafayette, IN, USA, 2003.

38. Chiu, J.C.; Petty, G.W. Bayesian Retrieval of Complete Posterior PDFs of Oceanic Rain Rate from Microwave Observations. *J. Appl. Meteorol. Climatol.* **2006**, *45*, 1073–1095. [CrossRef]

39. Okamoto, K. Tropical Rainfall Measuring Mission (TRMM) Precipitation Radar Algorithm Instruction Manual for Version 6. TRMM Precipitation Radar Team. Available online: http://www.eorc.jaxa.jp/TRMM/documents/PR_algorithm_product_information/pr_manual/PR_Instruction_Manual_V7_L1.pdf (accessed on 27 October 2015).

40. Yeh, N.C.; Chen, W.J.; Wei, C.H.; Liu, C.Y. The Analysis of Hydrometeor Sensitivity on TRMM/TMI. *J. Aeronaut. Astronaut. Aviat.* **2014**, *46*, 203–207.

41. Chien, F.C.; Hong, J.S.; Chang, W.J.; Jou, J.D.; Lin, P.L.; Lin, T.E.; Liu, S.P.; Miou, H.J.; Chen, C.Y. A Sensitivity Study of the WRF Model Part II: Verification of Quantitative Precipitation Forecasts. *Atmos. Sci.* **2006**, *34*, 261–276. (In Chinese)

42. Iguchi, T.; Kozu, T.; Meneghini, R.; Awaka, J.; Okamoto, K. Rain-profiling algorithm for the TRMM precipitation radar. *J. Appl. Meteorol.* **2000**, *39*, 2038–2052. [CrossRef]

Article

An Hourly Streamflow Forecasting Model Coupled with an Enforced Learning Strategy

Ming-Chang Wu [1] and Gwo-Fong Lin [1,2,*]

[1] Taiwan Typhoon and Flood Research Institute, National Applied Research Laboratories, 11F., No. 97, Sec. 1, Roosevelt Rd., Taipei City 10093, Taiwan; mcwu@narlabs.org.tw

[2] Department of Civil Engineering, National Taiwan University, Taipei City 10617, Taiwan

* Correspondence: gflin@ntu.edu.tw; Tel.: +886-2-3366-4368; Fax: +886-2-2363-1558

Academic Editor: Kwok-wing Chau

Received: 17 September 2015; Accepted: 22 October 2015; Published: 28 October 2015

Abstract: Floods, one of the most significant natural hazards, often result in loss of life and property. Accurate hourly streamflow forecasting is always a key issue in hydrology for flood hazard mitigation. To improve the performance of hourly streamflow forecasting, a methodology concerning the development of neural network (NN) based models with an enforced learning strategy is proposed in this paper. Firstly, four different NNs, namely back propagation network (BPN), radial basis function network (RBFN), self-organizing map (SOM), and support vector machine (SVM), are used to construct streamflow forecasting models. Through the cross-validation test, NN-based models with superior performance in streamflow forecasting are detected. Then, an enforced learning strategy is developed to further improve the performance of the superior NN-based models, *i.e.*, SOM and SVM in this study. Finally, the proposed flow forecasting model is obtained. Actual applications are conducted to demonstrate the potential of the proposed model. Moreover, comparison between the NN-based models with and without the enforced learning strategy is performed to evaluate the effect of the enforced learning strategy on model performance. The results indicate that the NN-based models with the enforced learning strategy indeed improve the accuracy of hourly streamflow forecasting. Hence, the presented methodology is expected to be helpful for developing improved NN-based streamflow forecasting models.

Keywords: streamflow forecasting; neural networks; support vector machine; enforced learning strategy

1. Introduction

Floods caused by heavy rainfall often lead to loss of life and property damage. For flood damage mitigation, the development of flood warning systems has been recognized as an important task. In most flood warning systems, accurate and reliable forecasts of flow are essential information. Therefore, providing accurate and reliable forecasts of flow is always a major issue in flood management. However, it is difficult to develop a fully physically based forecasting model because of the high variability in space and time, and the complex mechanisms involved in the rainfall-runoff process during storm events. It is also difficult to construct a statistically based model using traditional regression techniques owing to the highly nonlinear influence of heavy rainfall on floods.

In recent years, neural networks (NNs) have been suggested as a promising alternative to the physically based models. Due to the powerful capability to deal with highly complicated problems and to model nonlinear systems without explicit physical consideration, NNs have found increasing applications for modeling hydrological processes. General introductions of NNs and comprehensive reviews of their applications in various aspects of hydrology have been presented by American Society of Civil Engineers (ASCE) Task Committee on Application of Artificial Neural Networks in Hydrology [1,2], Govindaraju and Rao [3], and Maier and Dandy [4]. Moreover, Maier *et al.* [5] present a review of using NNs for the prediction of water resource variables in river systems. In various kinds of NNs, the most commonly used in hydrology are back propagation neural networks (BPNs), radial basis function neural networks (RBFNs), self-organizing maps (SOMs), and support vector machines (SVMs). Hence, in this paper, these four familiar NNs are adopted to develop NN-based flow forecasting models. A brief review of using these four NNs to forecast flows is presented below.

Huang *et al.* [6] used a BPN to forecast the river flow in the Apalachicola River. Their results indicated that the BPN provides better accuracy in forecasting river flow than the ARIMA model. Chau *et al.* [7] proposed a genetic algorithm-based NN for water level forecasting. Lin and Chen [8] constructed a BPN-based rainfall-runoff model with a systematic input determination approach for providing improved flow forecasts. Cheng *et al.* [9] proposed an NN daily runoff forecasting model with a heuristic training technique, and indicated that much better forecast accuracy and efficiency can be achieved. More relevant studies are available in the literature (e.g., [10–17]). Dawson *et al.* [18] used RBFN to forecast flows in the Yangtze River, China. Their results showed that the RBFN performs the best when compared to several existing time-series forecasting models. Lin and Chen [19] used RBFN to construct the rainfall-runoff relation for providing the 1- to 3-h ahead forecasts of streamflow. Lin and Wu [20] proposed an RBFN-based mode with a two-step learning algorithm to successfully yield 6-h ahead forecasts of inflow. Related works can also be found in the literature (e.g., [21–25]). Liong and Sivapragasam [26] used SVM to forecast the 1- to 7-day ahead flood stages. Their results concluded that SVM appears to be a very promising forecasting tool. Wu *et al.* [27] compared the potential of different NN-based techniques in river stage prediction and indicated the distributed SVM with optimal parameters can provide the most satisfying results. Wu *et al.* [28] used SVM equipped with a data analysis technique to successfully provide the improved 1- to 3-h ahead forecasts of streamflow. Recent relevant studies can also be found in the literature (e.g., [29–36]). As to the use of SOM for rainfall-runoff estimation and forecasting, Hsu *et al.* [37] provided a self-organizing linear output map (SOLO) and applied this in streamflow forecasting. Their results indicated the SOLO can provide features that facilitate insight into the underlying processes as well as satisfying results. More relevant works can be found in the literature (e.g., [38–42]).

As mentioned by ASCE Task Committee on Application of Artificial Neural Networks in Hydrology [1], the quality and the quantity of data available will influence the success of NN applications. NNs are data-driven techniques and therefore their performance intimately hinges on the data used for learning. Usually, NNs require larger data sets for better learning. However, no clearly theoretical guideline exists for deciding the length of hydrologic record for NN learning. Generally, a longer time series of training data containing more events of different types will improve the generalization ability of NN-based models. This condition cannot be easily satisfied because many hydrologic records do not go back far enough. Quite often, the quantity of data is very limited even when long historic records are available. For example, the peak flows, which are the most valuable part in constructing flow forecasting models, are always rare. Due to the insufficient data of peak streamflow in size, NN-based models are usually unable to yield satisfactory solutions of extreme values in the streamflow [43]. To overcome this problem, studies that are attempted to improve the quality and the quantity of training data of NN-based models are available in the literature (e.g., [28,40,44–46]). Hence, in a similar manner, an enforced learning strategy is proposed in this paper. By quickly improving the quality and the quantity of data used in the training of NN-based models, the performance of NN-based models is expected to be improved.

The purpose of this paper is to propose improved NN-based models for providing more accurate forecasts of streamflow. To reach this aim, a modeling methodology is presented herein. Firstly, four familiar NNs, namely BPN, RBFN, SOM and SVM, are used to construct flow forecasting models. Then, these NN-based models are evaluated through the cross-validation test for detecting the models with superior performance. Moreover, to further improve the forecasting performance of these superior NN-based models, an enforced learning strategy is proposed. Finally, the proposed flow forecasting model is developed. This paper is organized as follows. An introduction is given firstly. Then, brief

Water **2015**, *7*, 5876–5895

descriptions of the proposed methodology including the NNs used to construct flow forecasting models and the enforced learning strategy are presented in the second section. In the third section, the statement of the study area and data is described. Results of actual application are also provided in this section. Additionally, the forecasting performances of these NN-based models are compared and the effect of the enforced learning strategy on NN-based models is investigated. Finally, conclusions are summarized in the fourth section.

2. The Proposed Methodology

In this paper, to improve the hourly streamflow forecasting, a modeling methodology concerning the development of NN-based models with the enforced learning strategy is proposed. A flowchart of the development of the proposed NN-based flow forecasting model is presented in Figure 1.

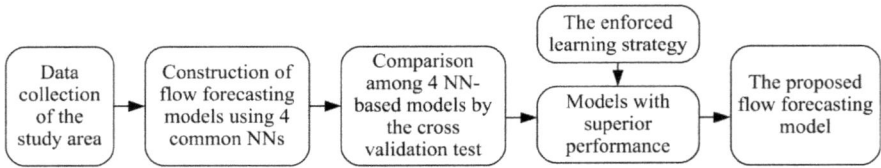

Figure 1. Flowchart of the development of the proposed flow forecasting model.

2.1. Neural Networks

As shown in Figure 1, four NNs, which are commonly used for hydrological forecasting, are adopted to construct NN-based flow forecasting models in this study. Brief introductions of these NNs, namely BPN, RBFN, SOM and SVM, are provided below.

2.1.1. Back Propagation Neural Network

Back propagation neural network proposed by Rumelhart *et al.* [47] is the most commonly used for hydrological forecasting. The network typically consists of an input layer, one or more hidden layers of computation neurons, and an output layer. During the learning step, the input signals proceed through the network in a forward direction, and the error signal back propagates from the output layer toward the input layer. The objective of learning is to minimize the error function F:

$$F = \frac{1}{2}\sum_{l=1}^{L}(d_l - y_l)^2 \tag{1}$$

where d_l and y_l are respectively the desired and the actual outputs for the lth sample. L is the total number of samples in the training data set. Mathematically, the y_l resulting from a three-layer network with I input neurons, J hidden nodes, and one output neurons can be expressed as:

$$y_l = f\left(\sum_{j=1}^{J} w_j^{ho} f\left(\sum_{i=1}^{I} w_{ij}^{ih} x_{il}\right)\right) \tag{2}$$

where x_{il} is the lth sample input to the ith neuron of the input layer, w_{ij}^{ih} is the connection weight between the ith neuron of the input layer and the jth neuron of the hidden layer, w_j^{ho} is the connection weight between the jth neuron of the hidden layer and the neuron of the output layer, and f is the activation function. The most common form of f, *i.e.*, the sigmoid function, is adopted herein. By using the back-propagation learning method, the connection weights are iteratively adjusted until the error function F converges to an acceptable value. In this study, the network with one hidden layer is adopted. The number of hidden neurons is varied from one to 10 to select the most appropriate network architecture. For each number of hidden neurons, 30 different sets of initial connection weights are tried during the training process. The learning rate and the maximum training epoch are set to 0.8 and 10,000, respectively.

2.1.2. Radial Basis Function Neural Network

The radial basis function neural network developed by Broomhead and Lowe [48] has been widely employed in non-linear system identification and time series prediction because of its powerful ability of universal function approximation. An RBF network consists of an input layer, a hidden layer with a number of neurons, and an output layer. The hidden layer transforms data from the input space to the hidden space using a nonlinear function. The nonlinear function of hidden units is symmetric in the input space, and the output of each hidden neuron depends only on the radial distance between the input and the hidden neuron. The response of each hidden neuron is scaled by its connecting weight to the output neuron and then summed to produce the overall network output. Therefore, the output of RBFN is written as:

$$\hat{y} = w_0 + \sum_{j=1}^{M} w_j h_j(\mathbf{x}) \tag{3}$$

where w_j is the connecting weight between the jth hidden neuron and the output neuron, and w_0 is the bias. The values of w_j and w_0 are estimated using the least mean square algorithm. M is the number of hidden neurons. The $h_j(\mathbf{x})$ is the output of the jth hidden neuron given by:

$$h_j(x) = \exp\left(\frac{-1}{2\rho^2}\|\mathbf{x} - \mathbf{c}_j\|^2\right), \quad j = 1, 2, \cdots, M \tag{4}$$

where $\|\cdot\|$ denotes the Euclidean norm, $\mathbf{x}$ is the input vector, $\mathbf{c}_j$ is the center vector of the jth hidden neuron, and ρ is the width of the hidden neurons. The value of ρ can be calculated as $d_{max}/\sqrt{2M}$, in which d_{max} is the maximum distance between two hidden neurons. As to the determination of the center vector of hidden neuron c_j, relevant works can be found in the literature (e.g., [19,20,24,49–51]). In this study, a simple method is applied. That is, the number of hidden neurons is set to 30 and the center vectors of these hidden neurons are selected randomly from the training data set. Moreover, to avoid the local optimal problem, a total of 30 sets of different selections of the center vectors are tried.

2.1.3. Support Vector Machine

Support vector machine, which is a novel kind of NN, is developed by Vapnik [52]. SVM is constructed based on both the structural risk minimization principle and the empirical risk minimization principle. This enables SVM to generalize well. Hence, SVM has emerged as an alternative tool in many conventional NNs dominated fields, especially for hydrological forecasting. Herein, a brief introduction of SVM is presented. More mathematical details can be found in several textbooks [52–54]. Based on N_d training data, the objective of the SVM learning is to find a non-linear regression function to yield the output $\hat{y}$, which is the best approximation of the desired output y with an error tolerance of ε. The regression function that relates the input vector $\mathbf{x}$ to the output $\hat{y}$ can be written as:

$$f(\mathbf{x}) = \mathbf{w}^T \varphi(\mathbf{x}) + b = \hat{y} \tag{5}$$

where $\varphi(\mathbf{x})$ is a non-linear function mapping input vector $\mathbf{x}$ to a high-dimensional feature space. $\mathbf{w}$ and b are weights and bias, respectively, and can be estimated by minimizing the following structural risk function:

$$R = \frac{1}{2}\mathbf{w}^T\mathbf{w} + C\sum_{i=1}^{N_d} L_\varepsilon(\hat{y}_i) \tag{6}$$

where C is a user-defined parameter representing the trade-off between the model complexity and the empirical error, and L_ε is the Vapnik's ε-insensitive loss function. Vapnik [52] transformed the SVM problem as an optimization problem:

$$\text{Maximize} \quad \sum_{i=1}^{N_d} y_i(\alpha_i - \alpha'_i) - \varepsilon \sum_{i=1}^{N_d} (\alpha_i + \alpha'_i) - \frac{1}{2} \sum_{i=1}^{N_d} \sum_{j=1}^{N_d} (\alpha_i - \alpha'_i)(\alpha_j - \alpha'_j)\varphi(\mathbf{x}_i)^{\mathrm{T}}\varphi(\mathbf{x}_j)$$

$$\text{subject to} \quad \sum_{i=1}^{N_d} (\alpha_i - \alpha'_i) = 0 \tag{7}$$

$$0 \le \alpha_i, \alpha'_i \le C, \quad i = 1, 2, ..., N_d$$

where α and α' are the dual Lagrange multipliers. The solution to Equation (7) is guaranteed to be unique and globally optimal because the objective function is a convex function. The optimal Lagrange multipliers α^* are solved by the standard quadratic programming algorithm. Then, the regression function can be rewritten as:

$$f(\mathbf{x}) = \sum_{i=1}^{N_d} \alpha_i^* \varphi(\mathbf{x}_i)^{\mathrm{T}}\varphi(\mathbf{x}) + b = \sum_{i=1}^{N_d} \alpha_i^* K(\mathbf{x}_i, \mathbf{x}) + b \tag{8}$$

where $K(\mathbf{x}_i, \mathbf{x})$ is the kernel function. The most used kernel function, *i.e.*, the radial basis function, is adopted herein. Some of solved Lagrange multipliers $(\alpha - \alpha')$ are zero and should be eliminated from the regression function. The regression function involves the nonzero Lagrange multipliers and the corresponding input vectors of the training data, which are called the support vectors. The final regression function can be rewritten as:

$$f(\mathbf{x}) = \sum_{k=1}^{N_{sv}} \alpha_k K(\mathbf{x}_k, \mathbf{x}) + b \tag{9}$$

where $\mathbf{x}_k$ denotes the kth support vector and N_{sv} is the number of support vectors. Herein, the parameter C, which means the trade-off between the model complexity and the empirical error, is set to 1. That means the model complexity is as important as the empirical error. In addition, it is acceptable to set the error tolerance ε to 1% for flow forecasting.

2.1.4. Self-Organizing Map

The self-organizing map proposed by Kohonen is a special class of NN. In an unsupervised manner, the learning of SOM is to define the weights so that the mapping is ordered and descriptive of the distribution of input data [55]. Therefore, the SOM is capable of clustering, classification, estimation, and data mining. Additionally, the SOM can provide features that facilitate insight into the hydrological processes and has been used for hydrological forecasting. An SOM network consists of one input layer and one output layer, *i.e.*, the Kohonen layer, with numerous neurons. Each neuron of the Kohonen layer has a synaptic weight vector having the same dimension as the input vector.

In this paper, the self-organizing linear output map (SOLO) proposed by Hsu *et al.* [37] is adopted to develop a flow forecasting model. The development of SOLO includes two steps: to classify the inputs using SOM and then to map the inputs into the outputs using multivariate linear regressions. In other words, SOLO uses piecewise linear regression functions to descript the nonlinear relationships between inputs and outputs. For example, if a $N \times N$ SOM is used to analyze the input data, then the input-output function mapping is therefore accomplished by a set of $N \times N$ piecewise linear regression functions that cover the entire input domain. For a certain input data $\mathbf{x}$ belonging to the ith neuron, the output of SOLO is:

$$\hat{y} = f_i(\mathbf{x}) = \sum \mathbf{a}^i \mathbf{x} + b_0^i, \quad i = 1, ..., N \times N \tag{10}$$

where $\mathbf{a}$ is the vector of regression parameters and b_0 is the bias. As reported by Hsu *et al.* [34], the structure of SOLO has been designed for rapid, precise, and inexpensive estimation of network parameters and system outputs. In this study, to reach a just conclusion, different dimensions ($N \times N$, $N = 2, 3, 4, 5$) are tried. The parameters of Equation (10) are decided by the least mean square algorithm.

2.2. Enforced Learning Strategy

In order to improve the performance of NN-based forecasting models, an enforced learning strategy is proposed herein. Because NNs are nonlinear data-driven techniques, both the quantity and the quality of data available have great influence on the modeling performance [1]. During the training of NNs, the weights are adjusted iteratively to minimize the overall error between the desired and the actual outputs. Owing to the fact that the data of peak flow are insufficient in size, NN-based models are usually unable to yield satisfactory solutions of extreme values in the river flow [43]. The idea to increase the rate of the data with specific characteristics in the entirety of the learning data is applied. This idea is close to the human learning process. When we try to grasp specific and important information, we tend to practice repeatedly for better results [45,56]. Hence, in this study, a simple and quick data processing procedure is used. Firstly, the data with special characteristics, *i.e.*, high-flow data herein, are extracted. At the present stage, based on authors' experience, the highest 10% or 20% of data in each event are regarded as the data with specific characteristics. For a certain training event, if the peak flow is relatively high among all events, the highest 20% of all flow data in this event are extracted. Otherwise, the highest 10% of flow data are extracted. Second, these extracted high-flow data are directly reproduced. The corresponding rainfall data are also reproduced. Then, a fictitious event is generated by recombining these reproductions in a manner similar to the ranking method commonly used in the construction of design hyetographs [57]. This event is regarded as a new event and finally involved in the original training data for constructing NN-based models. An illustration of the aforementioned description is presented in Figure 2. It should be noted that the enforced learning strategy is used to process the original training data. By means of the enforced learning strategy, the training events are enhanced. The inputs, the original structure, and the parameters of NNs are not changed. The effectiveness of the enforced learning strategy can finally be drawn by comparing the NN-based models with and without the enforced learning strategy.

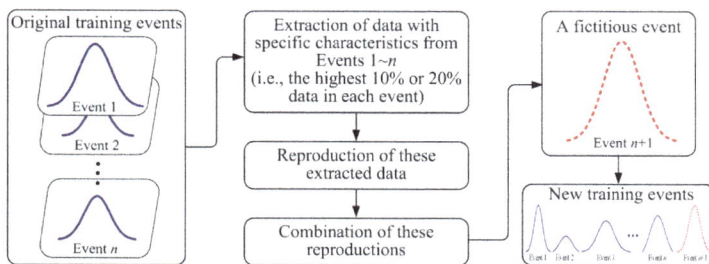

Figure 2. Graphical illustration of the enforced learning strategy.

3. Application and Result Discussion

3.1. The Study Area and Data

The study area of this paper is the Wu River basin located in central Western Taiwan. The lengths of the Wu River basin are 52 km in the north-south direction and 84 km in the east-west direction. The basin, with an area of 2026 km², ranks 4th in Taiwan. The length of the main river is 119 km, and the average slope is 1/92. In this basin, floods caused by heavy rainfalls are quite common. The metropolis of Taichung, which is a major city with a population of about three million in central Taiwan, is located downstream in the study area. Therefore, an accurate, efficient and robust flow forecasting model is needed for the study area.

As shown in Figure 3, there are seven rain gauges (Liu-Fen-Liao, Pei-Shan, Tsao-Tun, Chin-Liu, Hui-Suen, Tsui-Luan and Tou-Pien-Keng) and one water-level gauge (Wu-Chi Bridge) in the study area.

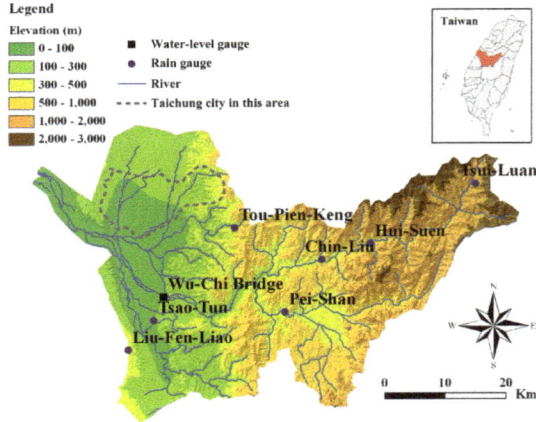

Figure 3. The study area and locations of rainfall and water level gauging stations.

The observed rainfall and flow data are collected from the computer archives of the Water Resources Agency, Taiwan. These data are hourly values. Heavy rainfall events with rainfall and flow data available simultaneously are collected. Moreover, events under the condition that the basin is without any extensive development or land cover change are suggested. Hence, a total of 10 typhoon events with a length of approximately 700 hourly data are used in this study. In Figure 4, the areal rainfall and the corresponding flows, as well as the information of these 10 typhoon events are presented.

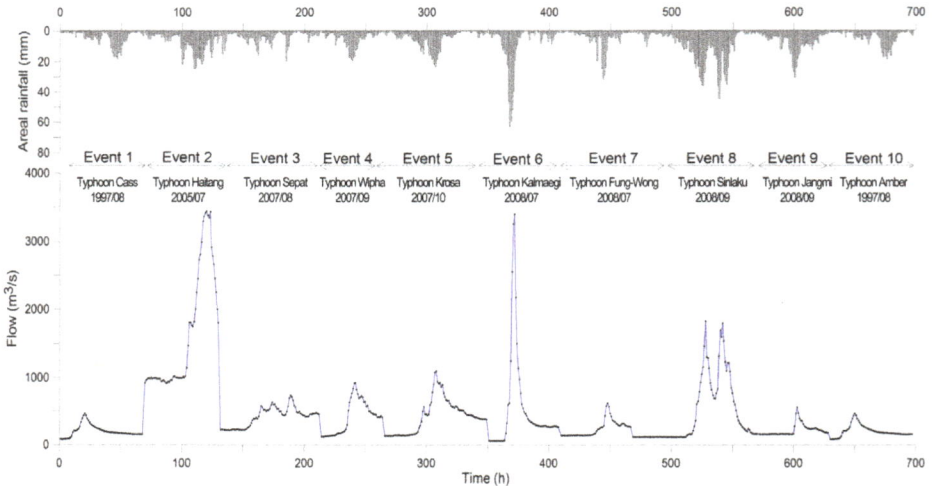

Figure 4. The areal rainfall and flow data used in this study.

3.2. Input Design and Parameter Setting of NN-Base Models

In the construction of NN-based models, the input determination is critical. Generally, the inputs of NN-based flow forecasting models are antecedent flow and rainfall. Therefore, in this study these two hydrological variables are used and the work of input design is to select the best lag length in this study area. Herein, the canonical correlation analysis is adopted. The correlation between input and output time-series data is calculated using the Pearson product-moment correlation coefficient written as:

$$\rho = \frac{\text{cov}(\mathbf{x}, \mathbf{y})}{\sigma_x \sigma_y} \tag{11}$$

where $\mathbf{x}$ and $\mathbf{y}$ are the input and output time-series data, respectively. The larger value of ρ means the higher correlation between $\mathbf{x}$ and $\mathbf{y}$. It is expected that the input, which has a higher correlation with the output, is helpful for forecasting the output. The ρ between the antecedent rainfall with different time lags and the flow with a lead time of 1 h are calculated. The result summarized in Table 1 shows the Q_{t+1} (where t is the current time) has the highest correlation with R_{t-2}. This indicates the concentration time of the study area is about 3 h. Hence, the forecasting lead-time should not exceed 3 h in this study. Additionally, it is observed that the Q_{t+1} has the highest correlation with Q_t and Q_{t-1}. Therefore, according to Table 1, the best inputs of the NN-based model are decided and can then be written in a general form as:

$$Q_{t+i} = f(R_{t+i-3}, Q_t, Q_{t-1}), \quad i = 1, 2, 3 \tag{12}$$

where R_{t+i-3} is the areal rainfall at time $t + i - 3$, Q_t, Q_{t-1} and Q_{t+i} are flow at time t, $t - 1$ and $t + i$, respectively. It should be noted that herein the best inputs mean the best lag length of input variables, which is influenced by the hydrological environment of the study area. Therefore, in this study, inputs of four NN-based flow forecasting models are all the same.

Table 1. Values of Pearson product-moment correlation coefficient.

Lag Length j	Pearson Product-Moment Correlation Coefficient ρ	
	Between Q_{t+1} and R_{t-j}	Between Q_{t+1} and Q_{t-j}
0	0.48	0.95
1	0.55	0.88
2	0.58	0.80
3	0.56	0.72
4	0.52	0.65
5	0.46	0.58

After the determination of model inputs, the parameter setting is then proceeded by trial and error. Finally, the BPN with one hidden layer included two neurons, the RBFN with 30 hidden neurons, and the SOM of the dimension of 3×3 are adopted in this study. To avoid the overtraining problem, the cross-validation test is adopted to evaluate the overall performance of NNs in this manuscript. Besides, a total of 30 repeats of NN learning are performed. Each NN is evaluated based on the mean performance of these 30 repeats, instead of the performance of only one learning. Hence, in this manner, the effect of overtraining on the training performance should be reduced and a just conclusion can be reached.

3.3. Cross Validation and Performance Measures

During the construction of NN-based models, the collected data are usually partitioned into two parts: training and testing. Training data are used to determine the architectures of NNs and adjust the weights of NN-based models. The performance of the trained NN-based models is then tested by the remaining data (*i.e.*, testing data) that are not used in the training step. However, different selections of training and testing events may yield different results and sometimes lead to different conclusions. To reach just conclusions, cross validations are conducted herein. That is, each single event is used in turn as the testing event and the remaining events are used as training events. Thus, a total of 10 tests corresponding to 10 heavy rainfall events will be performed.

To evaluate the forecasting performance of each test, four performance measures are employed. Firstly, the relative root mean square error (RRMSE) is used. For a single event, the RRMSE is defined as:

$$RRMSE = \sqrt{\frac{1}{n}\sum_{t=1}^{n}\left(\frac{\hat{Q}_t - Q_t}{Q_t}\right)^2} \tag{13}$$

where $\hat{Q}_t$ and Q_t are the forecasted and observed flows at time t, respectively, and n is the number of data points. For a total of N testing events, the mean RRMSE (MRRMSE) is then calculated. Second, the coefficient of efficiency (CE) is used [58,59]. For a single event, the CE is written as:

$$CE = 1 - \frac{\sum_{t=1}^{n}(Q_t - \hat{Q}_t)^2}{\sum_{t=1}^{n}(Q_t - \overline{Q})^2} \tag{14}$$

where $\overline{Q}$ is the average of observed flow. The CE is often used to assess the forecasting ability of hydrological models. If the forecasts are perfect, the CE value is equal to one. For N testing events, the mean CE (MCE) is calculated. Third, the error of time to peak flow (ET_p) is used. For a single typhoon event, the ET_p is written as:

$$ET_P = abs(\hat{T}_p - T_p) \tag{15}$$

where $\hat{T}_p$ and T_P are the time to peak for forecasted and observed flows, respectively, and abs( ) denotes the absolute value. For N typhoon events, the mean ET_p (MET_p) is calculated. Moreover, the percentage error of peak flow (EQ_p) is used. For a single typhoon event, the EQ_p is written as:

$$EQ_P = abs(\hat{Q}_p - Q_p)/Q_p \times 100 \tag{16}$$

where $\hat{Q}_p$ and Q_P are the forecasted and observed peak flows, respectively. For N typhoon events, the mean EQ_p (MEQ_p) is calculated.

These four criteria adopted herein are the most commonly used in hydrology for assessing the forecasting performance. The RRMSE represents the relative error between the observed and forecasted flows. The CE, namely the Nash-Sutcliffe efficiency, represents the forecasting efficiency. The above two criteria are used to assess the overall forecasting performance. As to the specific fragment, the ET_p, and EQ_p are used to measure the forecasting error related to the peak values. Moreover, since the cross-validation test is used in this paper, the mean values of these four criteria (i.e., MRRMSE, MCE, MET_p, and MEQ_p) are further used to compare the forecasting performance of different NNs. Hence, based on the use of these criteria, a just conclusion is expected to be reached.

3.4. Performance Comparisons among Four NN-Based Models

Firstly, we focus on the accuracy of four NN-based models. Four performance measures are calculated and presented in Table 2. As shown in Table 2, the MRRMSE, MET_p, and MEQ_p values increase with increasing forecast lead time, and the MCE values decrease with increasing forecast lead time. It is observed that the SOLO and the SVM models yield lower MRRMSE values and higher CE values than the BPN and the RBFN models for 1- to 3-h ahead forecasting. The results indicate the SOLO and the SVM models perform better than the BPN and the RBFN models. As to the comparison between the SOLO and the SVM models, the SOLO model performs better than the SVM model for 1-h ahead forecasting. For 2-h ahead forecasting, these two models perform equally well, and for 3-h ahead forecasting the SVM model performs better than the SOLO model. It may be speculated that for 1-h ahead forecasting the relation between rainfall and flow is slightly nonlinear, and hence the piecewise linear model (*i.e.*, SOLO) quickly captures the relationship hidden in the training data and yields better forecasts as compared to the nonlinear model (*i.e.*, SVM). For 3-h ahead forecasting the relation between rainfall and flow is very complicated and highly nonlinear, and therefore the SVM model performs better than the SOLO model. As to the MET_p and MEQ_p values, the SOLO model yields the lowest MET_p, while the SVM gives the lowest MEQ_p. Overall, it is concluded that the forecasts resulting from the SOLO and the SVM models are more accurate than those from the other two models in this study. Among these four models, the forecasting performance of the RBFN model is the worst. For 3-h ahead forecasting, the *CE* value from the RBFN model is even negative. That indicates the observed mean is a better forecast than the output of the RBFN model. Maybe the random selection procedure used herein cannot effectively obtain the best center vectors of RBFN hidden neurons.

Table 2. Results of four NN-based flow forecasting models.

Model	*MRRMSE* (%)			*MCE*			MET_p (h)			MEQ_P (%)		
	1-h ahead	2-h ahead	3-h ahead	1-h ahead	2-h ahead	3-h ahead	1-h ahead	2-h ahead	3-h ahead	1-h ahead	2-h ahead	3-h ahead
BPN	26.5	32.2	44.5	0.83	0.57	0.15	2.1	2.8	3.9	10.6	18.2	28.1
RBFN	15.4	32.0	42.2	0.87	0.48	−0.11	2.2	2.8	4.5	9.9	24.6	37.7
SOLO	9.1	19.0	28.8	0.94	0.72	0.34	0.7	1.3	2.2	8.8	16.5	23.1
SVM	12.1	18.8	27.5	0.90	0.72	0.47	2.1	2.8	2.7	7.2	12.9	18.6

Notes: *MRRMSE* is the mean relative root mean square error; *MCE* is the mean coefficient of efficiency; MET_p is the mean error of time to peak flow; MEQ_p is the mean error of peak flow.

Second, we focus on the robustness of these four NN-based models. To construct a robust NN-based model that can yield reliable forecasts, a robust weight optimization algorithm is important. For a robust optimization algorithm, the obtained optimal weights should slightly be influenced by the selections of initial weights. On the contrary, the optimization algorithm is less robust if obtained optimal weights are highly dependent on the initial weights. To demonstrate the robustness of these four models, an experiment that 30 repeats of each model under the same model inputs and architecture is executed herein. Hence, 30 *MCE* values are obtained for each model. Then, the lack of robustness can be evaluated by the variation in *MCE* values. The coefficient of variation (*CV*), which is calculated by dividing the standard deviation with the mean, is used herein. A higher *CV* value of *MCE* represents the higher variation in *MCE* and also indicates that the performance of the corresponding model is less reliable. The *CV* values listed in Table 3 are calculated from a data set of 30 *MCE* values. As shown in Table 3, the *CV* values resulting from the SOLO and SVM models are zero. That is, SOLO and SVM models yield a constant *MCE* value in 30 runs. As to the RBFN and BPN models, different initial weights lead to different *MCE* values even when the same training and testing data are used. Table 3 clearly shows that the robustness of the SOLO and SVM models are better than that of RBFN and BPN models. The obtained optimal weights of the SOLO and SVM models are not influenced by the selections of initial weights. The forecasts resulting from the SOLO and SVM models are more reliable than those from the RBFN and BPN models. Hence, according to the model accuracy and the model robustness (*i.e.*, the results in Tables 2 and 3), it is concluded that the SOLO and SVM models are the best two among the four NN-based models in this study. Consequently, the SOLO and SVM models are then used in the following section to evaluate the effect of the enforced learning strategy on NN-based models for developing the proposed flow forecasting models.

Table 3. *CV* values resulting from various NN-based models.

Lead Time (h)	CV (%)			
	BPN	**RBFN**	**SOLO**	**SVM**
1	0.1	2.4	0	0
2	0.3	23.1	0	0
3	16.1	−151.7	0	0

Note: Coefficient of variation (*CV*) is calculated from a data set of 30 *CE* values resulting from each model trained with 30 different sets of initial weights.

3.5. Effects of the Enforced Learning Strategy on NN-Based Models

For further improving the performance of SOLO and SVM, which are the superior NN-based forecasting models in this study, the enforced learning strategy is involved in the development of the SOLO and the SVM models. The comparisons of NN-based models with and without the enforced learning strategy are then executed to assess the effect of the enforced learning strategy on the NN-based models. It should be noted that the inputs, the architecture, and the parameter of these NN-based model are unchanged. Only the data used in the training step are different. By means of the enforced learning strategy, a fictitious event is added in the original training data for constructing the NN-based models. Additionally, in this section the enforced learning strategy is applied during the construction of two different NN-based models. Hence, a just conclusion regarding the effect of enforced learning strategy on NN-based models is expected to be reached.

3.5.1. Comparison of the SOLO Models with and without the Enforced Learning Strategy

In this subsection, the influence of the enforced learning strategy on the SOLO model is discussed. In contrast to the SOLO model constructed earlier, the SOLO model constructed with the enforced learning strategy is named the enforced SOLO model hereafter. The enforced SOLO model is also applied to forecast the streamflow with a lead time of 1- to 3-h. The bar charts corresponding to four performance measures from the SOLO and the enforced SOLO models are presented in Figure 5. As shown in Figure 5, the enforced SOLO model yielded lower *MRRMSE* and higher *MCE* values than the SOLO model. That is, the enforced SOLO model provides more accurate forecasts as compared to the SOLO model. As to the peak flow forecasting, the *MEQ$_p$* values from the enforced SOLO model are lower than those from the SOLO model. As to *MET$_p$*, the performance of the SOLO and the enforced SOLO models are the same. That is, the enforced SOLO model also provides more accurate forecasts for the peak flow.

Moreover, the observed flows *versus* corresponding forecasts resulting from the SOLO and from the enforced SOLO models are presented. The scatter plots and the forecasted hydrographs for 1- to 3-h ahead forecasting are shown in Figure 6. It is observed that the forecasts from the enforced SOLO are in better agreement with the observations as compared to those from the SOLO. Therefore, Figure 6 again confirms that the enforced SOLO model indeed provides improved forecasts as compared to the SOLO model. Furthermore, to show the superiority of the enforced SOLO model more clearly the events (Events 2 and 6), which yielded the maximum peak flows in our used data are highlighted. On average, the *EQ$_P$* values of the SOLO model are 12%, 27% and 55% for 1- to 3-h ahead forecasting. By using the enforced SOLO model, these corresponding *EQ$_P$* values are 6%, 11% and 37%. A significant improvement in reducing the error of peak flow forecasting is clearly observed. Hence, according to the comparison results above, it is clearly concluded that the improved streamflow forecasts are indeed obtained by the enforced SOLO model (*i.e.*, the SOLO model with the enforced learning strategy).

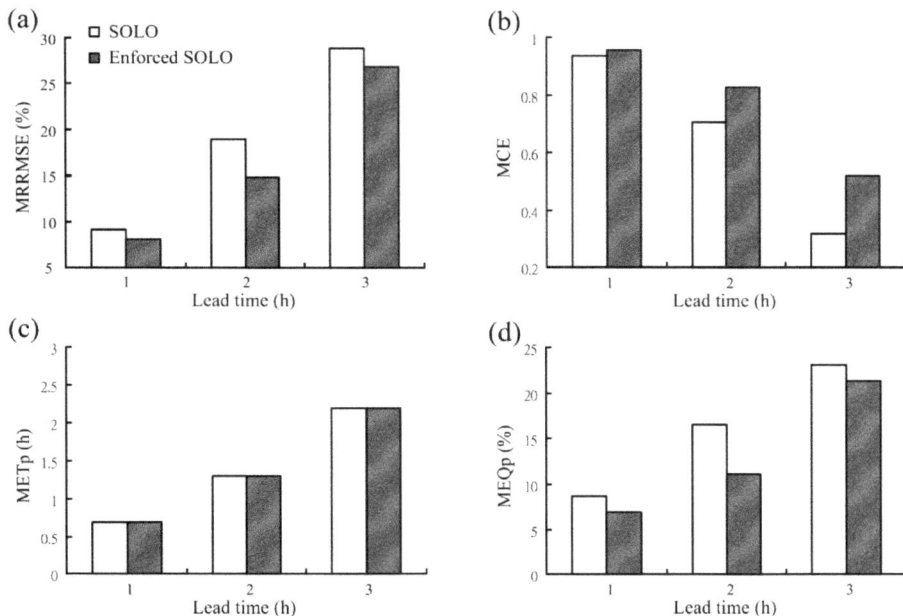

Figure 5. Performance comparison of the SOLO and the enforced SOLO models: (**a**) *MRRMSE*; (**b**) *MCE*; (**c**) *MET_p* and (**d**) *MEQ_p*.

3.5.2. Comparison of the SVM Models with and without the Enforced Learning Strategy

In this subsection, the influence of the enforced learning strategy on another NN-based model, *i.e.*, the SVM model, is discussed. The SVM model with the enforced learning strategy is named the enforced SVM model hereafter. Four performance measures resulting from the SVM and the enforced SVM models are graphically displayed in Figure 7. The results in Figure 7 show that as compared to the SVM model, the enforced SVM model provides the forecasts with lower *MRRMSE* values and the higher *MCE* values. Moreover, the *MET_p* and *MEQ_p* values from the enforced SVM model are lower than those from the SVM model. It is concluded that the enforced SVM model indeed improves the forecasts of overall flows as well as the peaks, and the enforced learning strategy successfully improves the forecasting performance of the SVM model.

Figure 8 shows the observed flow *versus* corresponding forecasts from the SVM and the enforced SVM models. Again, Figure 8 confirms the enforced SVM model indeed provides improved forecasts of flows due to the better agreement between the observations and forecasts. Furthermore, the events that yielded the maximum peak flows in our data are focused to show the superiority of the enforced SVM model. On average, the EQ_p values of the SVM model are 30%, 49% and 58% for 1- to 3-h ahead forecasting. Those are reduced to 6%, 16% and 42% by means of the enforced SVM. Again, a significant improvement in reducing the error of peak flow forecasting is clearly observed. Hence, based on the results above, it is concluded that the improved forecasts are indeed obtained by using the enforced SVM model (*i.e.*, the SVM model with the enforced learning strategy).

Due to the results concerning the comparison between the SOLO and the enforced SOLO and the comparison between the SVM and the enforced SVM, the use of the enforced learning strategy indeed let both the SOM and SVM provide improved forecasts. More accurate forecasts of overall streamflow as well as the peaks are obtained. That is, the enforced learning strategy is indeed helpful for improving the forecasting performance of NNs, even when different NNs are used.

117

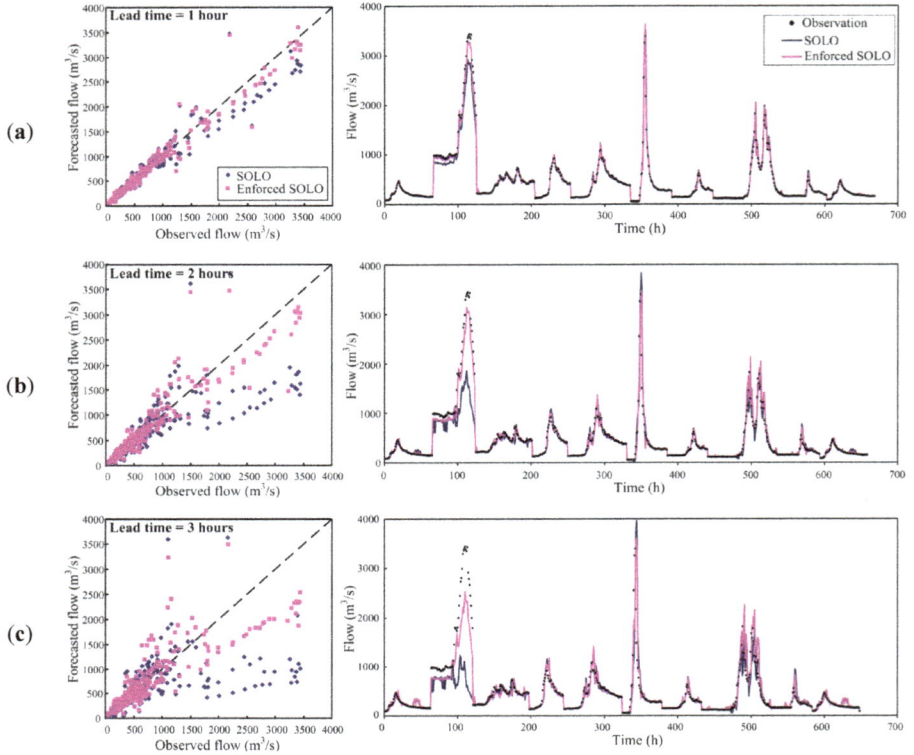

Figure 6. Observed flows *versus* corresponding forecasts resulting from the SOLO and the enforced SOLO models: (**a**) 1-h ahead; (**b**) 2-h ahead and (**c**) 3-h ahead.

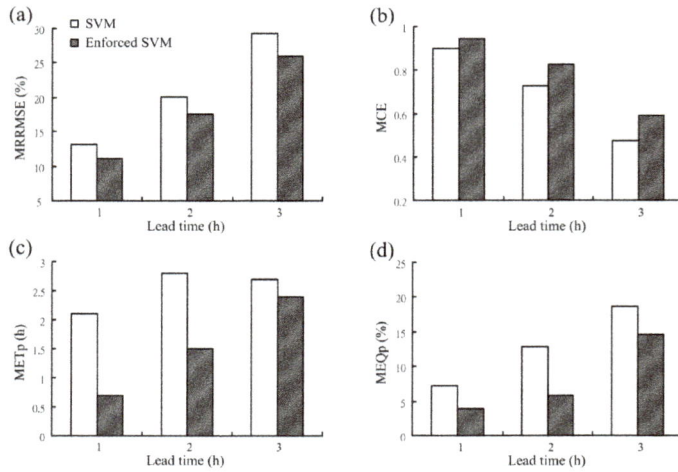

Figure 7. Performance comparison of the SVM and the enforced SVM models: (**a**) *MRRMSE*; (**b**) *MCE*; (**c**) *MET$_p$*; and (**d**) *MEQ$_P$*.

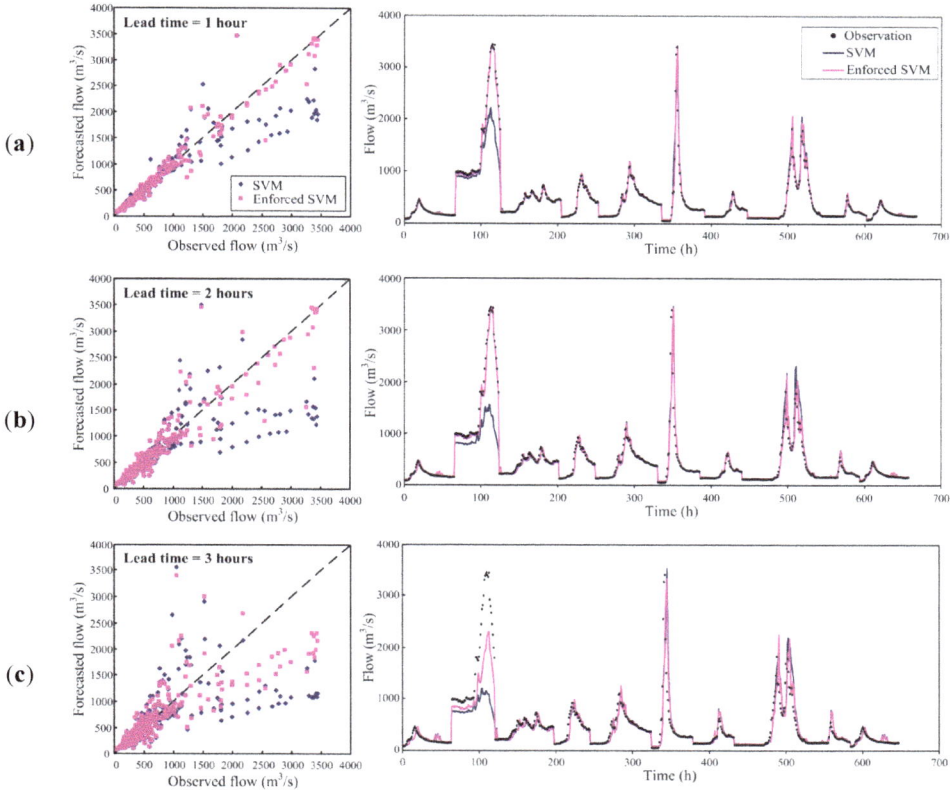

Figure 8. Observed flows *versus* corresponding forecasts resulting from the SVM and the enforced SVM models: (**a**) 1-h ahead; (**b**) 2-h ahead and (**c**) 3-h ahead.

4. Conclusions

To improve the performance of hourly flow forecasting, a methodology concerning the development of NN-based models with the enforced learning strategy is presented. Firstly, four common NNs (namely, BPN, BFN, SOLO and SVM) are used to construct NN-based flow forecasting models. Through the cross-validation test, it is observed that SOLO and SVM provide better and more robust forecasts than BPN and RBFN in our study. To further improve the performance of NN-based models, the enforced learning strategy is proposed. Therefore, the data with special characteristics (*i.e.*, the peak flows herein) are reproduced and recombined to be a fictitious event. This event is regarded as new training data and used for constructing the SOLO and the SVM models. Comparisons between NN-based models with and without the enforced learning strategy are performed. The results show that the improved forecasts are obtained through the enforced NN-based models (*i.e.*, the NN-based models constructed with the enforced learning strategy). Hence, it is confirmed that the enforced learning algorithm successfully improves the forecasting performance of the NN-based flow forecasting models. In conclusion, the proposed enforced NN-based model is recommended as an alternative to the existing NN-based models for flow forecasting. The presented methodology is also expected to be helpful for developing an NN-based forecasting model. Nevertheless, more applications of the methodology in different hydrologic environments should be conducted to further assess the methodology's potential. Additionally, further study on improving the enforced learning

Water **2015**, *7*, 5876–5895

strategy such as the objective determination of the data with special characteristics is still required in future research.

Acknowledgments: This paper is based on research partially supported by the Ministry of Science and Technology, Taiwan, under grants MOST 103-2221-E-492-033 and 101-2625-M-002-007. We would also like to thank the Editors and reviewers for their constructive suggestions that greatly improved the manuscript.

Author Contributions: Ming-Chang Wu contributed to the model development and applications. Gwo-Fong Lin contributed to the comments and supervision of this research. Both authors contributed about equally to the result discussion, and the manuscript composition and revision at all stages.

Conflicts of Interest: The authors declare no conflict of interest.

References

1. ASCE Task Committee on Application of Artificial Neural Networks in Hydrology. Artificial Neural Networks in Hydrology, part I: Preliminary concepts. *J. Hydrol. Eng.* **2000**, *5*, 115–123.
2. ASCE Task Committee on Application of Artificial Neural Networks in Hydrology. Artificial Neural Networks in Hydrology, part II: Hydrologic applications. *J. Hydrol. Eng.* **2000**, *5*, 124–137.
3. Govindaraju, R.S.; Rao, A.R. *Artificial Neural Networks in Hydrology*; Kluwer: Alphen aan den Rijn, The Netherlands, 2000.
4. Maier, H.R.; Dandy, G.C. Neural networks for the prediction and forecasting of water resources variables: A review of modelling issues and applications. *Environ. Model. Softw.* **2000**, *15*, 101–124. [CrossRef]
5. Maier, H.R.; Jain, A.; Dandy, G.C.; Sudheer, K.P. Methods used for the development of neural networks for the prediction of water resource variables in river systems: Current status and future directions. *Environ. Model. Softw.* **2010**, *25*, 891–909. [CrossRef]
6. Huang, W.; Xu, B.; Chan-Hilton, A. Forecasting flows in Apalachicola River using neural networks. *Hydrol. Process.* **2004**, *18*, 2545–2564. [CrossRef]
7. Chau, K.W.; Wu, C.L.; Li, Y.S. Comparison of several flood forecasting models in Yangtze River. *J. Hydrol. Eng.* **2005**, *10*, 485–491. [CrossRef]
8. Lin, G.F.; Chen, G.R. A systematic approach to the input determination for neural network rainfall-runoff models. *Hydrol. Process.* **2008**, *22*, 2524–2530. [CrossRef]
9. Cheng, C.T.; Niu, W.J.; Feng, Z.K.; Shen, J.J.; Chau, K.W. Daily reservoir runoff forecasting method using artificial neural network based on quantum-behaved particle swarm optimization. *Water* **2015**, *7*, 4232–4246. [CrossRef]
10. Xu, Z.X.; Li, J.Y. Short-term inflow forecasting using an artificial neural network model. *Hydrol. Process.* **2002**, *16*, 2423–2439. [CrossRef]
11. Coulibaly, P.; Haché, M.; Fortin, V.; Bobée, B. Improving daily reservoir inflow forecasts with model combination. *J. Hydrol. Eng.* **2005**, *10*, 91–99. [CrossRef]
12. Wu, C.L.; Chau, K.W. A flood forecasting neural network model with genetic algorithm. *Int. J. Environ. Pollut.* **2006**, *28*, 261–273. [CrossRef]
13. Muluye, G.V.; Coulibaly, P. Seasonal reservoir inflow forecasting with low-frequency climatic indices: A comparison of data-driven methods. *Hydrol. Sci. J.* **2007**, *52*, 508–522. [CrossRef]
14. Tayfur, G.; Moramarco, T.; Singh, V.P. Predicting and forecasting flow discharge at sites receiving significant lateral inflow. *Hydrol. Process.* **2007**, *21*, 1848–1859. [CrossRef]
15. Lin, G.F.; Huang, P.Y.; Chen, G.R. Using typhoon characteristics to improve the long lead-time flood forecasting of a small watershed. *J. Hydrol.* **2010**, *380*, 450–459. [CrossRef]
16. Taormina, R.; Chau, K.W. Neural network river forecasting with multi-objective fully informed particle swarm optimization. *J. Hydroinform.* **2015**, *17*, 99–113. [CrossRef]
17. Wang, Y.; Guo, S.; Xiong, L.; Liu, P.; Liu, D. Daily runoff forecasting model based on ANN and data preprocessing techniques. *Water* **2015**, *7*, 4144–4160. [CrossRef]
18. Dawson, C.W.; Harpham, C.; Wilby, R.L.; Chen, Y. Evaluation of artificial neural network techniques for flow forecasting in the River Yangtze, China. *Hydrol. Earth Syst. Sci.* **2002**, *6*, 619–626. [CrossRef]
19. Lin, G.F.; Chen, L.H. A non-linear rainfall-runoff model using radial basis function network. *J. Hydrol.* **2004**, *289*, 1–8. [CrossRef]

20. Lin, G.F.; Wu, M.C. An RBF network with a two-step learning algorithm for developing a reservoir inflow forecasting model. *J. Hydrol.* **2011**, *405*, 439–450. [CrossRef]

21. Sahoo, G.B.; Raya, C. Flow forecasting for a Hawaii stream using rating curves and neural networks. *J. Hydrol.* **2006**, *317*, 63–80. [CrossRef]

22. Sudheer, K.P.; Srinivasan, K.; Neelakantan, T.R.; Srinivas, V.V. A nonlinear data-driven model for synthetic generation of annual streamflows. *Hydrol. Process.* **2008**, *22*, 1831–1845. [CrossRef]

23. Mutlu, E.; Chaubey, I.; Hexmoor, H.; Bajwa, S.G. Comparison of artificial neural network models for hydrologic predictions at multiple gauging stations in an agricultural watershed. *Hydrol. Process.* **2008**, *22*, 5097–106. [CrossRef]

24. Chang, L.C.; Chang, F.J.; Wang, Y.P. Auto-configuring radial basis function networks for chaotic time series and flood forecasting. *Hydrol. Process.* **2009**, *23*, 2450–2459. [CrossRef]

25. Lin, G.F.; Wu, M.C.; Chen, G.R.; Tsai, F.Y. An RBF-based model with an information processor for forecasting hourly reservoir inflow during typhoons. *Hydrol. Process.* **2009**, *23*, 3598–3609. [CrossRef]

26. Liong, S.Y.; Sivapragasam, C. Flood stage forecasting with support vector machines. *J. Am. Water Resour. Assoc.* **2002**, *38*, 173–186. [CrossRef]

27. Wu, C.L.; Chau, K.W.; Li, Y.S. River stage prediction based on a distributed support vector regression. *J. Hydrol.* **2008**, *358*, 96–111. [CrossRef]

28. Wu, M.C.; Lin, G.F.; Lin, H.Y. Improving the forecasts of extreme streamflow by support vector regression with the data extracted by self organizing map. *Hydrol. Process.* **2014**, *28*, 386–397. [CrossRef]

29. Yu, X.Y.; Liong, S.Y.; Babovic, V. EC-SVM approach for real-time hydrologic forecasting. *J. Hydroinform.* **2004**, *6*, 209–223.

30. Sivapragasam, C.; Liong, S.Y. Flow categorization model for improving forecasting. *Nordic Hydrol.* **2005**, *36*, 37–48.

31. Yu, X.Y.; Liong, S.Y. Forecasting of hydrologic time series with ridge regression in feature space. *J. Hydrol.* **2007**, *332*, 290–302. [CrossRef]

32. Wang, W.C.; Chau, K.W.; Cheng, C.T.; Qiu, L. A comparison of performance of several artificial intelligence methods for forecasting monthly discharge time series. *J. Hydrol.* **2009**, *374*, 294–306. [CrossRef]

33. Lin, G.F.; Chen, G.R.; Huang, P.Y.; Chou, Y.C. Support vector machine-based models for hourly reservoir inflow forecasting during typhoon-warning periods. *J. Hydrol.* **2009**, *372*, 17–29. [CrossRef]

34. Lin, G.F.; Chen, G.R.; Huang, P.Y. Effective typhoon characteristics and their effects on SVM-based hourly reservoir inflow forecasting models. *Adv. Water Resour.* **2010**, *33*, 887–898. [CrossRef]

35. Noori, R.; Karbassi, A.R.; Moghaddamnia, A.; Han, D.; Zokaei-Ashtiani, M.H.; Farokhnia, A.; Gousheh, M.G. Assessment of input variables determination on the SVM model performance using PCA, Gamma test, and forward selection techniques for monthly stream flow prediction. *J. Hydrol.* **2011**, *401*, 177–189. [CrossRef]

36. Lin, G.F.; Chou, Y.C.; Wu, M.C. Typhoon flood forecasting using integrated two-stage support vector machine approach. *J. Hydrol.* **2013**, *486*, 334–342. [CrossRef]

37. Hsu, K.L.; Gupta, H.V.; Gao, X.; Sorooshian, S.; Imam, B. Self-organizing linear output map (SOLO): An artificial neural network suitable for hydrologic modeling and analysis. *Water Resour. Res.* **2002**, *38*, 10–26. [CrossRef]

38. Moradkhani, H.; Hsu, K.L.; Gupta, H.V.; Sorooshian, S. Improved streamflow forecasting using self-organizing radial basis function artificial neural networks. *J. Hydrol.* **2004**, *295*, 246–262. [CrossRef]

39. Hong, Y.; Hsu, K.; Sorooshian, S.; Gao, X. Self-organizing nonlinear output (SONO): A neural network suitable for cloud patch-based rainfall estimation at small scales. *Water Resour. Res.* **2005**, *41*. [CrossRef]

40. Chang, F.J.; Chang, L.C.; Wang, Y.S. Enforced self-organizing map neural networks for river flood forecasting. *Hydrol. Process.* **2007**, *21*, 741–749. [CrossRef]

41. Yang, C.C.; Chen, C.S. Application of integrated back-propagation network and self-organizing map for flood forecasting. *Hydrol. Process.* **2009**, *23*, 1313–1323. [CrossRef]

42. Kim, S.; Singh, V.P. Spatial disaggregation of areal rainfall using two different artificial neural networks models. *Water* **2015**, *7*, 2707–2727. [CrossRef]

43. Sudheer, K.P.; Nayak, P.C.; Ramasastri, K.S. Improving peak flow estimates in artificial neural network river flow models. *Hydrol. Process.* **2003**, *17*, 677–686. [CrossRef]

44. Venkatasubramanian, V. Drowning in data: Informatics and modeling challenges in a data-rich networked world. *AICHE J.* **2009**, *55*, 2–8. [CrossRef]

45. Fu, L.T.; Kara, L.B. Neural network-based symbol recognition using a few labeled samples. *Comput. Graph. UK* **2011**, *35*, 955–966. [CrossRef]

46. Chen, S.T. Mining informative hydrologic data by using support vector machines and elucidating mined data according to information entropy. *Entropy* **2015**, *17*, 1023–1041. [CrossRef]

47. Rumelhart, D.E.; Hinton, G.E.; Williams, R.J. *Learning Internal Representations by Error Propagation*; MIT Press: Cambridge, MA, USA, 1986.

48. Broomhead, D.S.; Lowe, D. Multivariable function interpolation and adaptive networks. *Complex Syst.* **1988**, *2*, 321–355.

49. Lin, G.F.; Chen, L.H. Time series forecasting by combining the radial basis function network and the self-organizing map. *Hydrol. Process.* **2005**, *19*, 1925–1937. [CrossRef]

50. Jayawardena, A.W.; Xu, P.C.; Tsang, F.L.; Li, W.K. Determining the structure of a radial basis function network for prediction of nonlinear hydrological time series. *Hydrol. Sci. J.* **2006**, *51*, 21–44. [CrossRef]

51. Lin, C.L.; Wang, J.F.; Chen, C.Y.; Chen, C.W.; Yen, C.W. Improving the generalization performance of RBF neural networks using a linear regression technique. *Expert Syst. Appl.* **2009**, *36*, 12049–12053. [CrossRef]

52. Vapnik, V.N. *The Nature of Statistical Learning Theory*; Springer: Berlin, Germany, 1995.

53. Vapnik, V.N. *Statistical Learning Theory*; John Wiley: New York, NY, USA, 1998.

54. Cristianini, N.; Shaw-Taylor, J. *An Introduction to Support Vector Machines and Other Kernel-Based Learning Methods*; Cambridge University Press: New York, NY, USA, 2000.

55. Kohonen, T. *Self-Organizing Maps*; Springer-Verlag: Berlin, Germany, 2001.

56. Tserng, H.P.; Lin, G.F.; Tsai, L.K.; Chen, P.C. An enforced support vector machine model for construction contractor default prediction. *Autom. Constr.* **2011**, *20*, 1242–1249. [CrossRef]

57. Kimura, N.; Tai, A.; Chiang, S.; Wei, H.P.; Su, Y.F.; Cheng, C.T.; Kitoh, A. Hydrological flood simulation using a design hyetograph created from extreme weather data of a high-resolution atmospheric general circulation model. *Water* **2014**, *6*, 345–366. [CrossRef]

58. Nash, J.E.; Sutcliffe, J.V. River flow forecasting through conceptual models, Part 1: A discussion of principles. *J. Hydrol.* **1970**, *10*, 282–290. [CrossRef]

59. Gupta, H.V.; Kling, H.; Yilmaz, K.K.; Martinez, G.F. Decomposition of the mean squared error and NSE performance criteria: Implications for improving hydrological modeling. *J. Hydrol.* **2009**, *377*, 80–91. [CrossRef]

water

Article

Applying a Correlation Analysis Method to Long-Term Forecasting of Power Production at Small Hydropower Plants

Gang Li *, Chen-Xi Liu, Sheng-Li Liao and Chun-Tian Cheng

Institute of Hydropower and Hydroinformatics, Dalian University of Technology, Dalian 116024, China; howardliuchenxi@163.com (C.-X.L.); shengliliao@dlut.edu.cn (S.-L.L.); ctcheng@dlut.edu.cn (C.-T.C.)
* Correspondence: glee@dlut.edu.cn; Tel.: +86-411-84708468; Fax: +86-411-84708768

Academic Editor: Kwok-wing Chau
Received: 13 July 2015; Accepted: 28 August 2015; Published: 2 September 2015

Abstract: Forecasting long-term power production of small hydropower (SHP) plants is of great significance for coordinating with large-medium hydropower (LHP) plants. Accurate forecasting can solve the problems of waste-water and abandoned electricity and ensure the safe operation of the power system. However, it faces a series of challenges, such as lack of sufficient data, uncertainty of power generation, no regularity of a single station and poor forecasting models. It is difficult to establish a forecasting model based on classical and mature prediction models. Therefore, this paper introduces a correlation analysis method for forecasting power production of SHP plants. By analyzing the correlation between SHP and LHP plants, a safe conclusion can be drawn that the power production of SHP plants show similar interval inflow to LHP plants in the same region. So a regression model is developed to forecast power production of SHP plants by using the forecasting inflow values of LHP plants. Taking the SHP plants in Yunnan province as an example, the correlation between SHP and LHP plants in a district or county are analyzed respectively. The results show that this correlation method is feasible. The proposed forecasting method has been successfully applied to forecast long-term power production of SHP plants in the 13 districts of the Yunnan Power Grid. From the results, the rationality, accuracy and generality of this method have been verified.

Keywords: SHP; power production; prediction; correlation analysis

1. Introduction

As a generally accepted renewable energy, small hydropower (SHP) has been greatly developed in the past few decades because of its small scale, lower investment, quick returns, lack of pollution and the promotion of local economic development [1–6]. With large-scale SHP plants accessing the power grid, problems of wasting water resources and abandoning electricity have been increasing, and the safe operation of the power grid is also threatened [7,8]. Therefore, it is necessary to forecast the power production of SHP plants to solve the above problems by means of coordination and dispatching of SHP and large-medium hydropower (LHP) plants.

Currently, the LHP forecasting method, which focuses on the forecasting of inflow in reservoirs and stream flow [9–21], is very mature, but the study of SHP has not formed a complete theoretical model. Greatly different from the forecasting problems of LHP, the long-term forecasting of SHP faces a series of challenges: (1) Problems arise from the weakness in management, difficulty of information collection, and lack of available data accumulation; (2) SHP is typically derived from run-off river plants with little regulating capacity, so their power production is determined to a great extent by the reservoir inflow. Because the installed capacity of a single plant is very small, it is difficult to forecast its power production because of strong uncertainty and fluctuation; (3) The power production of SHP plants shows great spatiotemporal diversity, and thus, it is difficult to establish a commonly used model; (4) Because SHP is widely distributed and large in quantity, building forecasting models for all SHP plants is unnecessary and cannot satisfy the demand of precision. Due to the challenges, forecasting power production of SHP plants is a complex task; therefore, a few researchers have explored this issue and have obtained some useful results [22,23].

The power production of SHP indicates the maximum generation capacity of an SHP plant under certain meteorological and hydrological conditions, which are easily influenced by factors, such as hydrology, climate, and installation capacity. Therefore forecasting the power production of an SHP plant is a nonlinear, multi-factor complicated problem. However, it is difficult to establish a prediction model based on classical and mature models for forecasting long-term power production because of the lack of observed data of SHP plants. As we know, SHP and LHP plants in the same region or neighborhood have similarities in some aspects of hydrology, meteorology and geography. As a result, some correlation exists between SHP and LHP in some aspects. LHP plants can provide long-term historical data and accurate forecast values. Thus, historical data are used as a reference for the study of forecasting long-term SHP power production.

To solve the problems mentioned above, this paper presents a correlation analysis method of LHP and SHP for forecasting long-term power production of SHP plants. First, the SHP plants are considered to belong to the same area as a whole. Then, the interval flow of the LHP plant is screened as the correlation factor. Then, the correlation analysis of LHP and SHP is performed, and the significance of the correlation is tested. Finally, a regression model is developed to forecast the power production of SHP through the predictive value of LHP. This forecast model has been successfully applied to the Yunnan Power Grid. The LHP plants have a higher level of automation than SHP plants, which can collect long series of observed data. Thus, we could obtain relatively accurate interval flow values of the LHP plant because considerable research activity of forecasting models for LHP plants has been conducted. In addition, there is much stronger correlation between power production of SHP plants and the interval flow of the LHP plant through the numerical simulation analysis. Therefore, the proposed forecast model is capable of achieving accurate forecasting results.

2. Spatiotemporal Characteristics of SHP

2.1. Randomness of a Single Plant

Because of the small installation capacity and the lack of regulation ability, SHP plants are predominantly influenced by rainfall and it is difficult to achieve stable regularity of power production. Therefore, the power production of a single plant shows strong randomness and fluctuation. Figure 1 shows the power production of a single SHP plant and the total generation from 75 SHP plants in the region each month in 2013. In this figure, the box shaped diagrams are used to represent the data dispersion degree. It is obvious that the box-shaped diagrams of a single plant have apparently longer "tentacles" than that of the overall region integrity. This suggests that power production in the sequence of a single plant has more outliers, stronger randomness and greater fluctuation.

2.2. Spatial Differences

SHP plants are mostly concentrated in remote mountain areas and small watersheds. Because each plant has different topography and landforms, the power production presents spatial differences. Taking Yunnan Province as an example, the climate condition has significant spatial differences that make meteorological phenomena unique, as in the old saying, "A mountain is divided into four seasons; 10 miles have different types of weather." For example, Jingdong and Jinggu are two adjacent counties located north of Puer district, the daily rainfall of which is shown in Figure 2. However, significant differences in rainfall and runoff formation occur because of Wuliang Mountain, Ailao Mountain and other mountains in this area, which results in spatial differences of power production of SHP plants.

(a)

(b)

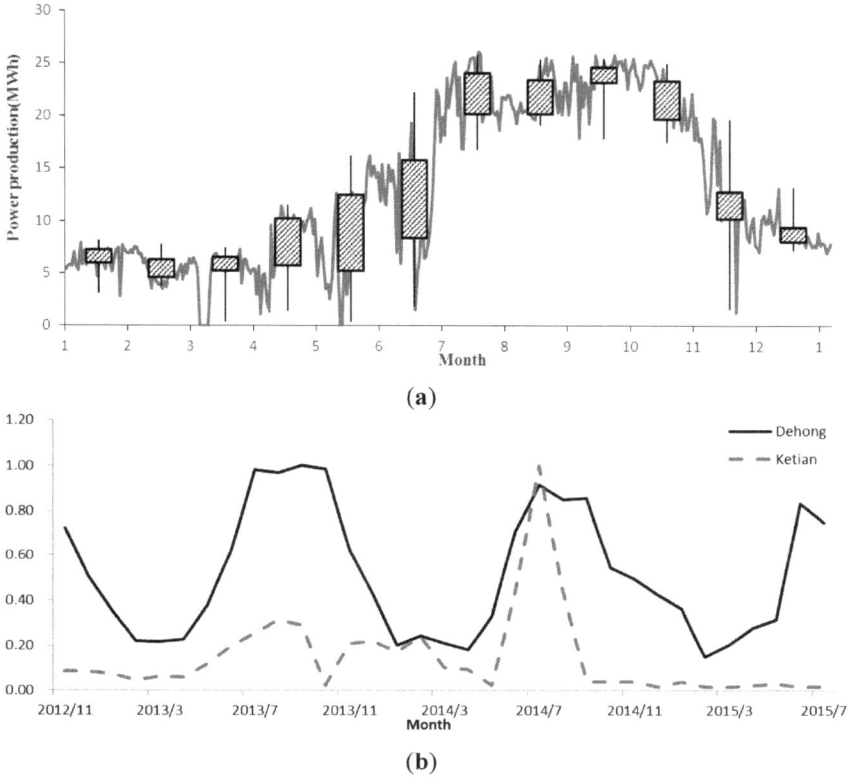

Figure 1. Power production curve and its box plot of a single small hydropower (SHP) plant and SHP plants in a county. (**a**) Power production and box plot of a single SHP plant; (**b**) Power production and box plot of SHP plants in county.

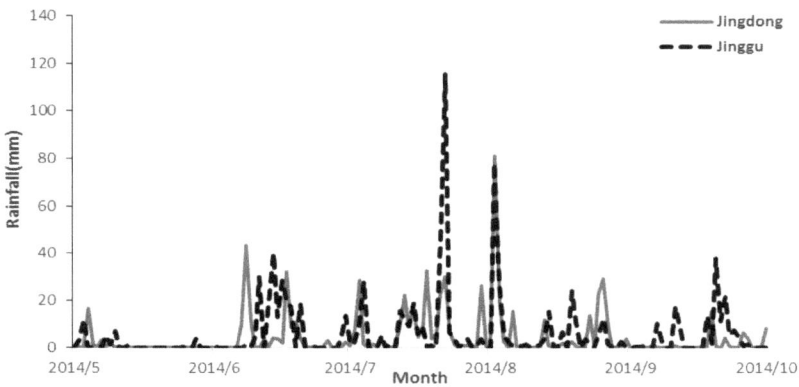

Figure 2. Rainfall curves of Jingdong and Jinggu during the flood season.

2.3. Similarity of Regions

SHP plants in the same region have some similarities in terms of hydrological and meteorological conditions. As shown in Figure 3, the generation data are different in terms of the degree of smoothing between a single SHP plant and all of the SHP plants in the same region. However, the change trend of generation data during the year is essentially the same as the two-trend line shown in Figure 3. In other words, there is a similarity between the single SHP plant and the regional integrity.

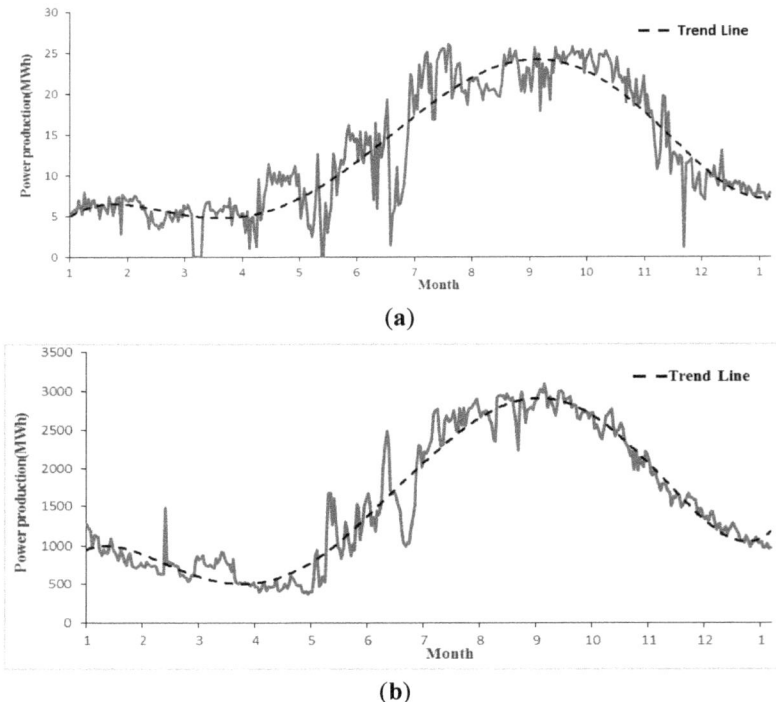

(a)

(b)

Figure 3. Power production curve and its tread line of SHP plant (a) Monthly power production and trend line of single SHP plant; (b) Monthly power production and trend line of SHP plants in county.

Overall, the power production of SHP plants has spatiotemporal characteristics such as randomness, spatial differences and regional similarity, which can provide strategy support for this paper in developing the forecasting method based on the correlation between the LHP plant and SHP plants.

3. Forecasting Method for Long-Term Power Production of SHP Plants

3.1. Selection of the Correlation Factor

LHP plants predictions are usually dependent on water level and flow (inflow or interval flow). These hydrological factors can form a set of candidate factors for the correlation analysis method. The significantly related factors of power production of SHP should be screened out before establishing the correlation analysis model.

The power production of an SHP plant is directly contributed by the reservoir inflow because most SHP plants are run-off river plants. The geographical and hydrological conditions of SHP plants are similar to that of LHP plant in the same region or neighborhood. SHP plants are usually located at different levels along tributaries. According to the Strahler classification of River Law, the power discharge generated by the SHP plants will flow into the mainstream where LHP plants are usually located. Thus, the interval flow of a set of candidate factors of LHP plants can reflect the runoff in the region where SHP plants are located, and there must be some correlationship between the interval flow of LHP plants and the power production of SHP plants in the same region. Then the correlativity of LHP and SHP in the region can be established. In addition, we had tried to analyze the correlation between the power production of SHP plants and other factors of LHP plants, such as water level, inflow and power generation. The inflow or release from LHP in the cascade hydropower plants is significantly influenced by human impact, which cannot reflect the natural runoff of SHP. Therefore, there is no correlation with the factors except for the interval flow.

From the above-mentioned facts, the interval flow of LHP plant is selected as the related factor to perform the correlation analysis in this paper.

3.2. Correlation Analysis of LHP and SHP

The statistician Karl Pearson designed a statistical index, the correlation coefficient, to reflect the intimate level between variables [24]. This paper utilizes the correlation coefficient to indicate the correlation between interval inflow of LHP plants and power production of SHP plants.

As mentioned in Section 2, the power production of the SHP plants in a region is expressed as:

$$E_m = \sum_{i=1}^{s} E_{m,i} \tag{1}$$

where E_m is the power production of all SHP plants in month m (MWh). $E_{m,i}$ is the power production of the ith SHP plant in month m (MWh), and s is the number of SHP plants in month m.

Considering dynamic operations and the constant changes of the installed capacity, the monthly utilization hour of the SHP plant is used to replace the power production in analyzing the correlation. The monthly utilization hour is as follows:

$$t_m = \frac{E_m}{N_{m,capa}} \tag{2}$$

where $N_{m,cap}$ is the installed capacity of SHP plants in month m (MW).

The correlation coefficient (R) can be calculated using Equation (3). R is between –1 and 1. The larger the absolute value is, the more significant the correlation is:

$$R = \frac{\sum\limits_{j=1}^{n} (t_{m,j} - \bar{t}_m)(q_j - \bar{q})}{\sqrt{\sum\limits_{j=1}^{n} (t_{m,j} - \bar{t}_m)^2 \cdot \sum\limits_{j=1}^{n} (q_j - \bar{q})^2}} \tag{3}$$

In the above equation, $t_{m,j}$ is the monthly utilization hour of the SHP plants in month j (h). $\bar{t}_m$ is the average value of monthly utilization hour (h). q_j is the interval flow of LHP plants in month j (m³/s). $\bar{q}$ is the average value of monthly interval flow (m³/s). n is the size of sample data.

3.3. Correlation Validation

The probability density function of R between two uncorrelated variables X and Y is:

$$f(R) = \frac{n-2}{\pi}(1 - R^2)^{\frac{n-4}{2}} \int_0^1 z^{n-2}(1 - z)^{-\frac{1}{2}}dz \tag{4}$$

The equation is transformed as:

$$t = \frac{R}{\sqrt{1 - R^2}} \sqrt{n - 2} \tag{5}$$

Based on Equation (5), the critical value of R can be obtained as follows:

$$R_{a,n} = \sqrt{\frac{t_{a,n}^2}{(n - 2) + t_{a,n}^2}} \tag{6}$$

Thus,

$$P(|r| \geq R_{a,n}) = a \tag{7}$$

where $R_{a,n}$ is the correlation coefficient of LHP and SHP plants at the level of a. By using this method, the LHP plant, which is significantly correlated, can be screened out.

3.4. Regression Model of the Power Production Forecast

To forecast the power production of SHP plants in a region, the LHP plant, which is significantly correlated to it, can be selected. Then a regression model is built to analyze the correlation between LHP and SHP. If the correlation is significant, it will be presented by a linear relationship between the LHP and SHP plants, in which the interval flow of LHP is the independent variable and the monthly utilization hours of SHP is the dependent variable. The linear regression model is built as follows:

$$\begin{aligned} t_{m,fore} &= b \times q_{fore} + a \\ a &= \overline{t_m} - b\overline{q} \\ b &= \frac{\sum_{i=1}^{n} t_{m,i} q_i - nt_m \overline{q}}{\sum_{i=1}^{n} t_{m,i}^2 - n\overline{t_m}^2} \end{aligned} \tag{8}$$

where $t_{m,fore}$ is the forecast value of monthly utilization hours of SHP plants (h). q_{fore} is the forecast value of monthly interval flow of LHP (m^3/s). a and b are the regression coefficients.

The forecast value of power production $E_{m,fore}$ can be calculated.

$$E_{m,fore} = t_{m,fore} \times N_{m,cap} \tag{9}$$

4. Case Study

The SHP plants in Yunnan Province, China, were taken as a case study. The river system of Yunnan province has been well developed, including six river systems: Yangtze River, Pearl River, Red River, Lancangjiang River, Nujiang River, and Irrawaddy River. A considerable number of LHP plants with long historical operation data exist; therefore, Yunnan province has suitable conditions for the correlation analysis of LHP and SHP plants. The hydropower dispatching automation system has been established for many years in the Yunnan Power Grid, which involves many of the classical and intelligent prediction models. By continually modifying the model parameters using real-time observed data, accurate forecasting results of the interval inflow of the LHP plant can be obtained. Therefore, the forecasted interval inflow values of the LHP plant, which are used in the forecasting process, will be obtained from the system.

In this section, the correlation between LHP and SHP plants at different scales (*i.e.*, the district scale and the county scale) was analyzed, and then the power production of SHP plants was forecasted.

4.1. Correlation Analysis of SHP Plants in a District

To demonstrate the correlation between SHP plants of district dispatch and the LHP plant, three districts that belonged to different basins were selected as typical examples: Dehong, Puer and Kunming (Figure 4). Yunnan is a low latitude region with a monsoonal climate and a plateau mountain, which leads to a significant difference between different districts and significant vertical variation. The Dehong district is located in western Yunnan and belongs to the Irrawaddy Basin; it contains several LHP plants, such as the cascade hydropower station of Dayingjiang River, Nongling Station, and Longjiang Station. The Puer district is located in southwestern Yunnan and contains Dachaoshan Station and Nuozhadu Station in Lancangjiang River Basin, and Jufudu Station and Gelantan Station in the Red River Basin. The Kunming district is located in central Yunnan and belongs to the Yangtze River Basin, which contains Ketian Station. Dayingjiang III station, Dachaoshan station and Ketian station are selected as reference stations in this section.

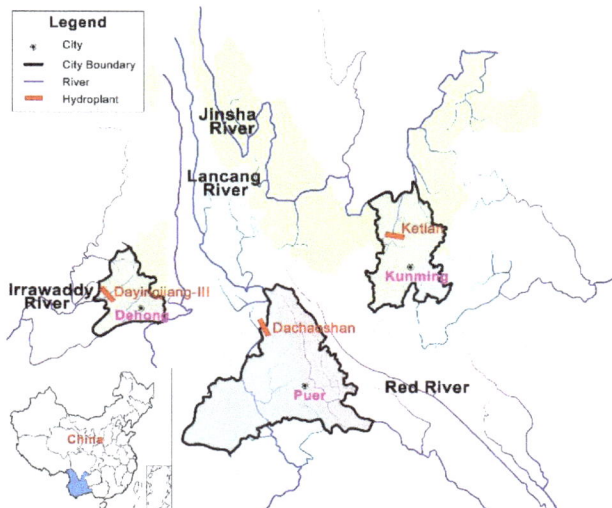

Figure 4. Map of typical basins, prefectures and large-medium hydropower (LHP) plants in Yunnan Province.

The data sequence of the interval flow of the LHP plant and the power production of the SHP plants was selected from November 2012 to July 2015. The correlation between the SHP plants of the three districts and the LHP plant in the same district was analyzed based on Equations (1) to (3), and the significance was tested based on Equations (4) to (6).

Table 1 shows the correlation coefficient between the LHP plant and the SHP plants. The SHP plants in Dehong have the most significant correlation with the Dayingjiang III plant, with a correlation coefficient of 0.94. These plants also have correlation coefficients of 0.77 with the Dachaoshan plant located in the Lancangjiang Basin and 0.46 with the Ketian plant located in the Yangtze Basin. Both of these plants are located far away from Dehong. Figure 5 shows the normalized trend graphs of the power production of SHP plants in Dehong district and the interval flow of the three LHP plants. It can easily be seen that the more significant the correlation is, the more similar the trend of SHP and LHP is. The correlation of SHP plants in Puer and Kunming districts also have similar regularity. From the result of Table 1, the LHP plants that are correlated to the SHP plants in Puer and Kunming districts respectively are Dachaoshan plant, with a correlation coefficient of 0.92 and Ketian plant with 0.89.

Table 1. The correlation coefficient between SHP and LHP plants in a district.

LHP Plant\District	Dehong	Puer	Kunming
Dayingjiang III	0.94 **	0.81 **	0.82 **
Dachaoshan	0.77 **	0.92 **	0.75 **
Ketian	0.46 *	0.39	0.89 **

Notes: ** denotes significantly correlated at the 0.01 level, * denotes significantly correlated at the 0.05 level.

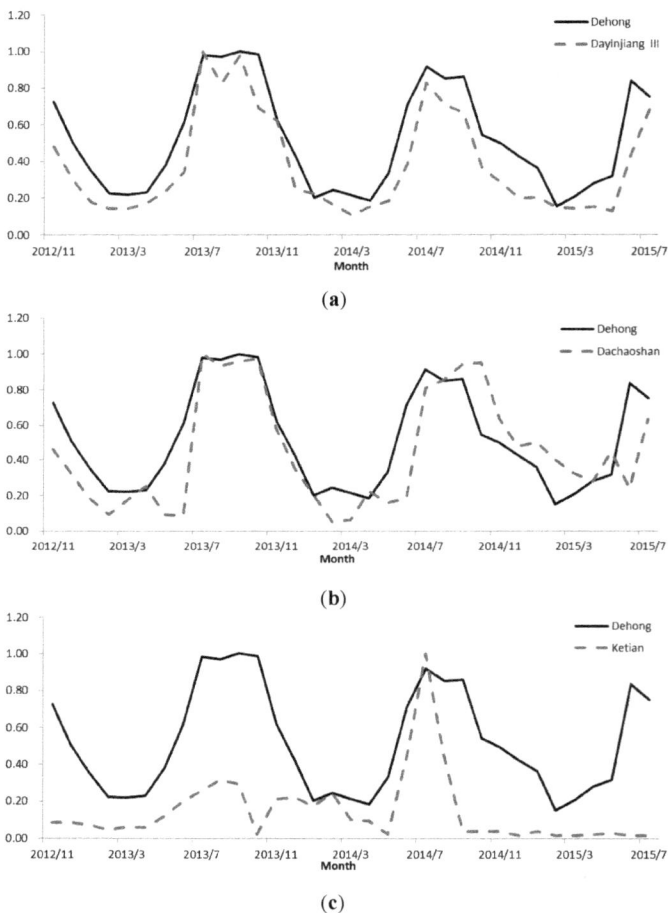

(a)

(b)

(c)

Figure 5. Normalized trend of power production of SHP plants in Dehong and interval flow of the LHP plant. (**a**) Trend Chart of SHP plants in Dehong and Dayingjiang III hydropower plant; (**b**) Trend Chart of SHP plants in Dehong and Dachaoshan hydropower plant; (**c**) Trend Chart of SHP plants in Dehong and Ketian hydropower plant.

Several regularities of the correlation between SHP plants in a district and the LHP plant can be concluded as follows:

(1) A correlation exists between the power production of SHP plants in a district and the interval flow of the LHP plant.

(2) The power production of SHP plants shows significant correlation with the LHP plant of the same basin, whereas the correlation with the LHP plant in other basins is not significant.

(3) As the power production of SHP plants shows spatial differences, the further the distance in space is, the less significant the correlation relationship is.

4.2. Correlation Analysis of SHP Plants in a County

To demonstrate the correlation between SHP and LHP plants in a county, Puer was selected as an example, as two river basins flow into this region (Figure 6). Puer is located in southwestern Yunnan and is affected by subtropical monsoon climate, with mountainous area accounting for 98.3% of the total areas, and the Tropic of Cancer pass through its center. Affected by terrain and altitude, the vertical differences in Puer are obvious. Separated by Mount Wuliang, the eastern region of Puer is the Red-River Basin and the western region is the Lancangjiang Basin. In this section four counties were chosen as examples: Jingdong, Jinggu, Ninger and Mojiang.

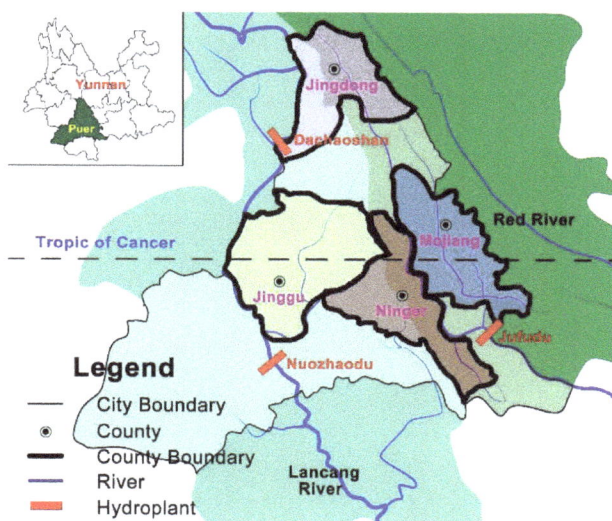

Figure 6. Map of typical basins, counties and LHP plants in Puer county.

Figure 6 shows that Jingdong and Ninger are located at the borderline of the two basins, Jinggu is located in Lancangjiang Basin, and Mojiang is located along a branch of the Red River. The data sequence of the interval flow of the LHP plant and the power production of SHP plants was selected from November 2012 to July 2015. The correlation between SHP plants in the three counties and the LHP plant are analyzed, and the significance of the correlation is tested.

Table 2 shows the correlation coefficient between the LHP and SHP plants. All of the SHP plants in a given county are significantly correlated with the LHP plant at the 0.01 confidence level, but the degree of significance varies obviously. From the results, it can be seen that the LHP plant that are correalted to the SHP plants in Jingdong and Jinggu county is Dachaoshan plant with a correlation coefficient of 0.92 and 0.84. The Ninger county is Nuozhadu plant with 0.93 and the Mojiang county is Jufudu plant with 0.85.

The regularity of the correlation between the SHP plants in a county and the LHP plant can be concluded as follows:

(1) As well as in district, there exists correlation between SHP plants and LHP plant in county. The degree of the correlation is associated with spatial distance.

(2) The correlation between SHP plants in a county and the LHP plant has similar regularity with the district correlation. Influenced by the river basin, SHP plants in different counties have differences in terms of correlation to the LHP plant.

(3) As the power production of SHP plants shows similarity of regions, the difference of the correlation in different counties (maybe in the same district) is less than that in different districts.

Table 2. The correlation coefficients between SHP plants in a county and the LHP plant.

LHP Plant\County	Jingdong	Jinggu	Ninger	Mojiang
Dachaoshan	0.92 **	0.84 **	0.90 **	0.75 **
Nuozhadu	0.91 **	0.81 **	0.93 **	0.81 **
Jufudu	0.70 **	0.76 **	0.90 **	0.85 **

Note: ** denotes significantly correlated at the 0.01 level.

4.3. Forecast Results of the Correlation Analysis Method

The SHP plants in Puer are selected as an example in this section. Several LHP plants that are correlated to the SHP plants are the Dachaoshan plant (correlation coefficient: 0.92), the Dayingjiang III plant (correlation coefficient: 0.81), and the Ketian plant (correlation coefficient: 0.39). So the Dachaoshan plant was chosen as the correlated plant to establish the regression model of LHP and SHP (Figure 7) based on Equation (8).

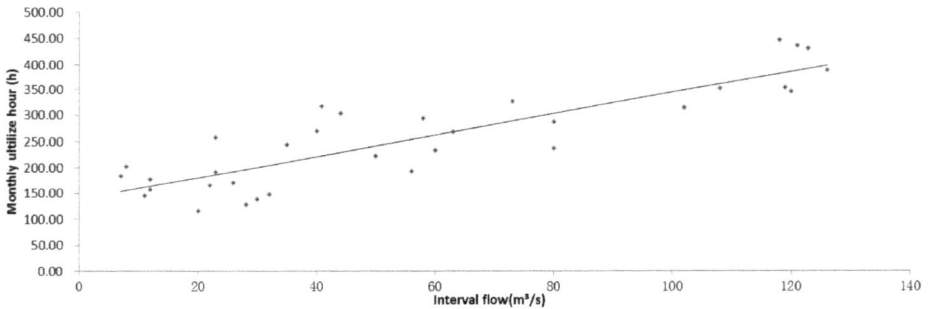

Figure 7. Linear curve fitting of LHP and SHP in Puer County.

After establishing the regression model, the power production of SHP plants in Puer was forecasted using the interval flow of Dachashan plant based on Equations (8) and (9). The prediction accuracy is 87.9%. The average relative error is 18.5%, and the maximum and minimum relative error is 43.8% and 5.6%, respectively. Figure 8 shows that the prediction value of this method shows the same trend with the real value regardless of the season. This indicates that this method could achieve an accurate result, even during the flood season, which can provide the reliable forecasted data for arranging the coordinate power generation schedule between SHP plants and LHP plants in order to reduce wasting water resources and abandoning electricity.

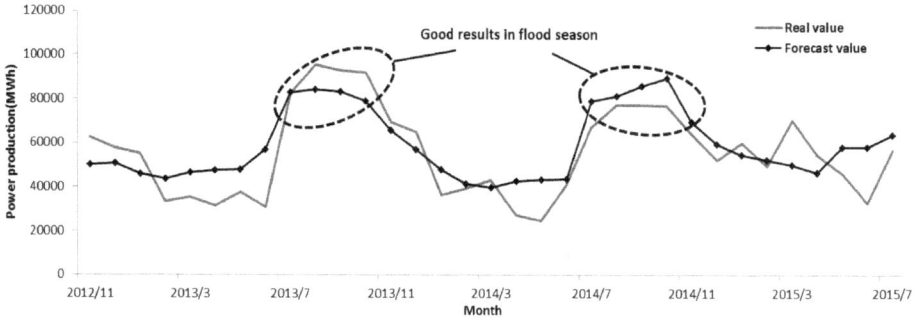

Figure 8. Prediction results of power production of SHP plants in Puer district.

4.4. Generality Analysis of Forecasting Method

The power production of SHP plants shows significant spatial differences. The regular mathematical method does not show good generality, as it was built based on the mathematical statistics rule of power production sample sequence. The generality of the correlation analysis method is determined by the correlation of LHP and SHP and the forecast accuracy of LHP. Therefore the correlation analysis method can solve the problem effectively.

This model is applied to forecast the long-term power production of SHP plants in 13 districts of Yunnan province, and the results are shown in Figure 9. The results indicate that the forecast accuracy is positively correlated to the correlation coefficient. Twelve districts have correlation coefficients greater than or equal to 0.7, and forecasting qualified rates of greater than 70%. These results have verified the generality of the correlation analysis method for the forecasting of long-term power production of SHP plants.

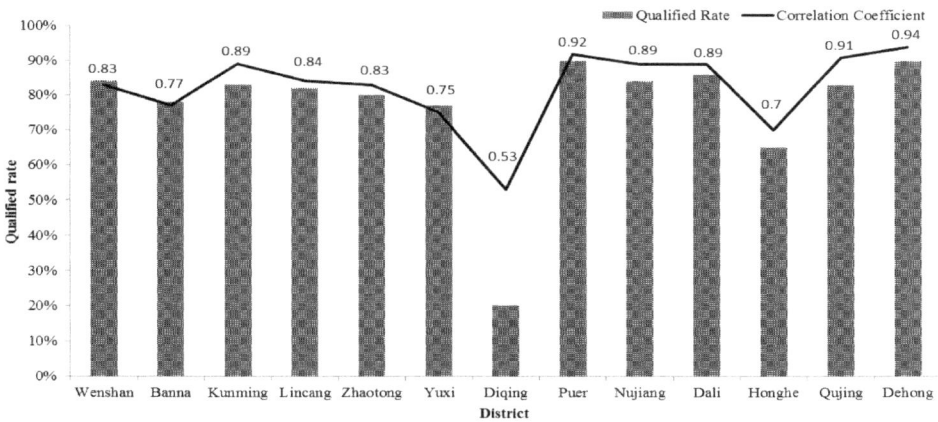

Figure 9. Prediction results of the thirteen districts in Yunnan province.

5. Conclusions

Forecasting the long-term power production of SHP plants is of great significance for realizing the coordination with LHP plants, solving the problem of the waste water and abandoned electricity and ensuring the safe operation of the power grid. In this paper, the similarity between LHP and SHP plants and the spatiotemporal characteristics of SHP plants have been analyzed, based on which, the correlation analysis method of LHP and SHP has been proposed. Taking the SHP plants in Yunnan province as examples, the correlation between the power production of SHP plants and the interval inflow of LHP plants has been verified, and the correlation characteristics in space and at the basin-scale have been obtained. Based on the interval flow of the Dachaoshan plant, the power production of the SHP plants in the Puer district was forecasted. The prediction accuracy of this method has been verified. Lastly, by analyzing the forecast results of the 13 districts in Yunnan province, the generality of the correlation analysis method is demonstrated. From the discussion above, we may safely draw the conclusion that the correlation analysis method is a feasible solution for forecasting the long-term power production of SHP plants.

From the discussion above, it can be seen that the proposed forecasting method has some limitation. Because SHP plants are lack of sufficient information for establishing a forecasting model, there must be a LHP plant with long-term observed data in district or county, which has significant correlation with the SHP plants. The prediction accuracy of SHP plants depends on the LHP plant. Therefore, how to use the classical and mature prediction models based on existing data for forecasting long-term power production of SHP plants may be future study directions.

Acknowledgments: This work was supported by the National High Technology Research and Development of China 863 Program (2012AA050205).

Author Contributions: All authors contributed extensively to the work presented in this paper. Gang Li contributed to the subject of the research, literature review and finalized the manuscripts. Chen-Xi Liu contributed to modeling and data analysis. Sheng-Li Liao contributed to the manuscript review. Chun-Tian Cheng contributed to the manuscript review and supervision.

Conflicts of Interest: The authors declare no conflict of interest.

References

1. Yuksel, I. As a renewable energy hydropower for sustainable development in Turkey. *Renew. Sustain. Energy Rev.* **2010**, *14*, 3213–3219. [CrossRef]
2. Dudhani, S.; Sinha, A.K.; Inamdar, S.S. Assessment of small hydropower potential using remote sensing data for sustainable development in India. *Energy Policy* **2006**, *34*, 3195–3205. [CrossRef]
3. Bakken, T.H.; Sundt, H.; Ruud, A. Development of small *versus* large hydropower in Norway comparison of environmental impacts. *Energy Procedia* **2012**, *20*, 185–199. [CrossRef]
4. Bøckman, T.; Fleten, S.E.; Juliussen, H.J. Investment timing and optimal capacity choice for small hydropower projects. *Eur. J. Oper. Res.* **2008**, *190*, 255–267. [CrossRef]
5. Kosnik, L. The potential for small scale hydropower development in the US. *Energy Policy* **2010**, *38*, 5512–5519. [CrossRef]
6. Li, G.; Liu, B.; Li, S.Z. An overview of large scale small hydropower in Yunnan Power Grid: situations, challenges and measures. In Proceedings of World Environmental and Water Resources Congress, Cincinnati, OH, USA, 19–23 May 2013.
7. Cheng, C. China's small hydropower and its dispatching management. *Renew. Sustain. Energy Rev.* **2015**, *42*, 43–55. [CrossRef]
8. Abbasi, T.; Abbasi, S.A. Small hydro and the environmental implications of its extensive utilization. *Renew. Sustain. Energy Rev.* **2011**, *15*, 2134–2143. [CrossRef]
9. Nikam, V.; Gupta, K. SVM-based model for short-term rainf all forecasts at a local scale in the Mumbai Urban area, India. *J. Hydrol. Eng.* **2014**, *19*, 1048–1052. [CrossRef]
10. Golob, R.; Štokelj, T.; Grgič, D. Neural-network-based water inflow forecasting. *Control Eng. Pract.* **1998**, *6*, 593–600. [CrossRef]
11. Coulibaly, P.; Anctil, F.; Bob´ee, B. Daily reservoir inflow forecasting using artificial neural networks with stopped training approach. *J. Hydrol.* **2000**, *230*, 244–257. [CrossRef]
12. Paravan, D.; Stokelj, T.; Golob, R. Improvements to the water management of a run-of-river HPP reservoir: Methodology and case study. *Control Eng. Pract.* **2004**, *12*, 377–385. [CrossRef]

13. Dutta, D.; Welsh, W.D.; Vaze, J.S.; Kim, S.H.; Nicholls, D. A comparative evaluation of short-term streamflow forecasting using time series analysis and Rainfall-Runoff models in eWater source. *Water Resour. Manag.* **2012**, *26*, 4397–4415. [CrossRef]

14. Vafakhah, M. Application of artificial neural networks and adaptive neuro-fuzzy inference system models to short-term streamflow forecasting. *Can. J. Civil Eng.* **2012**, *39*, 402–414. [CrossRef]

15. Zealand, C.M.; Burn, D.H.; Simonovic, S.P. Short term streamflow forecasting using artificial neural networks. *J. Hydrol.* **1999**, *214*, 32–48. [CrossRef]

16. Saeidifarzad, B.; Nourani, V.; Aalami, M.T.; Chau, K.W. Multi-site calibration of linear reservoir based geomorphologic rainfall-runoff models. *Water* **2014**, *6*, 2690–2716. [CrossRef]

17. Taormina, R. Neural network river forecasting with multi-objective fully informed particle swarm optimization. *J. Hydroinformatics* **2015**, *17*, 99–113.

18. Wu, C.L. Methods to improve neural network performance in daily flows prediction. *J. Hydrol.* **2009**, *372*, 80–93. [CrossRef]

19. Wang, W.C. Improving forecasting accuracy of annual runoff time series using ARIMA based on EEMD decomposition. *Water Resour. Manag.* **2015**, *29*, 2655–2675. [CrossRef]

20. Chen, X.Y. A Novel hybrid neural network based on continuity equation and fuzzy pattern-recognition for downstream daily river discharge forecasting. *J. Hydroinformatics* **2015**, *17*, 733–744. [CrossRef]

21. Chau, K.W. A hybrid model coupled with singular spectrum analysis for daily rainfall prediction. *J. Hydroinformatics* **2010**, *12*, 458–473. [CrossRef]

22. Monteiro, C.; Ramirez-Rosado, I.J.; Fernandez-Jimenez, L.A. Short-term forecasting model for electric power production of small-hydro power plants. *Renew. Energy* **2013**, *50*, 387–394. [CrossRef]

23. Li, G. Short-term power generation energy forecasting model for small hydropower stations using GA-SVM. *Math. Probl. Eng.* **2014**, *2014*, 1–9.

24. Joseph, L.R.; Nicewander, W.A. Thirteen ways to look at the correlation coefficient. *Am. Stat.* **1988**, *42*, 59–66.

Article

Heuristic Methods for Reservoir Monthly Inflow Forecasting: A Case Study of Xinfengjiang Reservoir in Pearl River, China

Chun-Tian Cheng *, Zhong-Kai Feng, Wen-Jing Niu and Sheng-Li Liao

Institute of Hydropower and Hydroinformatics, Dalian University of Technology, Dalian 116024, China; myfellow@mail.dlut.edu.cn (Z.-K.F.); dgniuwenjing@mail.dlut.edu.cn (W.-J.N.); shengliliao@dlut.edu.cn (S.-L.L.)
* Correspondence: ctcheng@dlut.edu.cn; Tel./Fax: +86-411-84708768

Academic Editor: Miklas Scholz
Received: 24 June 2015; Accepted: 27 July 2015; Published: 17 August 2015

Abstract: Reservoir monthly inflow is rather important for the security of long-term reservoir operation and water resource management. The main goal of the present research is to develop forecasting models for the reservoir monthly inflow. In this paper, artificial neural networks (ANN) and support vector machine (SVM) are two basic heuristic forecasting methods, and genetic algorithm (GA) is employed to choose the parameters of the SVM. When forecasting the monthly inflow data series, both approaches are inclined to acquire relatively poor performances. Thus, based on the thought of refined prediction by model combination, a hybrid forecasting method involving a two-stage process is proposed to improve the forecast accuracy. In the hybrid method, the ANN and SVM are, first, respectively implemented to forecast the reservoir monthly inflow data. Then, the processed predictive values of both ANN and SVM are selected as the input variables of a newly-built ANN model for refined forecasting. Three models, ANN, SVM, and the hybrid method, are developed for the monthly inflow forecasting in Xinfengjiang reservoir with 71-year discharges from 1944 to 2014. The comparison of results reveal that three models have satisfactory performances in the Xinfengjiang reservoir monthly inflow prediction, and the hybrid method performs better than ANN and SVM in terms of five statistical indicators. Thus, the hybrid method is an efficient tool for the long-term operation and dispatching of Xinfengjiang reservoir.

Keywords: monthly inflow; reservoir; forecast; artificial neural networks; support vector machine; genetic algorithm; hybrid method

---

1. Introduction

Long-term hydrological prediction is of significance for water resource activities, such as reservoir operation [1–5], water resource planning [6–9], risk management [10–13], and urbanization [14,15]. Hence, hydrologic time-series forecasting, especially monthly inflow, has triggered great interest in hydrology and water resources fields [16,17]. In the past several decades, the study of the hydrologic time-series forecasting has produced tremendous excitement and attention, and a large number of models and approaches have been proposed to improve the quality of forecasting accuracy. These developed models can be divided approximately into statistical methods, physical methods, and intelligent approaches. However, there was no one method that was appropriate, universally, for any reservoirs because the hydrological characteristics of river basins and regions change with variation of time and space, and each kind of method has various merits and defects. Statistical methods represented by autoregressive moving-average models are rather simple and mature but with lower accuracy [18,19]. Physical models like soil and water assessment tool (SWAT) [20] have the clear physical mechanism of the rainfall-runoff relation and reflect the nature and features of the hydrologic data series from different angles. However, the parameters of these models are not easy to determine and the predictive ability is limited in many situations [21–23]. Intelligent methods usually have strong robustness and are widely used in many areas, while have a low identifying speed and easy to encounter local optimum [24–28].

Reservoir monthly inflow data is influenced by various unstable factors and always present such characteristics as time-varying, non-stationary, and significant outliers. The characteristics of inflow data change the correlation between the past and the future. Moreover, there are many noise levels in different time-series regions, which further increase the difficulty of forecasting models. Hence, it is hard for a single time-series forecasting model to capture the dynamic changing processes and features, which may encounter local under-fitting or over-fitting problems [29–33]. The accuracy of a single forecast method always has limited effects. In order to obtain better performance, researchers have been constantly developing new technologies and methods for the hydrological prediction. In recent years, many hybrid approaches take advantage of more than one forecasting method to carry out the research work and engineering practice related to the reservoir inflow [34–39]. Application results indicate that the hybrid methods have higher forecasting precision than a single forecasting method.

Many successful applications demonstrate that, with the advantages of good generalizability and forecast accuracy, both artificial neural network (ANN) and support vector machine (SVM) are two types of efficient and promising approaches in hydrological prediction. Moreover, the research can be promoted rapidly on the basis of our early works on ANN and SVM [8,40,41]. Hence, we choose ANN and SVM for reservoir monthly inflow forecasting. However, when handling with the monthly inflow prediction of Xinfengjiang reservoir, both methods are inclined to acquire relatively poor performances. Thus, there are certain promotion spaces for the hydrological series forecasting in Xinfengjiang reservoir. Therefore, in this paper, based on the thought of refined prediction by model combination, we propose a hybrid forecasting approach for the reservoir monthly inflow based on three classical heuristic algorithms: ANN, SVM, and GA (genetic algorithm). The proposed method involves a two-stage forecasting process. In the first phase, with multiple hydrological input parameters, ANN and SVM are, respectively, implemented to forecast the reservoir monthly inflow data to identify the characteristic correlation, and GA is used for the parameter selection of SVM to reduce its performance volatility. In the second stage, in order to enhance the forecasting accuracy further, the results of the aforementioned ANN and SVM are selected as the input values of a newly-built ANN model, while the observed monthly inflow data are the output variables. When the training process is finished, the newly-built ANN model will be used for forecasting, and its forecasting results are the final values for operational prediction. In this research, the hybrid method was developed and compared with conventional ANN model and SVM model for one month-ahead forecasting of inflow data from Xinfengjiang reservoir in Guangdong province, China. It can be revealed from the result analysis that the proposed method is characterized by reasonable operation and high accuracy.

The rest of this paper is organized as follows. The description of the Xinfengjiang reservoir and data sets are given in Section 2. Section 3 introduces the information of the forecasting methodologies. Five different types of error measurements are introduced in Section 4. In Section 5, the implementation, including the input variables determination and model developments, and results of the forecast models are discussed, and the proposed hybrid method has the best forecasting performance. Section 6 briefly presents the major conclusions, limitations and future directions of the study.

2. Study Area and Data Sets

2.1. Study Area

The Pearl River (named Zhujiang in Chinese) is one of the world's 25 largest rivers in terms of annual water discharge and sediment load [42]. The Pearl River originates from the Yunnan Plateau, crosses hill country and mountainous areas, and drains into the South China Sea. The Pearl River controls a drainage area of 450,000 km^2 and reaches a total length of 2400 km. The rainy season extends from April to September, followed by a dry season from October to March.

The Xinfengjiang reservoir, also known as Evergreen Lake, is within the boundaries of Guangdong Province, about six kilometers away from Heyuan City. Figure 1 shows the location of the study area and the Xinfengjiang reservoir. The reservoir is located on the outlet of Xinfengjiang River, which is a tributary of the East River. The East River is one of the three main tributaries of the Pearl River. The drainage area of the reservoir is 5740 km², which accounts for about one quarter of the East River Basin area. The average annual rainfall is about 1974.7 mm. The annual inflow at the dam site is about 192 m³/s. Since being put into production in October 1960, the reservoir began to play comprehensive benefit in power generation, flood control, navigation, water supply, *etc.* The reservoir is equipped with four units and its installed capacity arrives 302 million watts. The average annual energy generation is 0.99 billion kW·h. As the largest artificial reservoir with multi-year regulating storage in south China, the reservoir has the total capacity of 13.90 billion m³, where the dead storage capacity is 4.31 billion m³. Its normal water level is 116 m at non-flood season while the corresponding storage is 10.8 billion m³. Its flood control level is 114 m during the first half of flood season from 1 April to 30 June, whilst that is 115 m during the second half of flood season from 1 July to 30 September.

Figure 1. Location of the study area and Xinfengjiang reservoir.

2.2. Division of Data

For meta-heuristic algorithms, such as ANN and SVM, the overtraining problem is likely to happen, which means that the models have excellent performance on the training data, but do not fit well to new data. In order to prevent the overtraining problem, Chau *et al.* (2005) suggested dividing the data into three subsets [5]: Training set for model training, testing set for monitoring the training process and validation set for model validation. Hence, in this study, the available data are divided into these above three data sets. The feasible monthly inflow data consists of 71 years (852 months) from 1944 to 2014 in Xinfengjiang reservoir. The first 55 years' monthly inflow data were used as the training set while the last 16 years' data were for validation. Moreover, of the training data, the first 40 years' data was for model training, and the other 15 years' data was for the purpose of confirming and validating the initial analysis.

It is hard to extrapolate for forecasting methods when the validation data contains variables beyond the range of training data. Table 1 shows the statistical parameters of various data sets, where X_{mean}, S_d, X_{min}, X_{max}, and R_{ange} respectively stand for the mean, standard deviation, minimum, maximum, and range of various data sets. We can find that the monthly inflow data for Xinfengjiang reservoir varies over a relative wide range from 9.3 to 1506 m³/s. The scope of the training data set includes that of testing and validation sets fully. The statistical parameters of the training set are close to the testing and validation sets. Hence, the data used for various data sets are representative of the same population, so there is no need to extrapolate beyond the range of the data for training.

Table 1. The information of various datasets in Xinfengjiang reservoir.

Datasets	Statistic				
	X_{mean}	S_d	X_{min}	X_{max}	R_{range}
Training set	204.1	14.3	9.3	1506.0	1496.7
Testing set	192.1	13.9	24.5	1300.2	1275.7
Validation set	176.3	13.3	22.3	1496.4	1474.1
Original data	195.3	14.0	9.3	1506.0	1496.7

2.3. Data Preprocessing

Moreover, according to Lin *et al.* in 2006 [41] and Wang *et al.* in 2009 [17], in consideration of the numerical difficulties caused by the large attribute values dominating the smaller ones, the normalization is an essential process for the raw data before applying the forecasting models to prediction in various data sets. Using the following Equation, the values have to be scaled to the range between 0 and 1 in the modeling process.

$$q'_i = \frac{q_i - q_{min}}{q_{max} - q_{min}} \tag{1}$$

where q_i and q'_i is the original inflow value and scaled inflow value, respectively. q_{max} and q_{min} are the maximum and minimum of flow series, respectively.

3. Forecasting Methodology

3.1. Artificial Neural Network (ANN)

As one of the most widely-used artificial intelligence methods, ANN has achieved great success in various fields by many researchers and scientists, like time-series prediction and simulation in water resources [5]. Through many investigations and practices, ANN has been proven that it is an efficient and reliable method in modeling nonlinear relationships between inputs and desired outputs in hydrologic time-series forecasting [16,17]. The ANN existence has much different kind of ways. ANN is commonly arranged in a series of layers composed of some close-connected processing neurons. Three-layer ANN, including one input layer, one hidden layer, and one output layer, is usually preferred in practical engineering applications because it can approximate almost any form of complex functional relationships between the inputs and desired outputs to arbitrary accuracy. Figure 2 shows the sketch map of a typical three-layer ANN. Every node usually gets an accumulated value by summing the values of its inputs multiplied by the corresponding weights associated with each interconnection, and then send the accumulated value to a nonlinear activation function to generate an output value which will be delivered to the following layer. Moreover, any one node of the previous layer is fully interconnected to all the nodes of the next layer, and there is no interconnection between any two nodes in the same layer.

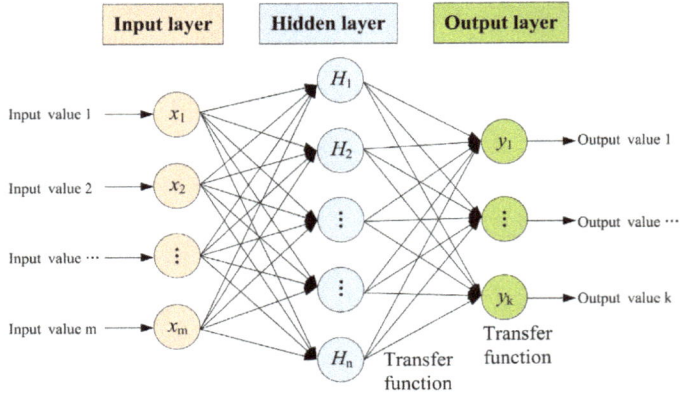

Figure 2. Sketch map of a typical three-layer ANN.

The back propagation algorithm is one of the most popular learning methods for the ANN training. In addition, with our early research works, back propagation can be easily implemented and integrated in practical forecasting system [40]. Back propagation can be roughly divided into two stages: a feed-forward stage and a backward stage. In the feed-forward stage, the input information is delivered to the input layer, the hidden layer and the output layer in sequence, to obtain the output information. In the backward stage, the connection weights and thresholds are modified by the differences between the computed and desired output values. Without knowing the detailed information about the nature of the complex system, ANN can approach the optimal or near-optimal relationship between the input data set and the output data set by optimizing the structure of the network constantly. Mathematically, the network can be expressed as follow:

$$Y = f\left(\sum WX + B\right) \tag{2}$$

where Y is the output vector. f is the transfer function. W is the weight vector. X is the weight vector. B is the bias vector.

3.2. Support Vector Machine (SVM)

Support Vector Machine (SVM), proposed by Vapnik in 1995 [41], is a novel and useful tool for data classification and regression analysis. SVM is built on the basis of statistical learning methods and the structural risk minimization principle instead of the empirical risk minimization [19,31]. SVM can achieve a global optimum, in theory, and has been applied in many fields over the past decades, such as hydrology and computer science [43–45]. There are abundant papers about the detailed theory of SVM. Here, we introduce the information of SVM in brief, and the interested readers can find the detailed theory of SVM by referring to more papers. The fundamental idea of the SVM technique is to take advantage of a linear or nonlinear model to map the target input data into a higher dimensional characteristic space, so that the primary problem can be solved in the new space. For example, as shown in Figure 3, the problem of data classification which cannot be linearly separated on the plane may be linearly separable in the space with three or higher dimensions.

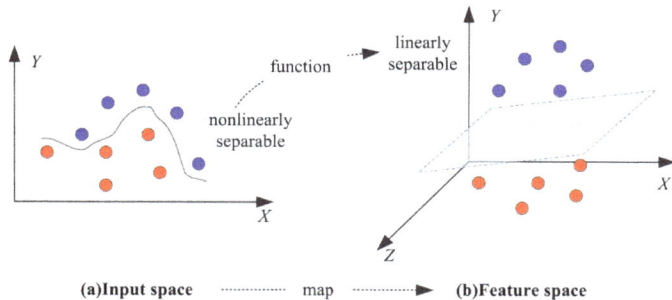

Figure 3. 2D input space mapping into 3D feature space to separate data linearly.

In SVM, the map model is usually defined as the kernel function to yield the inner products in the feature space and keep the calculated load reasonable. There are four kinds of commonly used kernel functions, including linear kernel, polynomial kernel, radial basis function (RBF) kernel, and sigmoid kernel [30,41]. Unlike the linear kernel, the RBF kernel can easily handle the non-linear relation between class labels and attributes. Compared with polynomial and sigmoid kernels, the RBF kernel has fewer tuning parameters, which reduces the complexity of model parameters selection. Moreover, the RBF kernel has good performance under general smoothness assumptions. In summary, the RBF kernel can improve the computational efficiency and enhance the generalization performance of SVM. Hence, the RBF kernel, as shown in Equation (3), is adopted as the kernel function in this study:

$$k(x_i, x) = \exp\left\{\frac{-\|x - x_i\|^2}{2\sigma^2}\right\} \tag{3}$$

where k represents the kernel function.

In the RBF kernel function, there are three parameters needed to be confirmed: the parameter C denotes the positive constant, the parameter ε represents the insensitive loss function, and the parameter σ denotes the Gaussian noise level of the standard deviation. Different parameter combinations can lead to large differences in the forecasting result. Thus, the combination of the three parameters has to be optimized, first, in order to improve the forecasting accuracy. Many methods are used to select these parameters, such as grid search technique, particle swarm optimization, and genetic algorithm. However, at present, no general guidelines are available for the parameter selection of SVM because each method has certain advantages and disadvantages. For example, the grid search technique has the advantages of simplicity and intuition but is more computationally expensive than other optimization techniques. As one of the most classic and popular evolutionary methods, genetic algorithm was widely employed to calibrate the combination of the three parameters due to its good robustness, adaptability, and simplicity, and satisfied results were also achieved in considerable research work. Therefore, for the better forecasting accuracy, we apply the GA to automatically choose the effective parameters combination of SVM kernel function.

3.3. Genetic Algorithm (GA)

In nature, for the limited resources, the grim competition exists in different individuals of the same or different species, resulting in the fittest individuals outmatching the weaker ones [2,23]. GA is a classical heuristic search algorithm which mimics the thought of natural selection and genetic evolution in Darwin's theory. By the power of evolution, GA can provide an efficient and robust search capability for the optimization problems associated with numerous complex constraints [34,35]. In GA, each potentially feasible or infeasible solution to the problem is encoded as a string of chromosomes. GA usually starts from a population of the given size which is generated randomly in the search space.

Then GA evolves through three essential operators: A selection operator representing the survival of the fittest, a crossover operator equating to the mating between individuals, and a mutation operator increasing the diversity. On the basis of the initial population, GA calculates the fitness values of all the individuals, and the fitness value $F(\theta)$ of the individual θ uses the following formula:

$$F(\theta) = \frac{1}{n}\sum_{i=1}^{n}[Y_i - SVM(X_i, \theta)]^2 \qquad (4)$$

where i represents the i-th data; n is the number of training data pairs; Y_i is the i-th observed data; X_i is the i-th input data vector; $SVM(X_i, \theta)$ represents the corresponding simulated value of SVM.

Then, the members with better fitness values are selected to form the population of the next generation. GA uses the crossover and mutation operators to enhance the population diversity. GA repeats the above-mentioned process until a certain terminal condition is met and the best individual represents the approximate optimal solution of the problem. Here, GA is employed to optimize the parameter combinations of the SVM model, and the objective is to minimize the fitness value of the optimal individual in the population, *i.e.*, $\min F(\theta)$. The flowchart is shown in Figure 4.

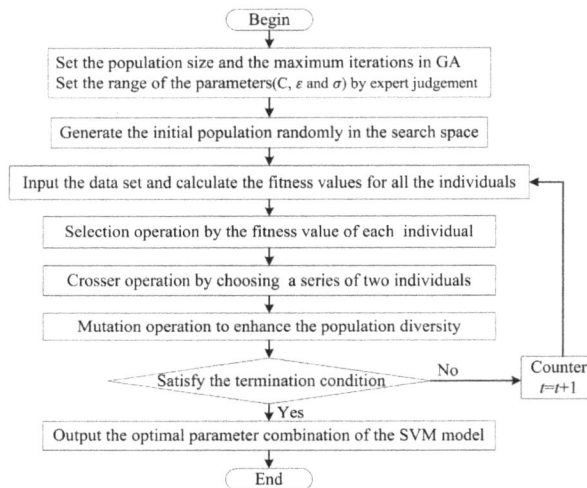

Figure 4. The flow chart of optimizing SVM using GA.

3.4. Hybrid Forecasting Method

The reservoir monthly inflow data series is controlled by a number of factors in the real world, including weather conditions, underlying surface, human activities, and others. These time-varying factors can introduce considerable uncertainty and noise, and affect the process of the inflow data series collection, pre-process, and prediction accuracy in the forecasting model. Hence, the reservoir monthly inflow data series usually presents the strong properties of randomness and volatility. On the one hand, a single forecasting model may reflect only one aspect of the character of the reservoir inflow in most cases so it is rather difficult to forecast the monthly inflow data accurately with one forecasting model because the bias or a large deviation always exists in the forecasting model. On the other hand, the results of two or more forecasting models can show the inflow characteristics from various perspectives. It is possible to further improve the prediction accuracy using different forecasting results. Therefore, to enhance the performance of the model, special treatment is required for the forecasting results to reduce the prediction errors of different models.

To deal with the problem of noise data caused by these aforementioned uncertain factors, this paper develops a hybrid forecast model based on ANN and SVM, which has many advantages discussed in the previous sections. The hybrid method is a two-stage process which can find an appropriate forecasting model to capture the complex relationship of the nonlinear system. First of all, the ANN A_1 and SVM S_1 forecasting model are driven to forecast the targeted reservoir inflow data, respectively, gaining two different forecasting results. Secondly, a new ANN model A_2 is built for the operational prediction, where the two different forecasting results of ANN and SVM are selected as the input variables and the real reservoir inflow data is used as the desired value. The two-stage forecasting process can be helpful to eliminate random errors of different models and improve the prediction ability to a certain degree. The framework of the proposed hybrid method is shown in Figure 5, and the process is described as below.

Step 1. Data processing. Divide the original valid monthly inflow data into various data sets, and these raw data are normalized to the preset range from 0 to 1.

Step 2. Model training in the first stage. Determine the structure of the ANN model A_1 and SVM model S_1, and use the abovementioned data to train both models, respectively, where GA is employed for the parameter selection of the SVM model S_1.

Step 3. Model training in the second stage. Determine the ANN model A_2 structure and use the processed data of the ANN model A_1 and SVM model S_1 as the input variables to train the model A_2.

Step 4. Model forecasting. The three optimized forecasting models are used to get the future values.

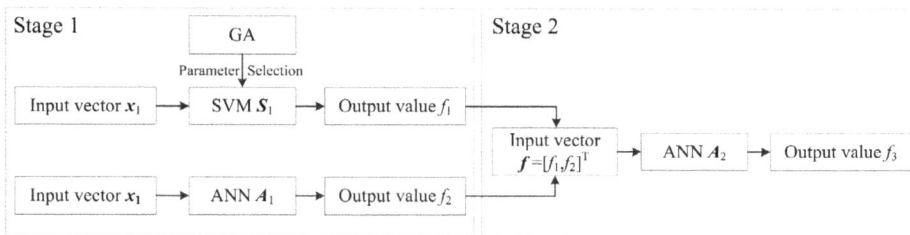

Figure 5. Sketch map of the hybrid method.

4. Statistical Measures

In this paper, the following five different types of error measurements are employed to evaluate the quality of the forecasting model. They are root mean square error (*RMSE*) and mean absolute error (*MAE*), mean absolute percentage error (*MAPE*), coefficient of correlation (*R*) and Nash-Sutcliffe (*NS*) efficiency coefficient. *RMSE* can be an arbitrary positive value and perform better when it is close to zero. *MAE* shows the degree of the absolute error between the forecasted and measured data. *MAPE* can express the relative absolute model error as a percentage. *R*, which ranges from −1 to 1, is a statistical measure of linear relationship between the observed and forecasted data. *NS* is less than or equal to 1, and has better forecasting capability when it is close to 1. The smaller the values of *RMSE*, *MAE* and *MAPE* are, the better the performance of the model shows. On the contrary, the larger the values of *NS* and *R* are, the better the forecasting model performs. The five criteria are calculated using the following Equations:

$$RMSE = \sqrt{\frac{1}{m}\sum_{i=1}^{m}\left(y_i - \widehat{y}_i\right)^2} \tag{5}$$

$$MAE = \frac{1}{m}\sum_{i=1}^{m}\left|y_i - \widehat{y}_i\right| \tag{6}$$

$$MAPE = \frac{1}{m} \sum_{i=1}^{m} \left| \frac{y_i - \widehat{y}_i}{y_i} \right| \times 100\% \tag{7}$$

$$R = \frac{\sum_{i=1}^{m} \left[(y_i - \bar{y}) \left(\widehat{y}_i - \bar{\tilde{y}} \right) \right]}{\sqrt{\sum_{i=1}^{m} (y_i - \bar{y})^2 \left(\widehat{y}_i - \bar{\tilde{y}} \right)^2}} \tag{8}$$

$$NS = 1 - \frac{\sum_{i=1}^{m} \left(y_i - \widehat{y}_i \right)^2}{\sum_{i=1}^{m} (y_i - \bar{y})^2} \tag{9}$$

where y_i and $\widehat{y}_i$ represent the i-th actual value and the i-th forecasted value of the forecasting model, respectively; m is the total number of data set for comparison; $\bar{y}$ represents the average value of the observed data, $\bar{y} = \frac{1}{m} \sum_{i=1}^{m} y_i$; $\tilde{y}$ is the average value of the forecasted data, $\tilde{y} = \frac{1}{m} \sum_{i=1}^{m} \widehat{y}_i$.

5. Results and Discussion

5.1. Input Variables Determination

Reasonable input variables can help capture the nonlinear features underlying the process and contribute to good model performance. For time-series forecasting, the autocorrelation function (ACF) and partial autocorrelation function (PACF) are two common parameters used to diagnose the order of the autoregressive process and determine the input vector of the model, too [17,41]. Figure 6 shows the ACF and PACF of the Xinfengjiang monthly inflow series with 95% confidence bands. Obviously, both ACF and PACF exhibit the peak value at lag 12, which indicates that twelve antecedent inflow values have the most useful information for the inflow forecasting. Hence, 12 antecedent inflow values are selected as the input vector based on autocorrelation coefficient analysis in this paper. The purpose of this study is to predict the inflow Q_{t+1} at the time $t+1$. Hence, the relationship between the output and input variables can be expressed as the following Equation:

$$Q_{t+1} = R(Q_t, Q_{t-1}, Q_{t-2}, Q_{t-3}, Q_{t-4}, Q_{t-5}, Q_{t-6}, Q_{t-7}, Q_{t-8}, Q_{t-9}, Q_{t-10}, Q_{t-11}) \tag{10}$$

where R denotes the nonlinear relationship, which are the corresponding model when ANN, SVM, and the hybrid method are used for inflow forecasting, respectively.

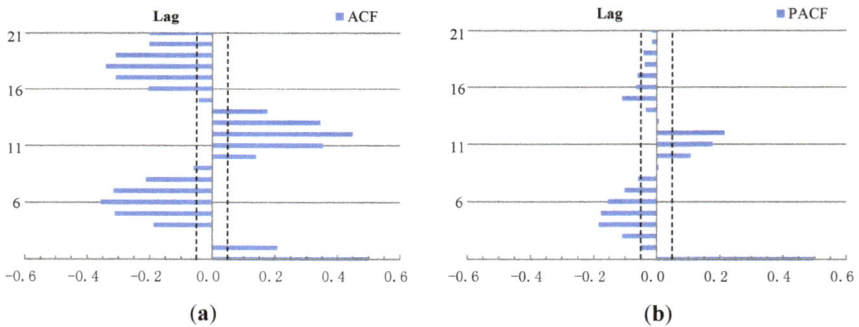

Figure 6. The (a) ACF and (b) PACF of Xinfengjiang monthly inflow series.

5.2. Development of Various Models

5.2.1. ANN Model A_1 Development

In the paper, we use a typical three-layer ANN model to forecast the monthly inflow in Xinfengjiang reservoir. All the neurons of hidden and output layers use the sigmoid transfer function. The twelve inputs and one output are applied to the ANN model, and all variables in the input and output data sets are normalized to the range between 0 and 1. The optimal network can be obtained using a trial and error procedure to train ANN models with various numbers of nodes in the hidden layer. As previously shown, the training data are further divided into the training set and the testing set. Based on the performances at different epochs, the cross-validation technique is used to select the optimum number of hidden neurons. Training is stopped when the error of the testing set starts to increase. Figure 7 shows the performances for the testing set with different hidden neurons from 2 to 25. When there are 15 neurons in the hidden layer, the testing error reached the minimum. Hence, the optimal ANN A_1 architecture is (12, 15, 1).

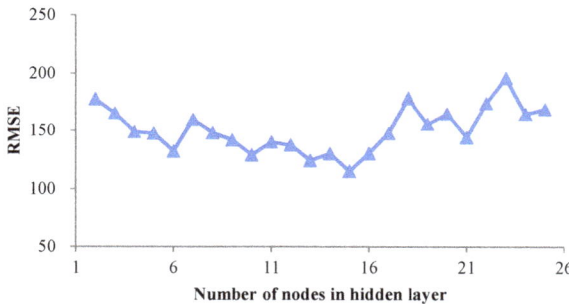

Figure 7. Performance of ANN model with different hidden nodes.

5.2.2. SVM Model S_1 Development

The setting of parameters plays an important role in the learning and generalization abilities of SVM. Larger search space is helpful for better parameters. Hence, the search scopes of three parameters are $C \in [2^{-5}, 2^{10}]$, $\sigma \in [2^{-5}, 2^{10}]$ and $\varepsilon \in [2^{-13}, 2^{5}]$. GA is used for the parameter selection of the SVM model. The SVM parameters are directly encoded using real value data in the chromosomes of the GA. The maximum iteration of GA is 500 and the population size is set to 300. Similar to the ANN model, the same data sets are used to optimize the parameters of SVM. To obtain more appropriate parameters, the overall process is repeated five times and the best model is selected as the final forecasting model. Table 2 displays the performance statistics of SVM models. The results indicate that, in the fourth run, SVM model with the optimal parameters $(C, \varepsilon, \sigma) = (9.425, 0.823, 0.081)$ behaved the best and should be selected as the forecast model for Xinfengjiang reservoir.

Table 2. The performance statistics of SVM models using GA over five runs.

Trial No.	Optimal Parameters (C, ε, σ)	Training					Validation				
		RMSE	*MAPE*	*MAE*	*NS*	*R*	*RMSE*	*MAPE*	*MAE*	*NS*	*R*
1	(10.653, 1.032, 0.078)	151.00	59.19	87.85	0.49	0.70	153.90	70.23	93.03	0.42	0.64
2	(9.827, 0.435, 0.064)	144.82	54.29	85.60	0.53	0.73	133.07	61.87	82.54	0.56	0.75
3	(2.783, 0.678, 0.125)	152.46	61.54	88.08	0.48	0.69	152.51	66.38	89.44	0.43	0.65
4	(9.425, 0.823, 0.081)	118.66	70.48	82.44	0.68	0.83	96.60	75.73	74.36	0.77	0.89
5	(11.803, 1.254, 0.708)	147.80	64.17	88.98	0.51	0.71	154.22	74.28	94.58	0.41	0.65

5.2.3. ANN Model A_2 Development

The two above models, ANN and SVM, are executed to respectively obtain the predicted data. The ANN model A_2 uses the results of both ANN model A_1 and SVM model S_1 as its input variables. There are two inputs and one output in the model. A typical three-layer network is used. The sigmoid transfer function is used in all neurons of the hidden layer and the output layer. To ensure the generalization, all variables are normalized, and a trial-and-error process is repeated to determine the optimal hidden layer nodes. The number of neuron in the hidden layer vary from two to nine, and all the statistical indexes of different network structures are recorded and compared during the calculation procedure. Finally, the optimal neural network adopted was (2, 5, 1), as shown in Figure 8, which was selected as the final forecasting model.

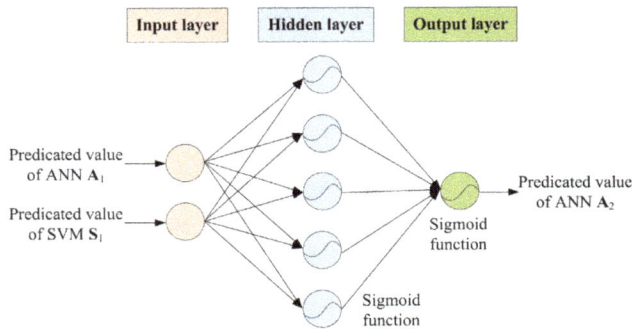

Figure 8. The optimal structure for ANN model A_2.

5.3. Comparison and Discussion

For the sake of comparison, three forecasting methods, namely ANN, SVM, and the hybrid method are tested under the same experimental conditions. The same data sets are used to verify the performance of various forecasting models in the same way. Every one-month step is predicted and compared with the actual inflow data to calculate the errors. The process is repeated over the whole time series, and then the average errors of all the months data are calculated. The obtained appropriate architectures of the ANN model A_1 and A_2 for Xinfengjiang reservoir are (12, 15, 1) and (2, 5, 1), respectively. Moreover, using GA for parameter selection, the SVM model with parameters $(C, \varepsilon, \sigma) = (9.425, 0.823, 0.081)$ is the forecasting model for Xinfengjiang reservoir.

Table 3 summarizes the statistical values of the three models in both training and validation periods. We can efficiently execute the analysis of the predictive ability of different models for Xinfengjiang reservoir. When compared to the original ANN and SVM, the hybrid method can produce better and closer prediction accuracy in term of all five measures during various periods. In the training period, the hybrid method achieves 19.21%, 24.26%, and 31.50% reduction in the *RMSE*, *MAE*, and *MAPE* values of SVM, respectively. Compared with ANN model, improvements of the hybrid model's forecast results regarding the R and NS were approximately 7.23% and 16.18%, respectively. In the validation period, the hybrid method can make 16.03%, 20.63%, and 21.83% improvements of the ANN forecast results related to the *RMSE*, *MAE*, and *MAPE*, respectively. The R and NS values of the hybrid method increase by 2.25% and 6.49% when compared with the SVM model, respectively. Thus, the above analysis indicates that the proposed method is able to obtain the best results in terms of all five different evaluation measures during both training and validation periods. The hybrid method starts the operational prediction using the processed data with more abundant information rather than original input vector, which help the forecasting model raise the cognitive level for the characteristics of time-variable monthly inflow data. By combining advantages of ANN and SVM, the hybrid method can effectively eliminate the noise of the original hydrological series. Therefore, the hybrid method can improve the forecasting accuracy of the monthly inflow data from Xinfengjiang reservoir.

Table 3. Model statistics of three models for Xinfengjiang reservoir.

Models	Training					Validation				
	RMSE	*MAPE*	*MAE*	*NS*	*R*	*RMSE*	*MAPE*	*MAE*	*NS*	*R*
SVM	118.66	70.48	82.44	0.68	0.83	96.60	75.73	74.36	0.77	0.89
ANN	118.60	55.20	79.73	0.68	0.83	102.09	63.68	73.49	0.74	0.87
Hybrid Method	95.86	48.28	62.44	0.79	0.89	85.72	49.78	58.33	0.82	0.91

Figures 9 and 10 respectively shows a comparison of forecasted *versus* observed values, and errors by predicted minus observed of the three models for the Xinfengjiang reservoir in the validation period. Figure 11 shows the scatterplots of observed inflow data *versus* forecast inflow of the three prediction models. Figure 9 demonstrates that the simulation results accord well with the observed results and the three models can capture the whole trend of the data series in the validation stage. The plots of errors in Figure 10 illustrate that a certain underestimation or overestimation exists in the monthly inflow predication value of each model. Due to the small magnitude and frequent occurrences of the low inflow pattern, all three models have slightly smaller errors and better generalization in these regions than high inflow pattern. The results are consistent with that in Tables 3 and 4. The linear trend line of the hybrid method in Figure 11 has the biggest R-squared value, which means that the trend line is closest to the perfect 45-degree line. From Figures 9–11, it can be observed that, when employed for monthly inflow data prediction, three models can achieve satisfactory performances for simulating the monthly inflow of Xinfengjiang reservoir, the hybrid method has high consistency and good stability, and performs better than SVM and ANN models in different inflow levels. To sum up, in the hybrid method, the ANN and SVM models are first used for the structure identification of different resolution in the hydrological time series, and then a newly-built ANN model is constructed for the refined prediction so as to enhance the prediction capability of the forecasting model. Therefore, the proposed method has satisfied performance when predicting the monthly inflow data series.

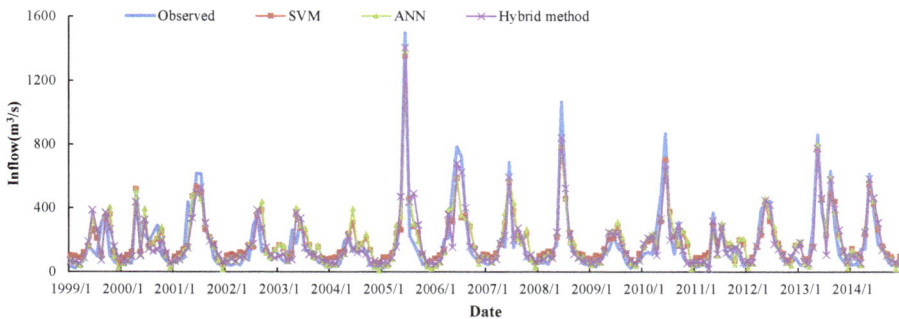

Figure 9. Comparison of forecasted *versus* observed data by various methods during the validation period.

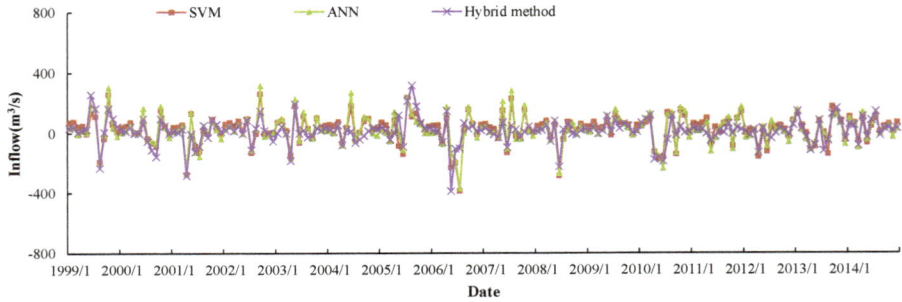

Figure 10. Comparison of errors by various methods during the validation period.

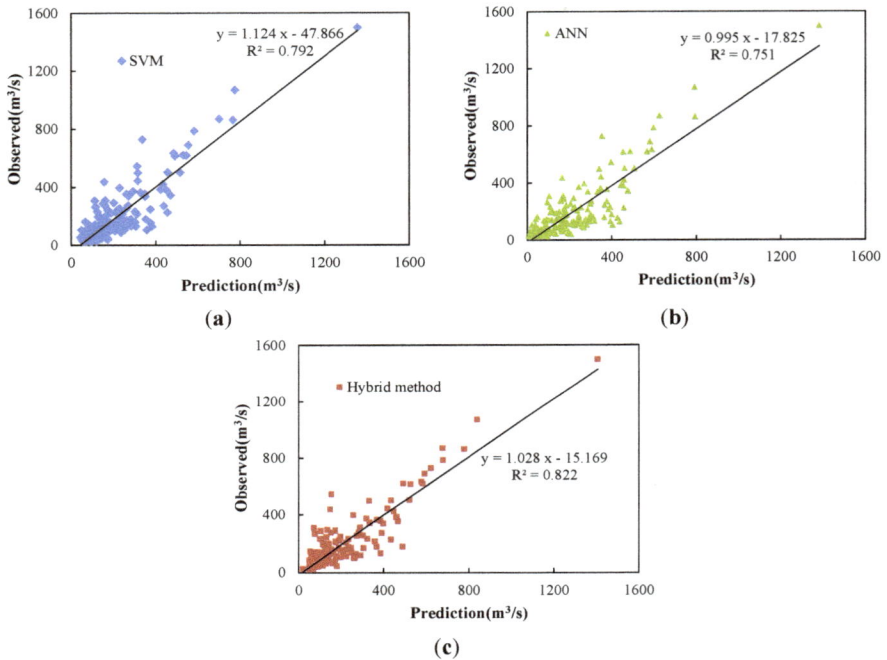

Figure 11. Scatter plots of forecasted *versus* observed data by various methods during the validation period. (a) SVM; (b) ANN and (c) Hybrid method.

Table 4 lists the peak flow estimation of SVM, ANN, and the hybrid method for Xinfengjiang reservoir during the validation period. The maximum observed peak inflow is 1496.4 m^3/s in June 2015, while the forecast value of the SVM, ANN, and hybrid method are 1355.5, 1381.3, and 1405.7 m^3/s, about 9.4%, 7.7% and 6.1% underestimation, respectively. For the second maximum peak inflow in June 2008, the SVM, ANN, and the hybrid method can obtain 776.5, 792.3, and 840.5 m^3/s instead of the observed 1066 m^3/s, about 27.2%, 25.7% and 21.2% underestimation, respectively. Moreover, for the 16 peak flows, the absolute average relative error of the SVM, ANN, and the hybrid method are 15.2%, 15.5% and 10.6%, respectively. Thus, it can be concluded that for peak inflow prediction, the hybrid method can obtain better forecast precision than SVM and ANN, while there is no significant difference between ANN and SVM.

Table 4. Peak flow estimates of three models for Xinfengjiang reservoir during the validation period.

Peak No.	Date	Observed	Forecast Peak			Relative Error (%)		
		Peak	SVM	ANN	Hybrid Method	SVM	ANN	Hybrid Method
1	1999/9	362.0	327.9	346.9	369.5	−9.4	−4.2	2.1
2	2000/4	497.9	516.0	507.5	434.9	3.6	1.9	−12.7
3	2001/6	618.1	530.3	488.4	492.9	−14.2	−21.0	−20.3
4	2002/8	352.6	349.1	376.7	386.2	−1.0	6.8	9.5
5	2003/6	336.2	272.0	285.6	334.4	−19.1	−15.1	−0.5
6	2004/5	202.8	237.3	236.8	225.8	17.0	16.8	11.3
7	2005/6	1496.4	1355.5	1381.3	1405.7	−9.4	−7.7	−6.1
8	2006/6	783.8	583.2	598.1	679.5	−25.6	−23.7	−13.3
9	2007/6	687.5	555.7	581.4	592.1	−19.2	−15.4	−13.9
10	2008/6	1066.0	776.5	792.3	840.5	−27.2	−25.7	−21.2
11	2009/6	228.2	211.5	252.4	236.1	−7.3	10.6	3.5
12	2010/6	867.5	701.4	626.7	677.5	−19.2	−27.8	−21.9
13	2011/5	369.6	293.5	244.1	319.3	−20.6	−34.0	−13.6
14	2012/6	442.3	315.6	348.7	419.6	−28.6	−21.2	−5.1
15	2013/5	860.9	766.5	794.2	778.3	−11.0	−7.7	−9.6
16	2014/5	616.2	544.8	567.0	584.9	−11.6	−8.0	−5.1
	Average (absolute)					15.2	15.5	10.6

6. Conclusions

In order to improve the forecasting accuracy of monthly inflow in Xinfengjiang reservoir, this paper develops a hybrid forecasting method based on artificial neural network (ANN), support vector machine (SVM) and genetic algorithm (GA) to forecast the monthly inflow data series. The forecasting process of the hybrid method can be divided into two stages. In the first stage, SVM and ANN are used to identify the complex nonlinear characteristic correlation between the input and the output data, and GA is implemented to seek for the parameter combination of the SVM model. In the second stage, for better forecasting accuracy, the results of the SVM and ANN are taken as input variables of a new ANN model, and the corresponding predicative results of the new ANN model is the final forecasting inflow value. Three different models, ANN, SVM, and the hybrid prediction model are applied to forecast the monthly inflow data from Xinfengjiang dam reservoir of Pearl River Basin in China, and five statistical measures are employed to evaluate the performances of these various models. From the detailed analysis in this work, it can be concluded that these three models can obtain the satisfactory forecasting accuracy for the monthly inflow data in Xinfengjiang reservoir, and the proposed hybrid method significantly outperforms the traditional ANN and SVM. Therefore, the hybrid forecasting method proposed in this paper can capture the potential information and relationship of the monthly inflow data series and will be helpful for Xinfengjiang reservoir managers to obtain more accurate and stable forecasting results. However, due to the limitation of the authors' time and energy, there are, undoubtedly, some defects needed to deepen in further research work. For example, only ANN and SVM are compared and considered in the present study for simplicity, more approaches can be considered and involved in the hybrid method, to enhance the generalizability of the forecasting model. In addition, the accuracy and applicability of the hybrid in different reservoirs' monthly or other-scale inflow under different climate conditions can also be further examined.

Acknowledgments: This study is supported by the Major International Joint Research Project from the National Nature Science Foundation of China (51210014) and the National Basic Research Program of China (973 Program, No. 2013CB035906).

Author Contributions: All authors contributed extensively to the work presented in this paper. Chun-Tian Cheng contributed to the subject of the research and literature review. Zhong-Kai Feng contributed to modeling and finalized the manuscripts. Wen-Jing Niu contributed to the data analysis and manuscript review. Sheng-Li Liao contributed to the manuscript review.

Conflicts of Interest: The authors declare no conflict of interest.

References

1. Zhao, T.; Zhao, J. Joint and respective effects of long and short-term forecast uncertainties on reservoir operations. *J. Hydrol.* **2014**, *517*, 83–94. [CrossRef]
2. Chiu, Y.C.; Chang, L.C.; Chang, F.J. Using a hybrid genetic algorithm-simulated annealing algorithm for fuzzy programming of reservoir operation. *Hydrol. Process.* **2007**, *21*, 3162–3172. [CrossRef]
3. Karamouz, M.; Ahmadi, A.; Moridi, A. Probabilistic reservoir operation using bayesian stochastic model and support vector machine. *Adv. Water Resour.* **2009**, *32*, 1588–1600. [CrossRef]
4. Lian, J.; Yao, Y.; Ma, C.; Guo, Q. Reservoir operation rules for controlling algal blooms in a tributary to the impoundment of three gorges dam. *Water* **2014**, *6*, 3200–3223. [CrossRef]
5. Chau, K.W.; Wu, C.L.; Li, Y.S. Comparison of several flood forecasting models in Yangtz River. *J. Hydrol. Eng.* **2005**, *10*, 485–491. [CrossRef]
6. Liu, P.; Lin, K.; Wei, X. A two-stage method of quantitative flood risk analysis for reservoir real-time operation using ensemble-based hydrologic forecasts. *Stoch. Env. Res. Risk A* **2014**, *29*, 803–813. [CrossRef]
7. Chau, K.W.; Wu, C.A. Hybrid model coupled with singular spectrum analysis for daily rainfall prediction. *J. Hydroinform.* **2010**, *12*, 458–473. [CrossRef]
8. Cheng, C.T.; Lin, J.Y.; Sun, Y.G.; Chau, K.W. Long-term prediction of discharges in Manwan hydropower using adaptive-network-based fuzzy inference systems models. *Lect. Notes Comput. Sci.* **2005**, *3612*, 1152–1161.
9. Fleming, S.W.; Weber, F.A. Detection of long-term change in hydroelectric reservoir inflows: Bridging theory and practice. *J. Hydrol.* **2012**, *470*, 36–54. [CrossRef]
10. Wu, C.L.; Chau, K.W.; Li, Y.S. Methods to improve neural network performance in daily flows prediction. *J. Hydrol.* **2009**, *372*, 80–93. [CrossRef]
11. Lund, J.R. Flood Management in California. *Water* **2012**, *4*, 157–169. [CrossRef]
12. Muttil, N.; Chau, K.W. Machine learning paradigms for selecting ecologically significant input variables. *Eng. Appl. Artif. Intell.* **2007**, *20*, 735–744. [CrossRef]
13. Coulibaly, P.; Haché, M.; Fortin, V.; Bobée, B. Improving daily reservoir inflow forecasts with model combination. *J. Hydrol. Eng.* **2005**, *10*, 91–99. [CrossRef]
14. Zhu, T.; Lund, J.R.; Jenkins, M.W.; Marques, G.F.; Ritzema, R.S. Climate change, urbanization, and optimal long-term floodplain protection. *Water Resour. Res.* **2007**, *43*, 122–127. [CrossRef]
15. Wu, C.L.; Chau, K.W. Data-driven models for monthly streamflow time series prediction. *Eng. Appl. Artif. Intell.* **2010**, *23*, 1350–1367. [CrossRef]
16. Valipour, M.; Banihabib, M.E.; Behbahani, S.M.R. Comparison of the ARMA, ARIMA and the autoregressive artificial neural network models in forecasting the monthly inflow of Dez dam reservoir. *J. Hydrol.* **2013**, *476*, 433–441. [CrossRef]
17. Wang, W.C.; Chau, K.W.; Cheng, C.T.; Qiu, L. A comparison of performance of several artificial intelligence methods for forecasting monthly discharge time series. *J. Hydrol.* **2009**, *374*, 294–306. [CrossRef]
18. Taormina, R.; Chau, K.W. Neural network river forecasting with multi-objective fully informed particle swarm optimization. *J. Hydroinform.* **2015**, *17*, 99–113. [CrossRef]
19. Lin, G.F.; Chen, G.R.; Huang, P.Y. Effective typhoon characteristics and their effects on hourly reservoir inflow forecasting. *Adv. Water Resour.* **2010**, *33*, 887–898. [CrossRef]
20. Demirel, M.C.; Venancio, A.; Kahya, E. Flow forecast by SWAT model and ANN in Pracana basin, Portugal. *Adv. Eng. Softw.* **2009**, *40*, 467–473. [CrossRef]
21. Saeidifarzad, B.; Nourani, V.; Aalami, M.; Chau, K.W. Multi-site calibration of linear reservoir based geomorphologic rainfall-runoff models. *Water* **2014**, *6*, 2690–2716. [CrossRef]
22. Chen, W.; Chau, K.W. Intelligent manipulation and calibration of parameters for hydrological models. *Int. J. Environ. Pollut.* **2006**, *28*, 432–447. [CrossRef]
23. Cheng, C.T.; Ou, C.P.; Chau, K.W. Combining a fuzzy optimal model with a genetic algorithm to solve multi-objective rainfall-runoff model calibration. *J. Hydrol.* **2002**, *268*, 72–86. [CrossRef]

24. Gupta, H.V.; Kling, H.; Yilmaz, K.K.; Martinez, G.F. Decomposition of the mean squared error and NSE performance criteria: Implications for improving hydrological modelling. *J. Hydrol.* **2009**, *377*, 80–91. [CrossRef]

25. Sattari, M.T.; Yurekli, K.; Pal, M. Performance evaluation of artificial neural network approaches in forecasting reservoir inflow. *Appl. Math. Model.* **2012**, *36*, 2649–2657. [CrossRef]

26. Maier, H.R.; Dandy, G.C. Neural networks for the prediction and forecasting of water resources variables: A review of modeling issues and applications. *Environ. Modell. Softw.* **2000**, *15*, 101–124. [CrossRef]

27. Taormina, R.; Chau, K.W.; Sethi, R. Artificial neural network simulation of hourly groundwater levels in a coastal aquifer system of the venice lagoon. *Eng. Appl. Artif. Intell.* **2012**, *25*, 1670–1676. [CrossRef]

28. Kisi, O.; Cimen, M. A wavelet-support vector machine conjunction model for monthly streamflow forecasting. *J. Hydrol.* **2011**, *399*, 132–140. [CrossRef]

29. Yang, J.S.; Yu, S.P.; Liu, G.M. Multi-step-ahead predictor design for effective long-term forecast of hydrological signals using a novel wavelet neural network hybrid model. *Hydrol. Earth Syst. Sci.* **2013**, *17*, 4981–4993. [CrossRef]

30. Noori, R.; Karbassi, A.R.; Moghaddamnia, A.; Han, D.; Zokaei-Ashtiani, M.H.; Farokhnia, A.; Gousheh, M.G. Assessment of input variables determination on the SVM model performance using PCA, Gamma test, and forward selection techniques for monthly stream flow prediction. *J. Hydrol.* **2011**, *40*, 177–189. [CrossRef]

31. Lin, G.F.; Chen, G.R.; Wu, M.C.; Chou, Y.C. Effective forecasting of hourly typhoon rainfall using support vector machines. *Water Resour. Res.* **2009**, *45*, 560–562. [CrossRef]

32. Bazartseren, B.; Hildebrandt, G.; Holz, K.P. Short-term water level prediction using neural networks and neuro-fuzzy approach. *Neurocomputing* **2003**, *55*, 439–450. [CrossRef]

33. Coulibaly, P.; Anctil, F.; Bobee, B. Daily reservoir inflow forecasting using artificial neural networks with stopped training approach. *J. Hydrol.* **2000**, *230*, 244–257. [CrossRef]

34. Su, J.; Wang, X.; Zhao, S.; Chen, B.; Li, C.; Yang, Z. A structurally simplified hybrid model of genetic algorithm and support vector machine for prediction of chlorophyll *a* in reservoirs. *Water* **2015**, *7*, 1610–1627. [CrossRef]

35. Kuo, J.T.; Wang, Y.Y.; Lung, W.S. A hybrid neural-genetic algorithm for reservoir water quality management. *Water Res.* **2006**, *40*, 1367–1376. [CrossRef] [PubMed]

36. Guo, Z.H.; Wu, J.; Lu, H.Y.; Wang, J.Z. A case study on a hybrid wind speed forecasting method using bp neural network. *Knowl. Based Syst.* **2011**, *24*, 1048–1056. [CrossRef]

37. Thirumalaiah, K.; Deo, M.C. River stage forecasting using artificial neural networks. *J. Hydrol. Eng.* **1998**, *3*, 26–32. [CrossRef]

38. Alvisi, S.; Mascellani, G.; Franchini, M.; Bardossy, A. Water level forecasting through fuzzy logic and artificial neural network approaches. *Hydrol. Earth Syst. Sci.* **2006**, *10*, 1–17. [CrossRef]

39. Seo, Y.; Kim, S.; Kisi, O.; Singh, V.P. Daily water level forecasting using wavelet decomposition and artificial intelligence techniques. *J. Hydrol.* **2015**, *520*, 224–243. [CrossRef]

40. Zhang, J.; Cheng, C.T.; Liao, S.L.; Wu, X.Y.; Shen, J.J. Daily reservoir inflow forecasting combining QPF into ANNs model. *Hydrol. Earth Syst. Sci.* **2009**, *6*, 121–150. [CrossRef]

41. Lin, J.Y.; Cheng, C.T.; Chau, K.W. Using support vector machines for long-term discharge prediction. *Hydrol. Sci. J.* **2006**, *51*, 599–612. [CrossRef]

42. Wu, C.S.; Yang, S.L.; Lei, Y.P. Quantifying the anthropogenic and climatic impacts on water discharge and sediment load in the Pearl River (Zhujiang), China (1954–2009). *J. Hydrol.* **2012**, *452*, 190–204. [CrossRef]

43. Yu, P.S.; Chen, S.T.; Chang, I.F. Support vector regression for real-time flood stage forecasting. *J. Hydrol.* **2006**, *328*, 704–716. [CrossRef]

44. Lin, G.F.; Chen, G.R.; Huang, P.Y.; Chou, Y.C. Support vector machine-based models for hourly reservoir inflow forecasting during typhoon-warning periods. *J. Hydrol.* **2009**, *372*, 17–29. [CrossRef]

45. Wu, C.L.; Chau, K.W.; Li, Y.S. River stage prediction based on a distributed support vector regression. *J. Hydrol.* **2008**, *358*, 96–111. [CrossRef]

water

MDPI

Article

Daily Reservoir Runoff Forecasting Method Using Artificial Neural Network Based on Quantum-behaved Particle Swarm Optimization

Chun-tian Cheng [1,*], Wen-jing Niu [1], Zhong-kai Feng [1], Jian-jian Shen [1] and Kwok-wing Chau [2]

[1] Institute of Hydropower and Hydroinformatics, Dalian University of Technology, Dalian 116024, China; dgniuwenjing@mail.dlut.edu.cn (W.N.); myfellow@mail.dlut.edu.cn (Z.F.); shenjj@dlut.edu.cn (J.S.)

[2] Department of Civil and Environmental Engineering, Hong Kong Polytechnic University, Hong Kong 999077, China; cekwchau@polyu.edu.hk

* Correspondence: ctcheng@dlut.edu.cn; Tel./Fax: +86-411-84708768

Academic Editor: Miklas Scholz

Received: 30 June 2015; Accepted: 27 July 2015; Published: 31 July 2015

Abstract: Accurate daily runoff forecasting is of great significance for the operation control of hydropower station and power grid. Conventional methods including rainfall-runoff models and statistical techniques usually rely on a number of assumptions, leading to some deviation from the exact results. Artificial neural network (ANN) has the advantages of high fault-tolerance, strong nonlinear mapping and learning ability, which provides an effective method for the daily runoff forecasting. However, its training has certain drawbacks such as time-consuming, slow learning speed and easily falling into local optimum, which cannot be ignored in the real world application. In order to overcome the disadvantages of ANN model, the artificial neural network model based on quantum-behaved particle swarm optimization (QPSO), ANN-QPSO for short, is presented for the daily runoff forecasting in this paper, where QPSO was employed to select the synaptic weights and thresholds of ANN, while ANN was used for the prediction. The proposed model can combine the advantages of both QPSO and ANN to enhance the generalization performance of the forecasting model. The methodology is assessed by using the daily runoff data of Hongjiadu reservoir in southeast Guizhou province of China from 2006 to 2014. The results demonstrate that the proposed approach achieves much better forecast accuracy than the basic ANN model, and the QPSO algorithm is an alternative training technique for the ANN parameters selection.

Keywords: quantum-behaved particle swarm optimization (QPSO); daily runoff; reservoir forecasting; artificial neural network; hybrid forecast

---

1. Introduction

Accurate daily runoff forecasting is extremely important for hydropower operation control and power grid operation scheduling [1–5]. Over the past decades, there have been abundant traditional classical research works for the daily runoff forecasting, which can be broadly separated into two categories: process-based model like Xin'anjiang model [6,7], and data-based model such as autoregressive model and moving average model [8,9]. These approaches entail exogenous input and rely on a number of assumptions for natural environment, leading to some deviation from the exact results in most cases. In recent years, with the booming development of heuristic methods, many researchers pay attention to applying them in daily runoff forecasting or the parameter selection of the hydrologic model, including artificial neural network [10,11], SCE-UA algorithm [12,13], support vector machine [14,15] and other hybrid methods [16,17].

As a typical artificial neural network, back propagation neural network (BP) can nearly simulate any complex linear or non-linear functional relationship without knowing the correlation between the input data and the output data [18,19]. After learning from the training data set, BP can be used to predict a new output data effectively with the corresponding input data. Compared with other methods, BP has high fault tolerance, strong robustness and easy adaptability to online learning. BP has been widely used in many practical areas, including load prediction, wind speed prediction and daily runoff forecasting. However, BP has some drawbacks, such as long computing time, slow convergence and easy to encounter local minimum. Hence, a variety of hybrid optimization methods using such global optimization algorithm like particle swarm optimization (PSO) are developed to improve the generalization ability of the artificial neural network [20,21]. These hybrid optimization methods can improve the BP forecasting performance in varying degrees. However, when PSO is applied for the ANN parameters selection, it may be trapped into the local optima of the objective function because PSO is restricted by search capability. Therefore, the promotion space is still large for ANN parameter selection using an evolutionary algorithm [22–24].

In recent years, a novel particle swarm optimization variant called quantum-behaved particle swarm optimization algorithm (QPSO) was proposed by Sun *et al.* [25] in 2004. In QPSO, the global optimal solution in the whole searching space can be guaranteed theoretically. Moreover, simulation results of numerous complex benchmark functions showed that QPSO has better global searching ability than the basic PSO [26,27]. Hence, QPSO are widely used to solve the complex optimization problems which includes hydrothermal scheduling and economic dispatch problem [28,29]. However, up to now, there are a few reports about using QPSO for parameter calibration of artificial neural network. Therefore, to improve the generalization ability and calculation efficiency of artificial neural network, a hybrid method, coupling artificial neural network and QPSO, is developed for daily reservoir runoff forecasting in this research, where QPSO algorithm is selected as training algorithm for artificial neural network to enhance hydrologic forecast accuracy.

The remaining is organized as follows. Artificial neural network is introduced briefly in Section 2. Section 3 explains the PSO and QPSO methods in details, then the proposed QPSO-ANN model is presented in Section 4. Section 5 provides the results of the proposed method and other methods and gives discussions on their performances. Finally, conclusions are summarized in Section 6.

2. Artificial Neural Network

In general, the relation between input vector and output vector of a nonlinear system can be expressed as $Y = H(X)$, where $X = [X_1, \ldots, X_i, \ldots, X_n]^T$ is input vector; X_i is the *i*th input data; n is the number of input data; $Y = [Y_1, \ldots, Y_j, \ldots, Y_u]^T$ is output vector; Y_j is the *j*th input data; u is the number of output data; $H(\cdot)$ denotes the complex nonlinear relation which can be estimated by some meta-heuristic methods like artificial neural network.

In our study, BP neural network is chosen as the basic approach to estimate input-output relations $H(\cdot)$ of the nonlinear hydrological system. The main advantage of BP is that it can reflect the complex nature of underlying process with less information than other traditional methods. A typical BP neural network consists of three layers, input layer, hidden layer and output layer, whose structure is shown in Figure 1. Each layer is composed of a series of interconnected processing nodes. As a specific neuron, each node in any layer uses a nonlinear transfer function to calculate the inner product of input vector and weight vector to get a scalar result. Two neighboring layers are connected via the weights of the nodes between these layers. The input layer receives and transmits input data to hidden layer. The hidden layer may contain a single layer or multi-layer that receives values from the previous layer. Each hidden layer is responsible for the input information conversion and then delivers them to the next hidden layer or output layer. The output layer presents the simulated results and has only one single layer with one or several nodes. In a single calculation, the BP neural network can obtain overall error between the estimated output values and the target output values, then loss function gradient is calculated. The gradient-descent algorithm is fed to update weights and thresholds to minimize loss function. The connection weights and thresholds between any two feed forward-connected neurons will be unceasingly adjusted until the error meets the termination conditions. Then, the optimized BP neural network can be used to forecast the target value with the corresponding input vector.

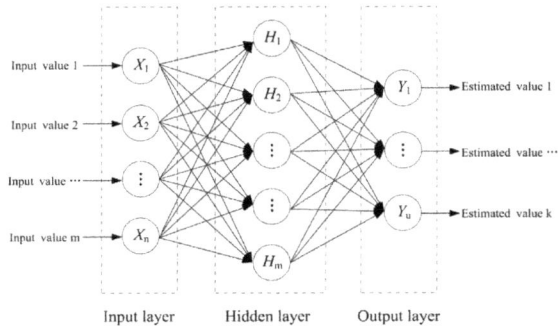

Figure 1. Schematic diagram of three-layer back propagation (BP) neural network.

Due to the defects of gradient descent method, the result may find a locally optimal solution instead of global optimum in most cases due to the existence of many local optima on the error surface. The convergence in back propagation learning cannot be guaranteed. Moreover, the computation speed is rather slow because the gradient descent algorithm requires small learning rates for stable learning.

3. Quantum-Behaved Particle Swarm Optimization

3.1. Particle Swarm Optimization

Particle Swarm Optimization (PSO), proposed by Kennedy and Eberhart in 1995 [30], is a well-known evolutionary population-based algorithm for global optimization problems [31,32]. The main concept of PSO is from analogy of biological and sociological feeding behavior of bird swarm, and its basic variant is a population (called a swarm) of candidate solutions (called particles). PSO is initialized with random solutions which search for optima by flying through problem space from generation to generation. The flight of each particle is guided continuously by its own best known position, ***pbest***, and the best known position of the whole population, ***gbest***. Each particle has position vector and velocity vector, and explores in the searching space by a few simple formulas.

There is extensive and profound homology or resemblance between PSO and other evolutionary computation techniques like genetic algorithm. Compared with genetic algorithm, PSO has faster convergence speed since it has no evolution operators like crossover and selection. Moreover, PSO has few parameters to adjust and depends directly upon function values rather than derivative information. In the past few years, PSO has been successfully applied to many research and application areas. However, the main defect of PSO is that global convergence cannot be guaranteed, especially when the number of decision variables or dimensions to be optimized are large. In other words, PSO is easily trapped into local optimum although it may have fast convergent rate [32,33].

3.2. Quantum-Behaved Particle Swarm Optimization

In order to deal with disadvantages of PSO, quantum-behaved particle swarm optimization (QPSO) was developed by Sun *et al.* [25] in 2004. From the quantum mechanics perspective, QPSO considers the particle possess quantum behavior and cannot determine the exact values of position vector and velocity vector simultaneously according to uncertainty principle [25,26]. Hence, there is no velocity vector in the particle of QPSO, and particle state is associated with an appropriate time-dependent Schrödinger equation and can be characterized by wave function ψ instead of position and velocity [27,28], where $|\psi|^2$ is the probability density function of its position. Let M particles in d

dimensional space with $\bar{k}$ maximum generations, the position vector of ith particle at kth generation can be expressed as $x_i(k) = [x_{i,1}(k), x_{i,2}(k), \ldots, x_{i,d}(k)]^T$. There will be $gbest(k) = [gbest_1(k), gbest_2(k), \ldots, gbest_d(k)]^T$ and $pbest_i(k) = [pbest_{i,1}(k), pbest_{i,2}(k), \ldots, pbest_{i,d}(k)]^T$. Employing Monte-Carlo method, particle moves according to the following iterative equation:

$$x_{i,j}(k+1) = \begin{cases} p_{i,j}(k+1) + a(k) \times \left| mbest_j(k+1) - x_{i,j}(k) \right| \times \ln(1/r_1), if\ r_2 \geq 0.5 \\ p_{i,j}(k+1) - a(k) \times \left| mbest_j(k+1) - x_{i,j}(k) \right| \times \ln(1/r_1), if\ r_2 < 0.5 \end{cases} \tag{1} \cdot$$

$$p_{i,j}(k+1) = r_3 \times pbest_{i,j}(k) + (1 - r_3) \times gbest_j(k) \tag{2}$$

$$mbest_j(k+1) = \frac{1}{M} \sum_{i=1}^{M} pbest_{i,j}(k) \tag{3}$$

$$a(k) = \frac{(a_1 - a_2) \times \left(\bar{k} - k \right)}{\bar{k}} + a_2 \tag{4}$$

for $i = 1,2,\ldots,M$; $j = 1,2,\ldots,d$; $k = 1,2,\ldots,\bar{k}$. Where $x_{i,j}(k)$ is position for jth dimension of ith particle in kth generation; r_1, r_2, r_3 are random variables distributed uniformly in [0,1]; $a(k)$ is contraction-expansion coefficient in kth generation which controls the convergence speed of the particle; a_1, a_2 are maximum and minimum value of $a(k)$, respectively; and there are usually $a_1 = 1.0$, $a_2 = 0.5$ [28]; $p_{i,j}(k)$ is the jth dimension of local attractor i in kth generation; $mbest$ represents the mean best position defined as mean of all $pbest$ position of the whole population.

4. Parameters Selection for Artificial Neural Network Based on QPSO Algorithm

In order to obtain better forecast accuracy, the novel QPSO algorithm is employed for parameters selection of BP neural network. In this paper, there is only one node in output layer, which is the daily runoff forecast value. If the node number of input layer and hidden layer are n and m, respectively, the architecture of the ANN neural network is n-m-1. The flow chart of the proposed method is shown in Figure 2, and the fundamental idea of the proposed method can be described as follows:

Step 0: Set basic parameters for the proposed method.
Step 0.1: Set maximize iterations $\bar{k}$ and population size M in QPSO.
Step 0.2: Divide data into training and testing sets.
Step 0.3: Define transfer function of neurons, which is a sigmoid function in this paper, *i.e.*:

$$f[x] = \frac{1}{1 + e^{-x}} \tag{5}$$

Step 1: The input and output data in both training and testing sets are normalized to ensure the quality of forecast results.

$$X = \{X_i'\} = a \times \frac{X_i - X_i^{min}}{X_i^{max} - X_i^{min}} + b \tag{6}$$

where X_i' and X_i is the normalized value and real value of each vector, respectively; X_i^{min} and X_i^{max} are the minimum and maximum value of input or output arrays; a and b are the positive normalized parameters, respectively. Based on large numbers of numerical experiments, we found that when the variable $a = 0.2$ and $b = 0.6$ are adopted to normalize the raw data, the forecasting models performs better. Hence, we use the variable $a = 0.2$ and $b = 0.6$ for data normalization in this paper.

Step 2: The QPSO algorithm is employed to select the parameters of BP neural network. The ith particle in the kth generation is denoted by $x_i(k) = \{w_i, b_i\}$. Here, w_i and b_i represent the connection weights and bias matrix between any two layers of the BP neural network, respectively.

Step 3: Set $k = 1$, and initialize the parameters w and b of every particle randomly in the searching space, which are the connection weight and bias on each node, respectively.

Step 4: Use the parameters to calculate the fitness of each particle. Here, the fitness is the forecasting error between the output values and the target ones.

Step 4.1: Calculate the outputs of all hidden layer nodes for each training sample.

$$y_j = f\left[\sum_{i=1}^{n} x_i w_{ji} + b_j\right], j = 1, 2, \cdots, m \tag{7}$$

where w_{ji} represents the connection weight from the input node i to the hidden node j, b_j stands for bias of neuron j, y_j is the output value of the hidden layer node j.

Step 4.2: Calculate the output data of the BP neural network for each training sample.

$$o_1 = f\left[\sum_{j=1}^{m} y_j w_{1j} + b_1\right] \tag{8}$$

where w_{1j} represent the connection weight from hidden node j to the output node 1, b_1 stands for the bias of the neuron; o_1 stands for the output data of network.

Step 4.3: Step 4.1 and 4.2 are repeated until all the training set samples are calculated. Then the forecasting error F is regarded as the fitness of the particle $x_i(k)$.

$$F[x_i(k)] = \frac{1}{S}\sum_{s=1}^{S}(o_s - t_s)^2 \tag{9}$$

where o_s and t_s is the sth normalized output value and target value in the training data, respectively. S is the number of training set samples.

Step 5: Update the best known position of each particle and the best known position of the whole population according to the following two formulas:

$$p_i(k) = \begin{cases} x_i(k) & if(k = 1) \\ \arg\min\{F[p_i(k-1)], F[x_i(k)]\} & otherwise \end{cases} \tag{10}$$

$$gbest(k) = \begin{cases} \arg\min\left\{\min_{1\leq i\leq M}\{F[p_i(k)]\}, F[gbest(k-1)]\right\} & if(k > 1) \\ \arg\min\left\{\min_{1\leq i\leq M}\{F[p_i(k)]\}\right\} & otherwise \end{cases} \tag{11}$$

Step 6: Calculate the mean best position and the contraction-expansion coefficient with Equations (3) and (4), respectively.

Step 7: Update current position of each particle by the Equation (1).

Step 8: Set $k = k+1$, if the maximum iterations $\bar{k}$ reached, the flow will go to Step 9, else go back to Step 4.

Step 9: Output the optimal parameter of the BP neural network, which will be used for new data forecasting process.

Step 10: Before starting the forecasting process, the input vector are needed to be normalized by Equation (6), then transmit the processed data into the calibrated artificial neural network model to obtain predictive value. The predictive data need to be renormalized to the original range of output data by Equation (12).

$$\hat{Y} = \{\hat{Y}_i\} = \frac{(Y'_i - b) \times (Y_i^{max} - Y_i^{min})}{a} + Y_i^{min} \tag{12}$$

where Y'_i and $\hat{Y}_i$ are normalized forecasting value and real forecasting value of the output vector, respectively; Y_i^{min} and Y_i^{max} are minimum and maximum value of the output arrays, respectively.

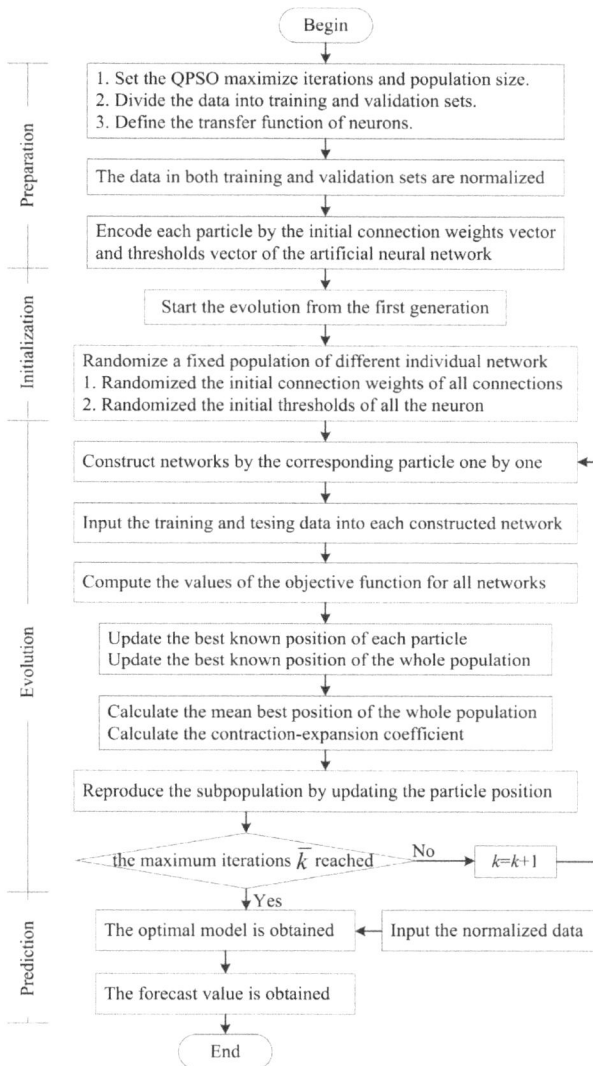

Figure 2. Flow chart of the proposed method.

5. Simulations

5.1. Study Area and Data Used

The study site is Hongjiadu reservoir in Wu River of Guizhou Province in southwest China. The Wu River is the biggest branch at southern bank of Yangtze River. Hongjiadu reservoir is the leading one with multi-year regulation ability of eleven cascade hydropower stations on Wu River. Rainfall produces most of the runoff. Its drainage area is 9900 km^2 and the mean annual runoff is 155 m$^3 \cdot$s^{-1} at the dam site. The total reservoir storage is 4.95 billion cubic meters and the regulated storage is 3.36 billion cubic meters. Locations of Wu River and Hongjiadu reservoir are shown in Figure 3.

Water **2015**, 7, 4232–4246

Figure 3. Location of study area.

All the daily runoff data collected from Hongjiadu reservoir operators is from 1 January 2006 to 31 December 2013. The data set between 1 January 2006 and 31 December 2012 is used for parameters calibration, while that from 1 January 2013 to 31 December 2013 is for testing. Moreover, before applying the proposed method for daily runoff predication, the data should be normalized to avoid numerical difficulties during calculation and guarantee consistency of greater numeric ranges as well as smaller ones. In the modeling process, input and output data sets are linearly scaled to [0.2, 0.8] as shown in Equation (6).

5.2. Performance Assessment Measures

Many performance measure methods have been developed to assess the forecast accuracy. However, so far, there is no unified standard since each measure can reflect one or more characteristics of the forecasting method. Hence, four commonly used metrics are selected to evaluate the forecast results: coefficient of correlation (*R*), Nash-Sutcliffe efficiency coefficient (*NSE*), root mean squared error (*RMSE*) and mean absolute percentage error (*MAPE*). *R* evaluates the linear relation between two data sequences, while *NSE* shows the capability of the model in predicting values away from the mean. The larger the value of *R* and *NSE*, the better the performances of the forecasting model. *RMSE* and *MAPE* measure the residual error and the mean absolute percentage error between the observed and forecasted data, respectively. The smaller the value of *RMSE* and *MAPE*, the better the performances of the forecasting model.

$$R = \sum_{i=1}^{n}\left[(Y_i - \overline{Y})(\hat{Y}_i - \widetilde{Y})\right] \Big/ \sqrt{\sum_{i=1}^{n}(Y_i - \overline{Y})^2(\hat{Y}_i - \widetilde{Y})^2} \tag{13}$$

$$NSE = 1 - \sum_{i=1}^{n}(Y_i - \hat{Y}_i)^2 \Big/ \sum_{i=1}^{n}(Y_i - \overline{Y})^2 \tag{14}$$

$$RMSE = \sqrt{\frac{1}{n}\sum_{i=1}^{n}(Y_i - \hat{Y}_i)^2} \tag{15}$$

$$MAPE = \frac{1}{n}\sum_{i=1}^{n}\left|\frac{Y_i - \hat{Y}_i}{Y_i}\right| \times 100 \tag{16}$$

where Y_i and $\hat{Y}_i$ are the observed value and predictive value of ith data, respectively. $\overline{Y}$ and $\widetilde{Y}$ represent the mean value of the observed value and predictive value, respectively. n is the total number of data set used for performance evaluation and comparison.

5.3. ANN Model Development

For ANN, proper selection of input variables will be helpful to find the best-fitted model. Based on the analysis of cross correlation coefficient and autocorrelation coefficient, four input combinations with different antecedent rainfalls and runoffs were developed for a comparative purpose. Table 1 summarizes these ANN models used for this study, where *Runoff*(*t*), *Rainfall*(*t*) are the runoff and rainfall value at the *t*-th period, respectively. To ensure the generalization capability of ANN, we use the trial and error method to determine the optimal network architecture. According to Chau *et al.* in 2005, the training process needs to be stopped when the error of the testing set starts to increase and that of the training set is still decreasing. Figure 4 shows the performance for the testing set against various numbers of neurons for model 1. The optimal ANN architecture adopted for model 1 is 2-4-1. The other three models have the same procedures as that for model 1. Table 2 shows the architecture and indices of various ANN forecasting models for Hongjiadu reservoir. We can find that antecedent two-day rainfalls and antecedent two-day runoff should be chosen as predictors, and ANN with the architecture of 4-7-1 performs best at this situation.

Table 1. Inputs and relation for various artificial neural network (ANN) forecasting models.

Model	Inputs	Relation between Output Variable and Input Variables
1	*Runoff*(*t*-1),*Rainfall*(*t*-1)	*Runoff*(*t*)=**H**[*Runoff*(*t*-1),*Rainfall*(*t*-1)]
2	*Runoff*(*t*-1),*Rainfall*(*t*-1),*Rainfall*(*t*-2)	*Runoff*(*t*)=**H**[*Runoff*(*t*-1),*Rainfall*(*t*-1),*Rainfall*(*t*-2)]
3	*Runoff*(*t*-1),*Runoff*(*t*-2),*Rainfall*(*t*-1)	*Runoff*(*t*)=**H**[*Runoff*(*t*-1),*Runoff*(*t*-2),*Rainfall*(*t*-1)]
4	*Runoff*(*t*-1),*Runoff*(*t*-2),*Rainfall*(*t*-1),*Rainfall*(*t*-2)	*Runoff*(*t*)=**H**[*Runoff*(*t*-1),*Runoff*(*t*-2),*Rainfall*(*t*-1),*Rainfall*(*t*-2)]

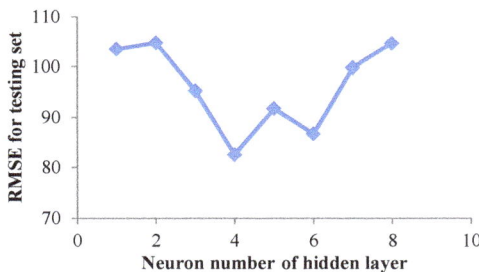

Figure 4. Performance of model 1 against different numbers of nodes in hidden layer.

Table 2. Architectures and indices of various ANN forecasting models for Hongjiadu reservoir.

Model	Model Architecture	Training				Testing			
		R	NSE	$RMSE$ $(m^3 \cdot s^{-1})$	$MAPE$ (%)	R	NSE	$RMSE$ $(m^3 \cdot s^{-1})$	$MAPE$ (%)
1	2-4-1	0.892	0.740	82.490	38.150	0.883	0.747	63.562	35.912
2	3-6-1	0.891	0.737	82.989	37.903	0.903	0.757	62.321	38.417
3	3-5-1	0.893	0.742	82.090	36.493	0.903	0.761	61.792	37.190
4	4-7-1	0.907	0.783	75.286	34.866	0.904	0.773	60.252	35.680

5.4. Comparison of Different Methods

In order to verify the effectiveness of the proposed method, the same training and verification samples are used for these two models, ANN and ANN-QPSO, and the above four quantitative indexes are employed to evaluate their performances. According to the above-mentioned analysis, the neural network architectures of both ANN and ANN-QPSO are 4-7-1 for Hongjiadu reservoir. Moreover, for ANN-QPSO, the number of population is set to be 300 whilst the maximize iterations is 500. The two algorithms are implemented by adopting JAVA language.

Table 3 presents the statistics results using various models developed for Hongjiadu study area. It can be seen that these two methods have different performances during both training and testing periods. Compared to the basic ANN, the proposed method is able to produce better forecast results for the daily runoff forecasting in Hongjiadu reservoir. In the training phase, the ANN-QPSO model improved the ANN forecasting ability with about 28.18% and 48.08% reduction in *RMSE* and *MAPE* values, respectively. The improvements of the forecasting results regarding the *R* and *NSE* were approximately 3.97% and 13.41%, respectively. In the testing phase, when compared with that of ANN, the statistical values of *R* and *NSE* of the proposed method increases by 5.42% and 17.46% respectively, while the value of *RMSE* and *MAPE* decreases by 36.34% and 28.81%. Figure 5 shows the convergence characteristic for objective functions of two methods in Hongjiadu reservoir. The objective function of the proposed method uses about 4 s to converge to a small neighborhood of the final result, whilst the ANN nearly stops the searching process since 1 second. In addition, in term of total computing time from Table 3, the ANN-QPSO decreases by 66.56% when compared to that of ANN. Thus, it can be concluded that the proposed method needs less computation time and has higher forecasting accuracy degree and global search capability than conventional ANN.

Table 3. Performance indices of two methods for Hongjiadu reservoir.

Method	Time(s)	Training				Testing			
		R	*NSE*	*RMSE* $(m^3 \cdot s^{-1})$	*MAPE* (%)	*R*	*NSE*	*RMSE* $(m^3 \cdot s^{-1})$	*MAPE* (%)
ANN-QPSO	10.1	0.943	0.888	54.074	18.102	0.953	0.908	38.354	25.401
ANN	30.2	0.907	0.783	75.286	34.866	0.904	0.773	60.252	35.680

The observed peak flow and forecasted peak flow of two models for Hongjiadu reservoir are shown in Table 4. Both ANN-QPSO and ANN models forecast the maximum peak discharge as 1641.8 $m^3 \cdot s^{-1}$ and 1258.3 $m^3 \cdot s^{-1}$ instead of the observed 1696.4 $m^3 \cdot s^{-1}$, corresponding to about 3.2% and 25.8% underestimation, respectively. Furthermore, the absolute averages of the relative error of the ANN-QPSO and ANN models for forecasting the 8 peak flow are 11.6% and 30.9%, respectively. In summary, the ANN-QPSO method performs better than ANN in term of peak flow estimation.

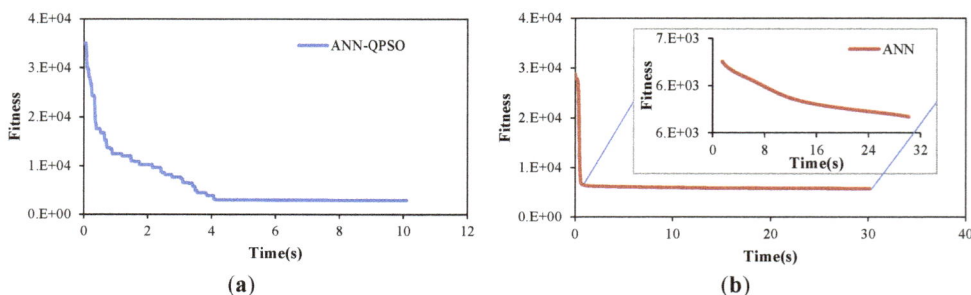

Figure 5. Convergence characteristic of the objective function of two methods for Hongjiadu reservoir (a) ANN-QPSO; (b) ANN.

The above analysis indicates that, for daily runoff forecasting, the proposed model can obtain better results than basic ANN model with significant improvements in terms of four different statistical indicators. Figures 6 and 7 demonstrate the scatter plots of observed data versus forecasted data using ANN and ANN-QPSO models during the training and testing period. The performances of both prediction models in the training period and testing period are respectively shown in Figures 8 and 9. From Figures 6–9, it can be clearly seen that the forecasting results of ANN model are inferior to that by the proposed ANN-QPSO model. For example, the model proposed in this paper can obtain the approximate maximum flows which is about 1700 $m^3 \cdot s^{-1}$ during the training period while an obvious deviation exists between the original observed data and the forecasted data in ANN model. Hence, the ANN-QPSO model can mimic daily runoff better than that by ANN model.

Table 4. Observed peak flow and forecasted peak flow of two models for Hongjiadu reservoir.

Period	Date	Observed Peak ($m^3 \cdot s^{-1}$)	Forecasted Peak ($m^3 \cdot s^{-1}$)		Relative Error (%)	
			ANNP-QPSO	QPSO	ANNP-QPSO	QPSO
Training	2006-06-30	854.3	792.7	747.6	−7.2	−12.5
Training	2007-07-30	1435.8	1234.2	1108.2	−14.0	−22.8
Training	2008-06-22	1663.8	1514.5	861.5	−9.0	−48.2
Training	2009-08-04	628.5	456.4	407.4	−27.4	−35.2
Training	2010-07-11	1076.0	1053.8	806.7	−2.1	−25.0
Training	2011-06-23	561.9	471.6	426.6	−16.1	−24.1
Training	2012-07-26	1696.4	1641.8	1258.3	−3.2	−25.8
Testing	2013-06-09	1343.0	1151.9	622.5	−14.2	−53.6
		Average (absolute)			11.6	30.9

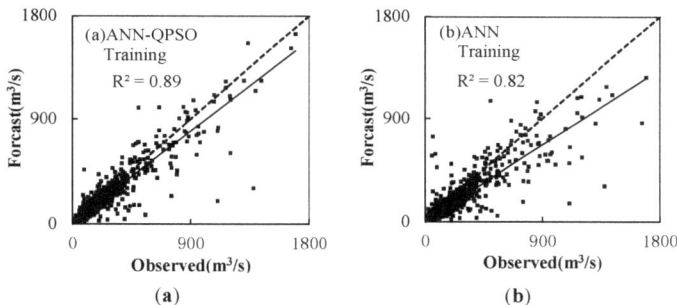

Figure 6. Scatter plots of observed data *vs.* forecasted data during the training period. (a) ANN-QPSO; (b) ANN.

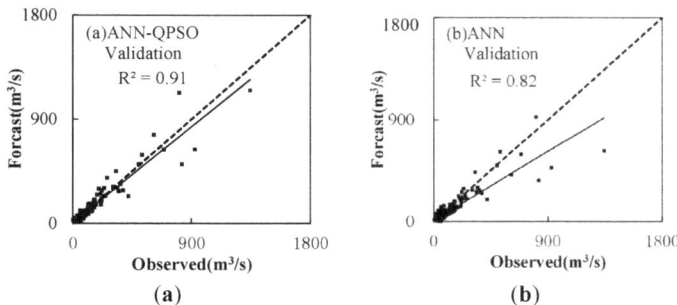

Figure 7. Scatter plots of observed data *vs.* forecasted data during the testing period. (a) ANN-QPSO; (b) ANN.

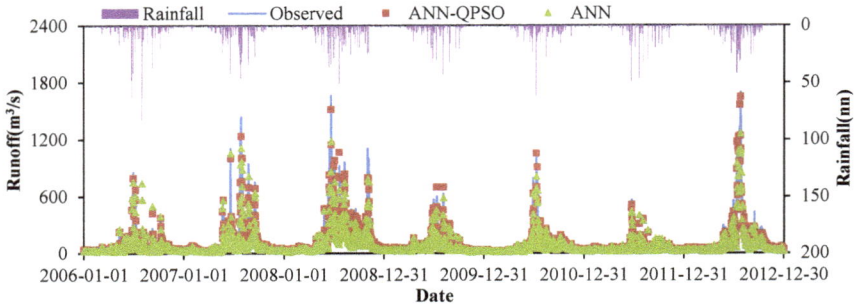

Figure 8. ANN, ANN-QPSO forecasted data and observed runoff data during the training period.

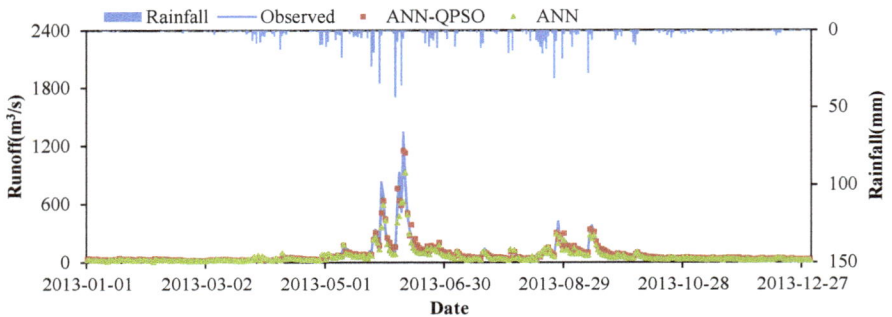

Figure 9. ANN, ANN-quantum-behaved particle swarm optimization (QPSO) forecasted data and observed runoff data during testing period.

6. Conclusions

Globally, hydropower energy has become one of the promising growing clean and renewable energy sources. It is of great significance to accurately predict daily reservoir runoff for integration of hydropower energy in power system. In this research, a novel method called ANN-QSPO, which is based on artificial neural network (ANN) and quantum-behaved particle swarm optimization (QPSO), was developed for daily reservoir runoff forecasting to help reservoirs plan and manage in a more sustainable manner. In the proposed ANN-QSPO method, QPSO was employed to select the ANN optimal parameters and the ANN was used for the prediction after the training process. The proposed approach was compared with ANN model for daily runoff forecasting of Hongjiadu reservoir in southeast China. From the experiment, the results show that the proposed method achieves much better forecast accuracy than basic ANN model. Compared with the statistical values of R and NSE of ANN, the improvements of the proposed method were approximately 3.97% and 13.41% in the training phase, while respectively increases by 5.42% and 17.46% in the testing phase. In term of total computing time, the ANN-QPSO decreases by 66.56% when compared to that of ANN. Thus, QPSO algorithm can act as an alternative training algorithm for the ANN parameters selection.

Acknowledgments: This study is supported by the Major International Joint Research Project from the National Nature Science Foundation of China (51210014) and the National Basic Research Program of China (973 Program) (No. 2013CB035906).

Author Contributions: All authors contributed extensively to the work presented in this paper. Chun-tian Cheng contributed to the subject of the research and literature review. Wen-jing Niu and Zhong-kai Feng contributed to modeling, data statistical analysis and finalized the manuscripts. Jian-jian Shen contributed to the manuscripts review and commented. Kwok-wing Chau contributed to the manuscripts revision and supervision.

Water **2015**, 7, 4232–4246

Conflicts of Interest: The authors declare no conflict of interest.

References

1. Zhang, J.; Cheng, C.T.; Liao, S.L.; Wu, X.Y.; Shen, J.J. Daily reservoir inflow forecasting combining QPF into ANNs model. *Hydro. Earth Syst. Sci.* **2009**, *6*, 121–150. [CrossRef]
2. Wang, W.C.; Chau, K.W.; Xu, D.M.; Chen, X.Y. Improving forecasting accuracy of annual runoff time series using ARIMA based on EEMD decomposition. *Water Resour. Manag.* **2015**, *29*, 1–21. [CrossRef]
3. Duan, Q.Y.; Sorooshian, S.; Gupta, V. Effective and efficient global optimization for conceptual rainfall-runoff models. *Water Resour. Res.* **1992**, *28*, 1015–1031. [CrossRef]
4. Valipour, M.; Banihabib, M.E.; Behbahani, S.M.R. Comparison of the ARMA, ARIMA, and the autoregressive artificial neural network models in forecasting the monthly inflow of Dez dam reservoir. *J. Hydrol.* **2013**, *476*, 433–441. [CrossRef]
5. Kneis, D.; Bürger, G.; Bronstert, A. Evaluation of medium-range runoff forecasts for a 500 km^2 watershed. *J. Hydrol.* **2012**, *414*, 341–353. [CrossRef]
6. Zhao, R.J. The Xinanjiang model applied in China. *J. Hydrol.* **1992**, *135*, 371–381.
7. Cheng, C.T.; Ou, C.P.; Chau, K.W. Combining a fuzzy optimal model with a genetic algorithm to solve multi-objective rainfall-runoff model calibration. *J. Hydrol.* **2002**, *268*, 72–86. [CrossRef]
8. Wang, W.C.; Chau, K.W.; Cheng, C.T.; Qiu, L. A comparison of performance of several artificial intelligence methods for forecasting monthly discharge time series. *J. Hydrol.* **2009**, *374*, 294–306. [CrossRef]
9. Lin, G.F.; Chen, G.R.; Huang, P.Y. Effective typhoon characteristics and their effects on hourly reservoir inflow forecasting. *Adv. Water Resour.* **2010**, *33*, 887–898. [CrossRef]
10. Hsu, K.; Gupta, H.V.; Sorroshian, S. Artificial neural network modeling of the rainfall-runoff process. *Water Resour. Res.* **1995**, *31*, 2517–2530. [CrossRef]
11. Machado, F.; Mine, M.; Kaviski, E.; Fill, H. Monthly rainfall-runoff modelling using artificial neural networks. *Hydrol. Sci. J.* **2011**, *56*, 349–361. [CrossRef]
12. Duan, Q.Y.; Sorooshian, S.; Gupta, V.K. Optimal use of the SCE-UA global optimization method for calibrating watershed models. *J. Hydrol.* **1994**, *158*, 265–284. [CrossRef]
13. Duan, Q.Y.; Gupta, V.K.; Sorooshian, S. Shuffled complex evolution approach for effective and efficient global minimization. *J. Optim. Theory Appl.* **1993**, *76*, 501–521. [CrossRef]
14. Lin, J.Y.; Cheng, C.T.; Chau, K.W. Using support vector machines for long-term discharge prediction. *Hydrol. Sci. J.* **2006**, *51*, 599–612. [CrossRef]
15. Lima, A.R.; Cannon, A.J.; Hsieh, W.W. Nonlinear regression in environmental sciences by support vector machines combined with evolutionary strategy. *Comput. Geosci.* **2013**, *50*, 136–144. [CrossRef]
16. Guo, W.J.; Wang, C.H.; Zeng, X.M.; Ma, T.F.; Yang, H. Subgrid parameterization of the soil moisture storage capacity for a distributed rainfall-runoff model. *Water* **2015**, *7*, 2691–2706. [CrossRef]
17. Kamruzzaman, M.; Shahriar, M.S.; Beecham, S. Assessment of short term rainfall and stream flows in South Australia. *Water* **2014**, *6*, 3528–3544. [CrossRef]
18. Chau, K.W.; Wu, C.L.; Li, Y.S. Comparison of several flood forecasting models in Yangtz River. *J. Hydrol. Eng.* **2005**, *10*, 485–491. [CrossRef]
19. Piotrowski, A.P.; Napiorkowski, J.J. Optimizing neural networks for river flow forecasting evolutionary computation methods *versus* the Levenberg-Marquardt approach. *J. Hydrol.* **2011**, *407*, 12–27. [CrossRef]
20. Chau, K.W. Particle swarm optimization training algorithm for ANNs in stage prediction of Shing Mun River. *J. Hydrol.* **2006**, *329*, 363–367. [CrossRef]
21. Asadnia, M.; Chua, L.H.C.; Qin, X.S.; Talei, A. Improved particle swarm optimization based artificial neural network for rainfall-runoff modeling. *J. Hydrol. Eng.* **2014**, *19*, 1320–1329. [CrossRef]
22. Liu, W.C.; Chung, C.E. Enhancing the predicting accuracy of the water stage using a physical-based model and an artificial neural network-genetic algorithm in a river system. *Water* **2014**, *6*, 1642–1661. [CrossRef]
23. Wu, C.L.; Chau, K.W. Rainfall-runoff modeling using artificial neural network coupled with singular spectrum analysis. *J. Hydrol.* **2011**, *399*, 394–409. [CrossRef]
24. Jeong, D.I.; Kim, Y.O. Combining single-value streamflow forecasts—A review and guidelines for selecting techniques. *J. Hydrol.* **2009**, *377*, 284–299. [CrossRef]

25. Sun, J.; Feng, B.; Xu, W.B. Particle swarm optimization with particles having quantum behavior. In Congress on Evolutionary Computation, 2004 (CEC2004), Proceedings of the 2004 Congress on Evolutionary Computation, Portland, OR, USA, 19–23 June 2004; pp. 325–331.

26. Fang, W.; Sun, J.; Ding, Y.; Wu, X.; Xu, W. A review of quantum-behaved particle swarm optimization. *IETE Tech. Rev.* **2010**, *27*, 336–348. [CrossRef]

27. Xi, M.; Sun, J.; Xu, W. An improved quantum-behaved particle swarm optimization algorithm with weighted mean best position. *Appl. Math. Comput.* **2008**, *205*, 751–759. [CrossRef]

28. Feng, Z.K.; Liao, S.L.; Niu, W.J.; Shen, J.J.; Cheng, C.T.; Li, Z.H. Improved quantum-behaved particle swarm optimization and its application in optimal operation of hydropower stations. *Adv. Water Sci.* **2015**, *26*, 413–422. (in Chinese).

29. Sun, C.; Lu, S. Short-term combined economic emission hydrothermal scheduling using improved quantum-behaved particle swarm optimization. *Expert Syst. Appl.* **2010**, *37*, 4232–4241. [CrossRef]

30. Eberhart, R.; Kennedy, J. A new optimizer using particle swarm theory. In Proceedings of the 6th International Symposium on Micro Machine and Human Science, New York, NY, USA, 4–6 October 1995; pp. 39–43.

31. Gaing, Z.L. Particle swarm optimization to solving the economic dispatch considering the generator constraints. *IEEE Trans. Pow. Syst.* **2003**, *18*, 1187–1195. [CrossRef]

32. Clerc, M.; Kennedy, J. The particle swarm-explosion, stability, and convergence in a multidimensional complex space. *IEEE Trans. Evol. Comput.* **2002**, *6*, 58–73. [CrossRef]

33. Ren, C.; An, N.; Wang, J.; Li, L.; Hu, B.; Shang, D. Optimal parameters selection for BP neural network based on particle swarm optimization: A case study of wind speed forecasting. *Knowl. Based Syst.* **2014**, *56*, 226–239. [CrossRef]

water

MDPI

Article

Daily Runoff Forecasting Model Based on ANN and Data Preprocessing Techniques

Yun Wang [1,2], **Shenglian Guo** [1,*], **Lihua Xiong** [1], **Pan Liu** [1] and **Dedi Liu** [1]

[1]   State Key Laboratory of Water Resources and Hydropower Engineering Science, Wuhan University,
     Wuhan 430072, China; wyun.1987@gmail.com (Y.W.); Xionglh@whu.edu.cn (L.X.); liupan@whu.edu.cn (P.L.);
     Dediliu@whu.edu.cn (D.L.)
[2]   China Yangtze Power Co., Ltd., Yichang, Hubei 443002, China
*   Correspondence: slguo@whu.edu.cn; Tel./Fax: +86-27-68773568

Academic Editor: Kwok-wing Chau
Received: 10 June 2015; Accepted: 20 July 2015; Published: 28 July 2015

Abstract: There are many models that have been used to simulate the rainfall-runoff relationship. The artificial neural network (ANN) model was selected to investigate an approach of improving daily runoff forecasting accuracy in terms of data preprocessing. Singular spectrum analysis (SSA) as one data preprocessing technique was adopted to deal with the model inputs and the SSA-ANN model was developed. The proposed model was compared with the original ANN model without data preprocessing and a nonlinear perturbation model (NLPM) based on ANN, *i.e.*, the NLPM-ANN model. Eight watersheds were selected for calibrating and testing these models. Comparative study shows that the learning and training ability of ANN models can be improved by SSA and NLPM techniques significantly, and the performance of the SSA-ANN model is much better than the NLPM-ANN model, with high foresting accuracy. The SSA-ANN1 model, which only considers rainfall as model input, was compared with the SSA-ANN2 model, which considers both rainfall and previous runoff as model inputs. It is shown that the Nash-Sutcliffe criterion of the SSA-ANN2 model is much higher than that of the SSA-ANN1 model, which means that the proper selection of previous runoff data as rainfall-runoff model inputs can significantly improve model performance since they usually are highly auto-correlated.

Keywords: daily runoff forecasting; data preprocessing; linear perturbation model; singular spectrum analysis; artificial neural network

1. Introduction

Real-time hydrological forecasting plays an important role in flood control and reservoir operation, and higher forecasting precision can increase the utilization efficiency of water resources. Traditionally, hydrological simulation modeling systems are classified into three main groups, namely empirical black box, lumped conceptual, and distributed physically-based models [1]. The last two groups focus on understanding hydrological processes and involve various physical phenomena. Owing to the complexity of the rainfall-runoff process, these physical process simulations and model calibrations require large amounts of hydrological data. On the contrary, black-box modeling does not require a deep knowledge of the underlying physics and also can solve the problem of the scarcity of the data. Several black-box models have been developed and used in hydrological forecasting, such as fuzzy theory [2,3], artificial neural network [4,5], chaos [6], genetic programming [7], support vector machine [8], and so on.

Artificial neural network, inspired by research into the biological neural networks, has a flexible structure, and self-learning and self-adaptive features. In 2000, the American Society of Civil Engineering (ASCE) Task Committee explicitly reviewed the application of artificial neural networks in hydrology [9,10]. Hsu *et al.* [5] mentioned that the artificial neural network (ANN) model can identify the complex nonlinear relationship between runoff and rainfall time series, even though the model structure and parameters cannot represent the physical process of the catchments. Maier and Dandy [11] reviewed using ANN models to deal with water resource variables prediction, outlined the steps that should be followed in the development of ANN models, and concluded that the ANN model has advantages in hydrological forecasting. Currently, ANN is still a research hot point and has been successfully applied in hydrological forecasting [12–22].

Due to the highly seasonal variation, and nonlinear and noisy characteristics of hydrological time series, preprocessing input data becomes an effective way to improve model precision [23–28]. Considering the highly seasonal variation of rainfall and runoff time series, Nash and Brasi [23] developed the linear perturbation model (LPM) based on the assumption that subtraction of the seasonal means from the original series would remove much of the non-linearity of the rainfall-runoff process. The relationship between the departures is simulated by the linear response function, but only part of the nonlinearity of the rainfall-runoff process can be removed by subtracting the seasonal means. Pang *et al.* [16] used the ANN model to replace the linear response function and proposed a nonlinear perturbation model (NLPM) based on ANN (NLPM-ANN). The advantage of the NLPM-ANN model is that it is capable of obtaining satisfactory results even if the explicit form of the relationship between the involved variables is unknown.

Considering that the hydrological time series can be viewed as a combination of quasi-periodic signals contaminated by noises to some extent [29], the singular spectrum analysis (SSA) proposed by Vautard *et al.* [30] can decompose the time series into a sum of a small number of interpretable components, such as a slowly varying trend, oscillatory components, and a "structureless" noise [31]. By performing a spectrum analysis on the input data, eliminating the noises, and inverting the remaining components to yield a "filtered" time series, the model performance could be improved. Sivapragasam *et al.* [25] proposed a prediction technique based on SSA coupled with support vector machines to predict runoff and rainfall, and showed that the proposed technique yields a significantly higher prediction accuracy than that of the nonlinear prediction method. Wu and Chau [29] also found that SSA can considerably improve the performance of the rainfall-runoff model and it is promising in hydrological forecasting.

In this paper, an approach of improving daily runoff forecasting accuracy in terms of data preprocessing and the selection of predictive factors is discussed. The artificial neural network (ANN) is used for rainfall-runoff simulation. The SSA and LPM techniques are adopted to deal with data preprocessing. Then SSA-ANN models are developed and compared with the NLPM-ANN model based on the daily data from the eight watersheds used by Pang *et al.* [16]. A comparative study is also conducted involving two different types of model inputs, namely considering rainfall as an input and considering both rainfall and runoff as inputs.

2. Data-Driven Models

2.1. NLPM-ANN Model

The structure of the NLPM-ANN model as shown in Figure 1 was proposed by Pang *et al.* [16] to consider the influence of seasonal changes and the nonlinearity of the rainfall-runoff process. The model input is divided into two parts. The first is the series of the seasonal expectations of the input (p_d) that is transformed to the series of the seasonal expectations of the output (q_d) through an undefined relation. The second part, which is the input perturbations (P_i-p_d), is transformed into the output perturbations (Q_i-q_d) through ANN. The total output is the sum of the seasonal expectations of the output and the output perturbations.

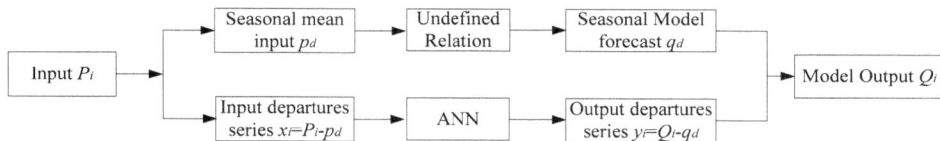

Figure 1. Schematic diagram of the NLPM-ANN model.

2.2. Singular Spectrum Analysis

Singular spectrum analysis (SSA) is a suitable analysis method for researching the period oscillatory behavior. It is also a statistical technique starting from a dynamic reconstruction of the time series and is associated with empirical orthogonal function (EOF). Generally, SSA can be considered as a special application of EOF decomposition. The main purpose of SSA is converting a one-dimensional time series into a multi-dimensional matrix with a given window length, and then the orthogonal decomposition of this matrix is obtained. If the obvious pairs of eigenvalues are produced and the corresponding EOF is almost periodic or orthogonal, this corresponding EOF can be considered the oscillatory behavior of the time series.

Brief operating procedures of SSA are summarized as follows. Assume that the series is a nonzero series $F = \{f_0, f_1, \ldots, f_{N-1}\}$ ($f_i \neq 0$), the length of series is N (>2). Given a window length L, the one-dimensional time series can be transferred into a sequence of L-dimensional vectors $\mathbf{X}_i = \{f_{i-1}, \ldots, f_{i+L-2}\}^T$, $(I = 1, \ldots, K = N-L+1)$. The K vectors $\mathbf{X}_i$ will form the columns of the $(L \times K)$ trajectory matrix:

$$\mathbf{X} = \begin{bmatrix} f_0 & f_1 & f_2 & \cdots & f_{K-1} \\ f_1 & f_2 & f_3 & \cdots & f_K \\ f_2 & f_3 & f_4 & \cdots & f_{K+1} \\ \vdots & \vdots & \vdots & \ddots & \vdots \\ f_{L-1} & f_L & f_{L+1} & \cdots & f_{N-1} \end{bmatrix} \tag{1}$$

Then the singular value decomposition (SVD) of the trajectory matrix $\mathbf{X}$ is conducted. Let $\mathbf{S} = \mathbf{X}\mathbf{X}^T$. The eigenvalues and eigenvectors of $\mathbf{S}$ can be calculated, and these eigenvalues range in the decreasing order of magnitude. According to the conventional computation of EOF, an expansion of the matrix $\mathbf{X}$ is represented as:

$$x_{i+j} = \sum_{k=1}^{L} a_i^k \mathbf{E}_j^k \tag{2}$$

where $i = 1, 2, \ldots, N - L + 1, j = 1, 2, \ldots, L, k = 1, 2, \ldots, L$, a_i^k is the time principal components (T-PC), $\mathbf{E}_j^k$ is the corresponding eigenvector denoted by T-EOF. The key step of SSA is to reconstruct a new one-dimensional series of length N using each component of the T-PC and T-EOF. The formula is expressed as follows:

$$x_i^k = \begin{cases} \frac{1}{i} \sum_{j=1}^{L} a_{ij}^k \mathbf{E}_j^k & 1 \leq i \leq L\text{-}1 \\ \frac{1}{L} \sum_{j=1}^{L} a_{ij}^k \mathbf{E}_j^k & L \leq i \leq N - L + 1 \\ \frac{1}{N-i+1} \sum_{j=i-N+L}^{L} a_{ij}^k \mathbf{E}_{ij}^k & N - L + 2 \leq i \leq N \end{cases} \tag{3}$$

Equation (3) produces an N-length time series F_k, thus the initial series F is decomposed into the sum of L series:

$$F = \sum_{k=1}^{L} F_k \tag{4}$$

If the number of contributing components is p, then the filtered series is the sum of p series:

$$F = \sum_{k=1}^{p} F_k \tag{5}$$

The sum of the remaining series is noise. As mentioned above, these reconstructed components can be associated with the trend, oscillations, or noise of the original time series with proper choices of L and p.

2.3. Artificial Neural Network

ANN can be categorized as single-layer, bilayer, and multilayer according to the number of layers, and as feed-forward, recurrent, and self-organizing according to the direction of information flow and processing [9]. Among these different architectures, the multilayer feed-forward networks, which consist of an input layer, several hidden layers, and an output layer, have been widely used. Each layer has different nodes, and the number of hidden layers and the hidden nodes of each hidden layer are usually determined by trial-and-error method.

Assuming the three-layer ANN denoted by $m \times h \times 1$, where m stands for the number of input nodes, namely the number of predictive factors, and h is the number of nodes in the hidden layer, the ANN prediction model can be formulated as:

$$\widehat{Q_{t+T}} = f(\mathbf{X}_t, w, \theta, m, h) = \theta_0 + \sum_{j=1}^{h} w_j^{out} \varphi \left(\sum_{i=1}^{m} w_{ji} \mathbf{X}_t + \theta_j \right) \tag{6}$$

where $\mathbf{X}_t$ is the input data; T is the length of lead time; φ denotes transfer functions; w_{ji} are the weights defining the link between the ith node of the input layer and the jth of the hidden layer; θ_j are biases associated with the jth node of the hidden layer; w_j^{out} are the weights associated with the connection between the jth node of the hidden layer and the node of the output layer; and θ_0 is the bias at the output node. The Levenberg–Marquardt algorithm is chosen to adjust the values of w and θ in this study [32].

2.4. Proposed SSA-ANN Models

The SSA-ANN models are proposed with the aim of analyzing the effect of data processing. The flowchart of SSA-ANN models is illustrated in Figure 2, where the original series is decomposed into oscillations and noise by SSA, firstly. Then the reconstructed series is selected as the ANN model input. If the input is the rainfall data series only, the SSA-ANN1 model is built to simulate the relationship between rainfall and runoff. If the input contains both the rainfall and runoff data series, the SSA-ANN2 model is built to simulate the relationship between rainfall and previous runoff with forecasting runoff.

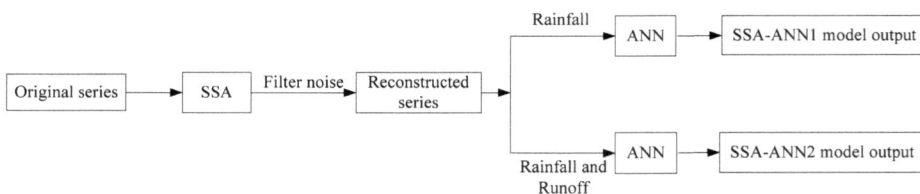

Figure 2. Schematic diagram of SSA-ANN models.

2.5. Evaluation of Model Performances

Two criteria are selected to evaluate the prediction performance based on Chinese Hydrological Forecasting (or prediction) guidelines (2008), they are:

(1)   Determination coefficient (or Nash-Sutcliffe criterion) (R^2)

$$R^2 = (1 - \frac{\sum_{t=1}^{n} (Q_t - Q_t')^2}{\sum_{t=1}^{n} (Q_t - \overline{Q_t})^2})$$ (7)

(2)   Water balance coefficient (WB)

$$WB = \frac{\sum_{t=1}^{n} Q_t'}{\sum_{t=1}^{n} Q_t}$$ (8)

where n is the number of year, Q_t and Q_t' are the observed and forecasted inflows, respectively, $\overline{Q_t}$ is the average value of observed flow; if the values of R^2 and WB are closer to one, the better the prediction results that are obtained.

3. Comparative Study

3.1. Data

To compare the proposed SSA-ANN models with the NLPM-ANN model, eight watersheds in China used by Pang *et al.* [16] were selected as case studies in this paper. The data include the daily rainfall and runoff data. Each of data series is divided into three parts, *i.e.*, training set, cross-validation set, and testing set. The training set is used to train the network and the cross-validation set is used to check the progress of the network and implement an early stopping approach in order to avoid the over-fitting of the training set. The testing set serves as model evaluation. Table 1 lists statistical information about all watersheds, including mean (μ), standard deviation (S_x), maximum (X_{max}), and minimum (X_{min}). As shown in Table 1, the training data does not cover the cross-validation or testing data totally. In order to ensure the extrapolation ability of ANN and avoid numerical difficulties during calculation, all data are scaled to the interval $[-0.9, 0.9]$ by normalization.

Table 1. List of the watershed statistical information.

Watershed and Datasets			Statistical Parameters				Data Period
			μ	S_x	X_{max}	X_{min}	
Jiahe area: 5578 km²	rainfall (mm)	whole data	2.3	5.9	71.4	0	January 1980–December 1990
		training data	2.3	6.0	68.9	0	
		cross-validation data	2.3	6.2	71.4	0	
		testing data	2.1	5.3	44.2	0	
	runoff (m³)	whole data	58.7	125.1	2620	6.5	
		training data	61.9	141.6	2620	6.5	
		cross-validation data	55.3	99.6	1220	7.9	
		testing data	50.7	76.4	1080	10.1	
Laoguanhe area: 4217 km²	rainfall (mm)	whole data	2.2	6.4	69.4	0	January 1980–December 1990
		training data	2.3	6.8	69.2	0	
		cross-validation data	2.0	5.8	56.0	0	
		testing data	2.0	5.7	69.4	0	
	runoff (m³)	whole data	27.1	73.6	1460	0.1	
		training data	33.5	84.1	1460	0.4	
		cross-validation data	16.8	50.6	586	0.1	
		testing data	14.8	46.1	793	0.2	

Table 1. Cont.

Watershed and Datasets			μ	S_x	X_{max}	X_{min}	Data Period
Baohe area: 3415 km²	rainfall (mm)	whole data	2.5	6.9	80.6	0	January 1980–December 1990
		training data	2.5	7.1	80.6	0	
		cross-validation data	2.2	6.0	51.3	0	
		testing data	2.6	6.8	80.5	0	
	runoff (m³)	whole data	46.5	129.4	4020	0	
		training data	49.7	150.7	4020	1.2	
		cross-validation data	31.4	54.8	523	3.8	
		testing data	50.3	96.8	2010	0.0	
Mumahe area: 1224 km²	rainfall (mm)	whole data	3.2	8.8	132.8	0	January 1980–December 1990
		training data	3.2	8.6	132.8	0	
		cross-validation data	3.3	9.3	98.6	0	
		testing data	2.9	9.1	94.4	0	
	runoff (m³)	whole data	39.3	80.3	1270	1.2	
		training data	41.0	80.8	1270	1.2	
		cross-validation data	40.6	82.1	796	4.6	
		testing data	32.1	76.4	990	2	
Nianyushan area: 924 km²	rainfall (mm)	whole data	3.8	11.6	269.5	0	January 1975–December 1999
		training data	3.9	12.2	269.5	0	
		cross-validation data	3.3	9.3	102.5	0	
		testing data	3.7	10.8	144.7	0	
	runoff (m³)	whole data	18.5	62.1	2095	0	
		training data	19.8	68.3	2095	0	
		cross-validation data	13.5	33.2	508	0	
		testing data	17.6	55.9	822	0	
Gaoguan area: 303 km²	rainfall (mm)	whole data	4.2	12.5	179.1	0	January 1984–December 1999
		training data	4.4	12.8	179.1	0	
		cross-validation data	3.5	11.3	143.8	0	
		testing data	4.2	12.7	116.0	0	
	runoff (m³)	whole data	5.8	15.1	246	0	
		training data	5.7	14.2	237	0	
		cross-validation data	5.1	13.5	246	0	
		testing data	7.7	20.5	214	0	
Shimen area: 271.25 km²	rainfall (mm)	whole data	3.8	11.4	141.3	0	January 1989–December 1999
		training data	3.5	10.1	114.9	0	
		cross-validation data	5.1	15.1	141.3	0	
		testing data	3.8	11.8	116.8	0	
	runoff (m³)	whole data	4.9	15.2	296	0	
		training data	3.7	9.9	150	0	
		cross-validation data	8.7	25.1	296	0	
		testing data	5.5	17.9	172	0	
Tiantang area: 220 km²	rainfall (mm)	whole data	3.7	12.1	193.4	0	January 1973–December 1984
		training data	3.6	11.6	175.0	0	
		cross-validation data	3.7	11.4	151.7	0	
		testing data	4.2	14.7	193.4	0	
	runoff (m³)	whole data	6.1	18.4	535	0	
		training data	5.6	16.5	400	0	
		cross-validation data	5.6	16.5	378	0.3	
		testing data	8.2	25.6	535	0.3	

3.2. Determination of Model Inputs

The suitable predictive factors have an important impact on model performance. If the model input is only rainfall, it can be expressed as:

$$y_i = f(x_i, x_{i-1}, \cdots, x_{i-n+1}) \tag{9}$$

where x is the rainfall series, y is the runoff series, and n is the number of antecedent rainfall components. In Pang *et al.*'s paper [16], only rainfall was selected as model input, so the SSA-ANN1 model, which only uses rainfall as model input, was developed. In order to ensure the comparability of model performance, the same n values for the SSA-ANN1 model and the NLPM-ANN model were selected. From Pang *et al.*'s results of the NLPM-ANN model [16], the values of n are 8, 6, 6, 8, 10, 8, 6, and 10 for Jiahe, Laoguanhe, Baohe, Mumahe, Nianyushan, Gaoguan, Shimen, and Tiantang, respectively.

As we know, the autocorrelation of the runoff series is strong and the impact of previous runoff on current runoff cannot be ignored, so the SSA-ANN2 model which uses rainfall and runoff as model inputs was developed in this paper. It can be expressed as:

$$y_i = f(y_{i-1}, \cdots, y_{i-m+1}, x_i, x_{i-1}, \cdots, x_{i-n+1}) \tag{10}$$

where m is the number of previous runoff data. The values of n for the SSA-ANN2 model are the same as the SSA-ANN1 model. In view of the convenience of operation and simplicity of computation, the autocorrelation function (ACF) is used to determine m. The smaller the values of correlation, the poorer the relationship is. Figure 3 plots the ACF values of the runoff series at the one-step prediction horizon. Then the number of model inputs can be taken with the values of 5, 5, 5, 3, 2, 3, 2, and 1 for Jiahe, Laoguanhe, Baohe, Mumahe, Nianyushan, Gaoguan, Shimen, and Tiantang, respectively. It can be seen that the number of previous daily runoff is obviously related with the watershed area.

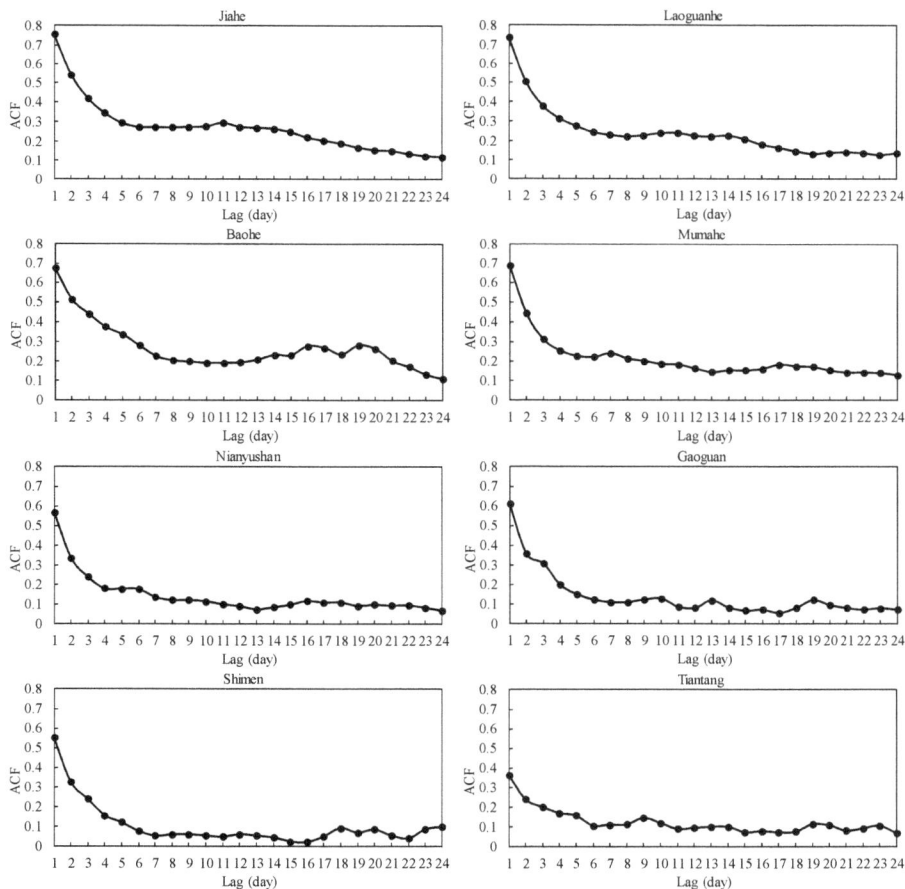

Figure 3. Autocorrelation function (ACF) values of runoff series for all watersheds.

3.3. Data Preprocessing

According to the theory of the SSA, the decomposition procedure requires identifying the parameter L. The value of an appropriate L should be able to clearly resolve different oscillations hidden in the original signal. In the current study, a small interval of [2,12] is examined to choose L [28]. L is considered as the target only if the singular spectrum can be markedly distinguished [33]. Figures 4 and 5 present the relation between singular values and singular numbers for the rainfall and runoff series, respectively, where the singular values associated with the appropriate L are highlighted by the dotted solid line. It can be seen that L is selected as 8, 8, 8, 8, 9, 10, 9, and 7 for the rainfall series, and L is set as 9, 8, 9, 10, 9, 10, 9, and 7 for the runoff series in the Jiahe, Laoguanhe, Baohe, Mumahe, Nianyushan, Gaoguan, Shimen, and Tiantang watersheds, respectively.

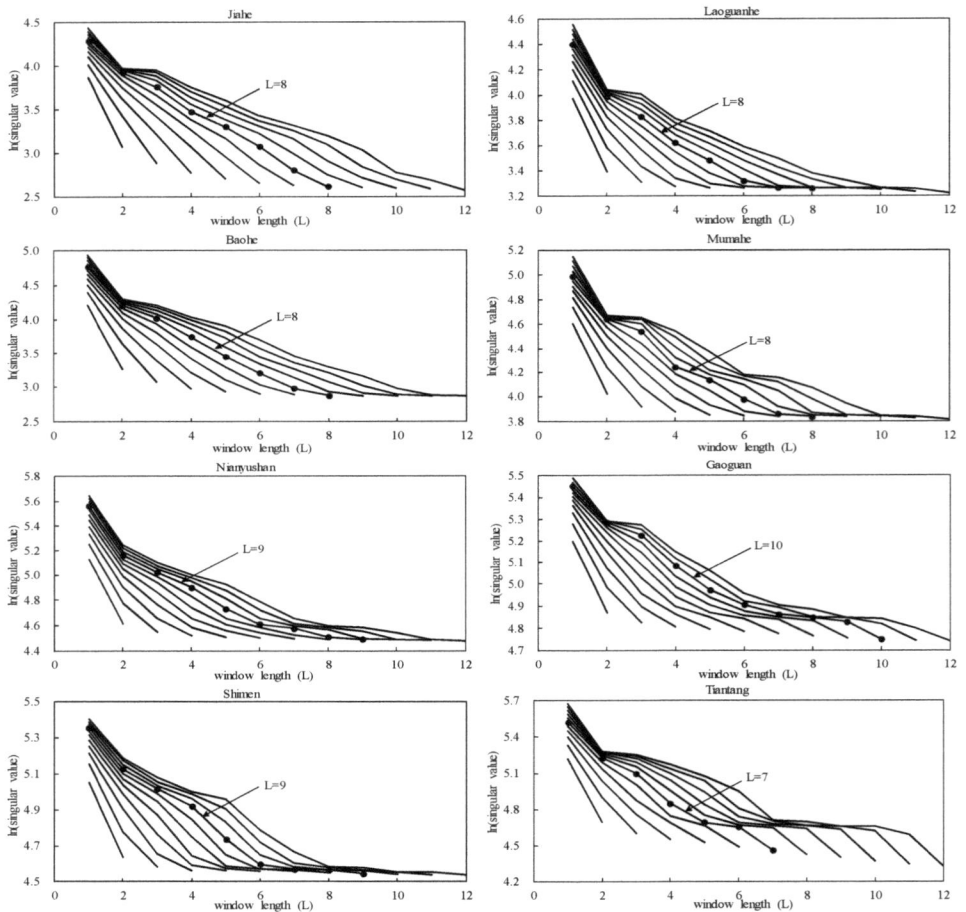

Figure 4. Singular values as a function of different window length L for rainfall series.

Once the original series is decomposed into L components, the subsequent task is to identify noise, choose the contributing components and reconstruct a new series as model inputs. This paper applied the cross-correlation function (CCF) to find the number of contributing components p ($\leq$L). From the perspective of linear correlation, the positive or negative CCF value indicates that the component makes a positive or negative contribution to the output of model. Table 2 listed all CCF values between each decomposed component and original series for all watersheds. Take Jiahe rainfall series as an example; the last four components have positive CCF values, which mean that they have positive correlation with the original series. So the number of contributing components p is equal to 4 and the sum of the last four components is reconstructed series. Meanwhile, the reconstructed series of other time series can be obtained by the same way.

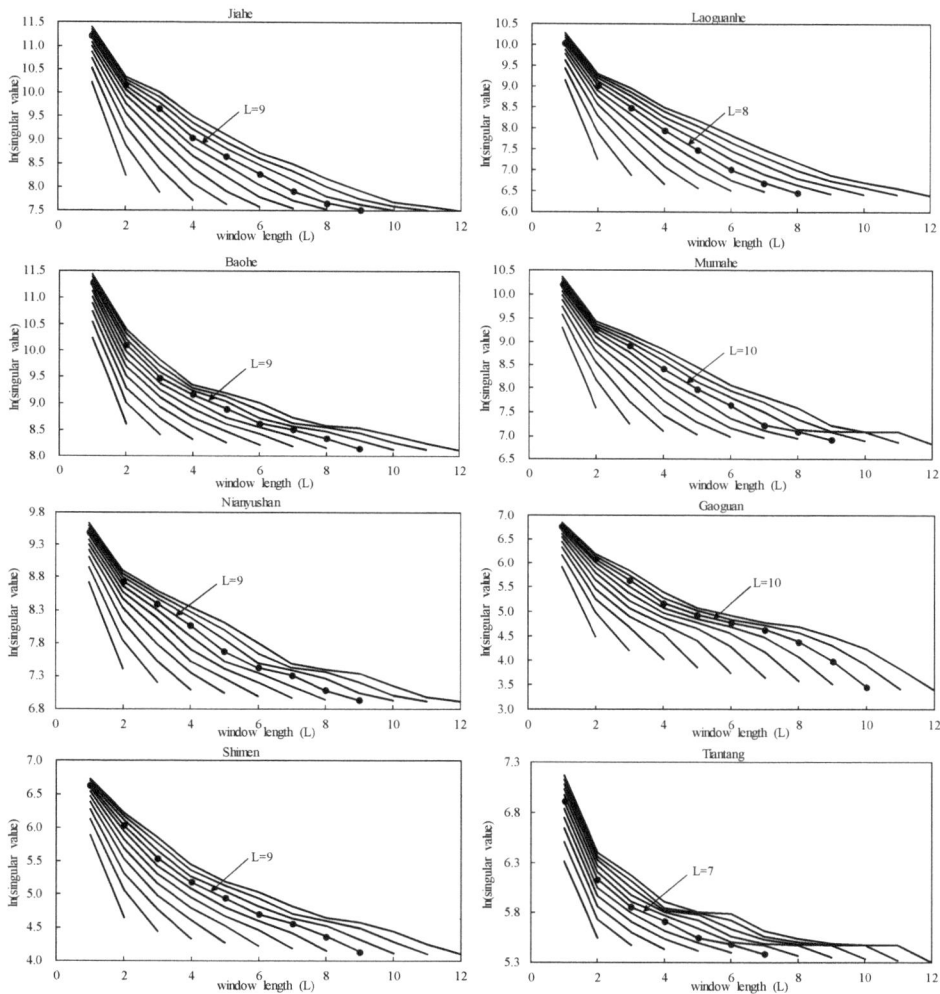

Figure 5. Singular values as a function of different window length L for runoff series.

Table 2. Cross-correlation function (CCF) values between each decomposed component and original series.

Watershed		Decomposed Components										L	p
		1	2	3	4	5	6	7	8	9	10		
Jiahe	rainfall	−0.26	−0.27	−0.19	−0.05	0.13	0.36	0.50	0.55	–	–	8	4
	runoff	−0.14	−0.15	−0.11	−0.05	0.05	0.18	0.39	0.55	0.77	–	9	5
Laoguanhe	rainfall	−0.36	−0.33	−0.24	−0.06	0.12	0.33	0.47	0.53	–	–	8	4
	runoff	−0.15	−0.15	−0.10	0.00	0.14	0.35	0.55	0.77	–	–	8	4
Baohe	rainfall	−0.26	−0.26	−0.18	−0.04	0.14	0.35	0.50	0.60	–	–	8	4
	runoff	−0.18	−0.20	−0.16	−0.08	0.04	0.16	0.33	0.54	0.76	–	9	5
Mumahe	rainfall	−0.34	−0.32	−0.22	−0.06	0.13	0.34	0.47	0.52	–	–	8	4
	runoff	−0.15	−0.18	−0.14	−0.09	−0.01	0.11	0.25	0.41	0.56	0.71	10	5
Nianyushan	rainfall	−0.33	−0.33	−0.26	−0.13	0.02	0.19	0.35	0.47	0.51	–	9	5
	runoff	−0.22	−0.22	−0.16	−0.03	0.15	0.34	0.54	0.68	–	–	8	4
Gaoguan	rainfall	−0.32	−0.37	−0.30	−0.18	−0.07	0.09	0.23	0.37	0.46	0.43	10	5
	runoff	−0.14	−0.19	−0.17	−0.12	−0.03	0.09	0.23	0.42	0.58	0.67	10	5
Shimen	rainfall	−0.34	−0.34	−0.32	−0.28	0.01	0.19	0.35	0.47	0.48	–	9	5
	runoff	−0.21	−0.23	−0.18	−0.09	0.04	0.19	0.39	0.58	0.66	–	9	5
Tiantang	rainfall	−0.32	−0.34	−0.19	0.03	0.28	0.46	0.53	–	–	–	7	4
	runoff	−0.31	−0.31	−0.16	0.03	0.25	0.46	0.62	–	–	–	7	4

4. Results Analysis

Table 3 summarized the model performances for each watershed during calibration and testing periods. The ANN model is the benchmark in which the input is the original rainfall series without data preprocessing. It is shown that the model performance is improved significantly by data preprocessing techniques. During the testing period, the mean values of R^2 and WB of eight watersheds are 70.16% and 0.879 by ANN, and are increased to 75.86% and 1.155 by NLPM-ANN, and 80.62% and 1.04 by SSA-ANN1, respectively. In the Tiantang watershed, the performance of the NLPM-ANN and SSA-ANN1 models is improved significantly, so the R^2 value increased from 59.79% to 81.96% and 79.54%, respectively, during the testing period.

Table 3. Summary of model performances during calibration and testing periods.

Watershed		ANN		NLPM-ANN		SSA-ANN1		SSA-ANN2	
		R^2 (%)	WB	R^2 (%)	WB	R^2 (%)	WB	R^2 (%)	WB
Jiahe	calibration	68.19	1.023	85.46	1.015′	80.97	0.982	96.09	1.013
	testing	61.48	0.866	61.31	1.119	74.91	0.975	92.40	1.013
Laoguanhe	calibration	69.72	1.048	85.66	1.042	82.29	0.972	96.31	1.186
	testing	60.42	1.058	68.25	1.412	78.44	1.464	93.20	1.407
Baohe	calibration	64.75	0.975	70.93	1.039	88.50	1.029	94.01	1.006
	testing	68.62	0.667	69.38	0.893	74.03	0.927	94.31	0.956
Mumahe	calibration	80.64	0.950	90.18	1.050	87.86	0.976	95.08	1.019
	testing	80.17	0.913	85.6	1.410	92.41	1.108	94.71	1.053
Nianyushan	calibration	75.8	0.941	83.44	1.084	84.89	0.910	85.86	1.020
	testing	82.38	0.803	85.39	1.329	88.30	0.939	88.39	1.077
Gaoguan	calibration	66.16	1.035	77.6	1.045	80.17	1.002	93.24	1.005
	testing	76.38	0.957	77.97	0.894	80.43	0.840	89.85	0.962
Shimen	calibration	65.03	0.848	64.85	1.068	73.85	1.141	94.53	1.084
	testing	72	0.772	75.72	1.281	76.90	1.089	87.99	1.055
Tiantang	calibration	65.47	0.985	73.06	1.049	78.08	0.960	88.66	1.131
	testing	59.79	0.895	81.96	0.956	79.54	1.015	91.32	1.043
Mean	calibration	69.47	0.976	78.41	1.046	82.08	1.00	92.97	1.06
	testing	70.16	0.879	75.86	1.155	80.62	1.04	91.52	1.07

The mean values of R^2 and WB for the SSA-ANN1 model are 82.08% and 80.62%, and 1.0 and 1.04, during calibration and testing periods, respectively, which are much better than that of the NLPM-ANN model. It means that the reconstructed series obtained by SSA has a strong regularity and is easy to simulate. It also demonstrated that the impact of noise in hydrological time series on model performance is bigger than the seasonal hydrological behavior. Therefore, SSA is an effective way to improve runoff forecasting accuracy. The mean values of R^2 for the SSA-ANN2 model are 92.97% and 91.52%, which are much better than those of the SSA-ANN1 model. It is concluded that considering previous runoff as a model input can improve model efficiency greatly.

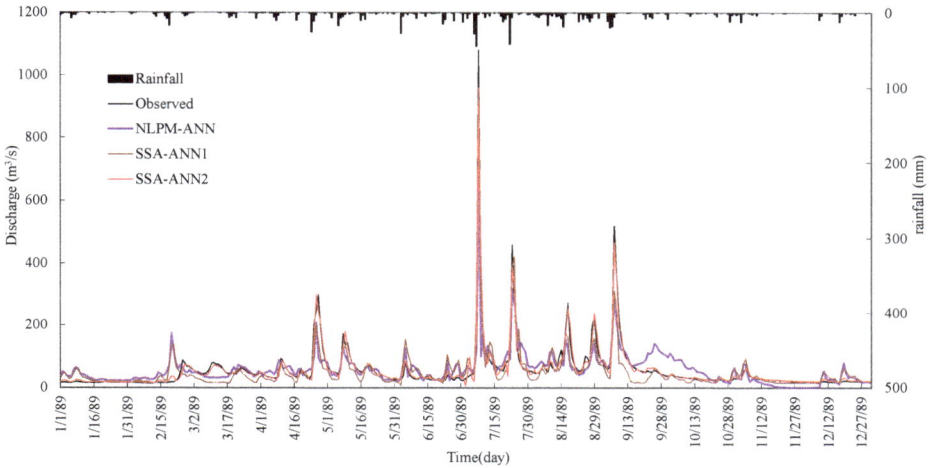

Figure 6. Observed and simulated runoff hydrographs by three models for Jiahe.

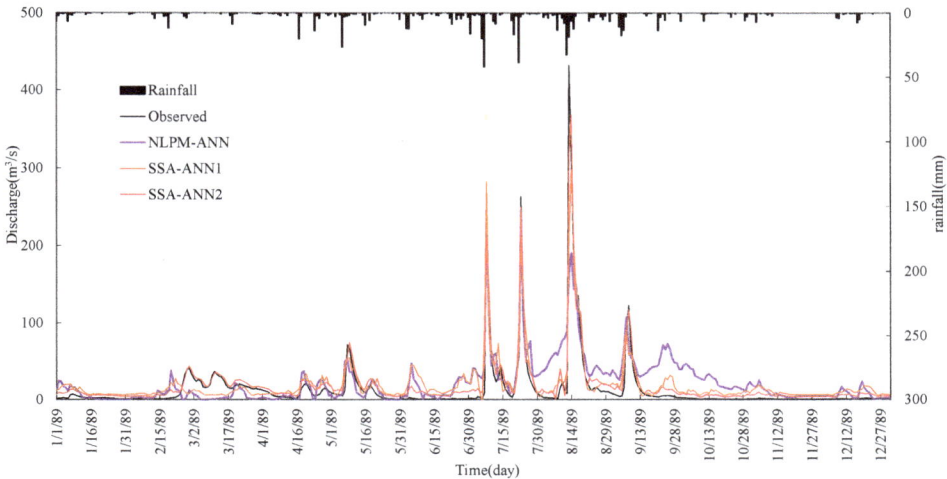

Figure 7. Observed and simulated runoff hydrographs by three models for Laoguanhe.

In order to compare the NLPM-ANN model, SSA-ANN1 model, and SSA-ANN2 model clearly and deeply, we selected one year during the testing period of four watersheds as an example, and the observed and simulated runoff hydrographs created by these three models for the Jiahe, Laoguanhe,

Baohe, and Shimen watersheds are plotted in Figures 6–9, respectively. These figures show that the runoff hydrograph simulated by the SSA-ANN2 model is much closer to the observational one. The peak and minimum flows simulated by the SSA-ANN2 model are the best among these models. Therefore, the SSA-ANN2 model can predict daily runoff very well in practice.

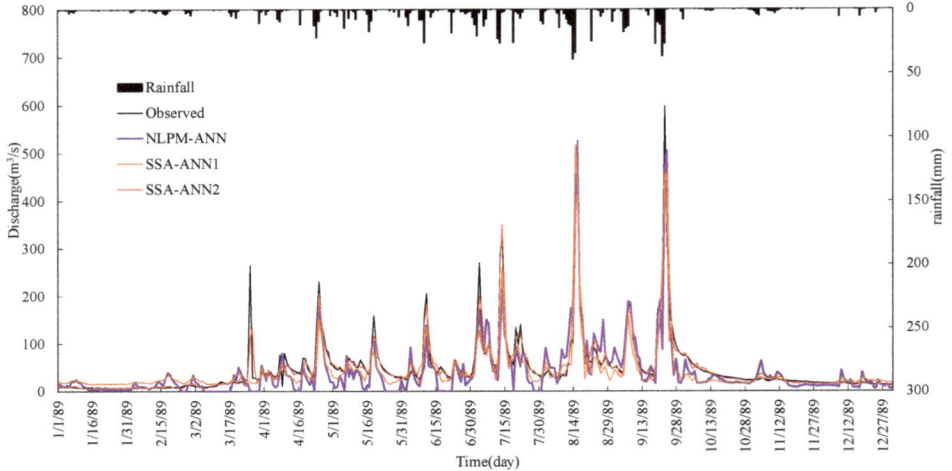

Figure 8. Observed and simulated runoff hydrographs by three models for Baohe.

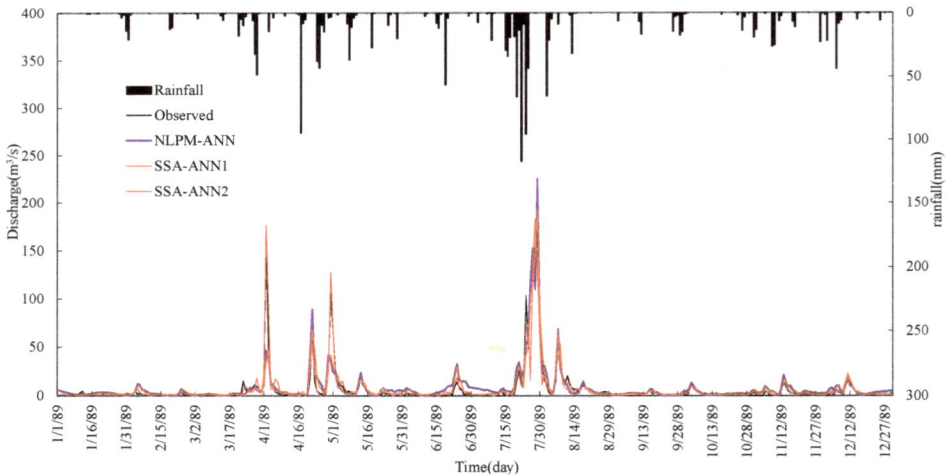

Figure 9. Observed and simulated runoff hydrographs by three models for Shimen.

5. Summary and Conclusions

The objective of this study is to investigate the approach of improving daily runoff forecasting in terms of data preprocessing and model input selection. The black-box model ANN is selected as the benchmark. Considering the subtraction of the seasonal means from the original series can remove the nonlinearity of the rainfall-runoff process, the NLPM method was used to preprocess model inputs. Considering the hydrological time series can be viewed as a combination of quasi-periodic signals contaminated by noises, the SSA method was used to filter the noise and choose reconstructed series as model inputs. These two data preprocessing techniques were compared and analyzed. Main findings and discussions were summarized as follows:

(1) The performance of the ANN model can be improved by data preprocessing techniques. SSA is more effective and it can improve the learning and training ability of the ANN type model significantly. Results also show that the impact of noise in hydrological time series on model performance is bigger than the seasonal hydrological behavior.

(2) Comparing the SSA-ANN1 model with the NLPM-ANN model, the mean values of R^2 and WB for the SSA-ANN1 model are 82.08% and 80.62%, and 1.0 and 1.04, during calibration and testing periods, respectively, which are much better than that of the NLPM-ANN model.

(3) The SSA-ANN2 model performs best for daily runoff forecasting for all selected watersheds. The effective way for increasing daily runoff forecasting accuracy is to preprocess data series by SSA and select both previous related rainfall and runoff as predictive factors.

(4) There are some limitations in this study. The method to select the contributing components relies on liner correlation analysis, which disregards the existence of nonlinearity in the hydrologic process. The sensitivities and uncertainties of model parameters are not analyzed. All of these will be the focus in our future research.

Acknowledgments: This study is financially supported by the National Natural Science Foundation of China (NSFC 51190094 and 51379148). The authors would like to thank the editor and anonymous reviewers whose comments and suggestions help to improve the manuscript.

Author Contributions: The SSA-ANN model was proposed and used to simulate the rainfall-runoff relationship. Results show that this model can improve daily runoff forecasting accuracy and it is worth of applying in practice.

Conflicts of Interest: The authors declare no conflict of interest.

References

1. Baratti, R.; Cannas, B.; Fanni, A.; Pintus, M.; Sechi, G.M.; Toreno, N. River flow forecast for reservoir management through neural networks. *Neurocomputing* **2003**, *55*, 421–437. [CrossRef]

2. Chang, F.J.; Chen, Y.C. A counterpropagation fuzzy-neural network modeling approach to real time streamflow prediction. *J. Hydrol.* **2001**, *245*, 153–164. [CrossRef]

3. Nayak, P.C.; Sudheer, K.P.; Ramasastri, K.S. Fuzzy computing based rainfall–runoff model for real time flood forecasting. *Hydrol. Process.* **2005**, *19*, 955–968. [CrossRef]

4. French, M.N.; Krajewski, W.F.; Cuykendall, R.R. Rainfall forecasting in space and time using a neural network. *J. Hydrol.* **1992**, *137*, 1–31. [CrossRef]

5. Hsu, K.L.; Gupta, H.V.; Sorooshian, S. Artificial neural network modeling of the rainfall–runoff process. *Water Resour. Res.* **1995**, *31*, 2517–2530. [CrossRef]

6. Sivakumar, B.; Liong, S.Y.; Liaw, C.Y. Evidence of chaotic behavior in Singapore rainfall. *J. Am. Water Resour. Assoc.* **1998**, *34*, 301–310. [CrossRef]

7. Whigam, P.A.; Crapper, P.F. Modelling rainfall–runoff relationships using genetic programming. *Math. Comput. Model.* **2001**, *33*, 707–721. [CrossRef]

8. Liong, S.Y.; Sivapragasm, C. Hood stage forecasting with SVM. *J. Am. Water Resour. Assoc.* **2002**, *38*, 173–186. [CrossRef]

9. Govindaraju, R.S. Artificial neural networks in hydrology. I: Preliminary concepts. *J. Hydrol. Eng.* **2000**, *5*, 115–123.

10. Govindaraju, R.S. Artificial neural networks in hydrology. II: Hydrological applications. *J. Hydrol. Eng.* **2000**, *5*, 124–137.

11. Maier, H.R.; Dandy, G.C. Neural networks for the prediction and forecasting of water resources variables: A review of modelling issues and applications. *Environ. Modell. Softw.* **2000**, *15*, 101–124. [CrossRef]

12. Dawson, C.W.; Wilby, R.L. Hydrological modeling using artificial neural networks. *Progr. Phys. Geogr.* **2001**, *25*, 80–108. [CrossRef]

13. Sudheer, K.P.; Gosain, A.K.; Ramasastri, K.S. A data-driven algorithm for constructing artificial neural network rainfall-runoff models. *Hydrol. Process.* **2002**, *16*, 1325–1330. [CrossRef]

14. Xiong, L.H.; O'Connor, K.M.; Guo, S.L. Comparison of three updating schemes using Artificial Neural Network in flow forecasting. *Hydrol. Earth Syst. Sci.* **2004**, *8*, 247–255. [CrossRef]

15. Kumar, A.R.S.; Sudheer, K.P.; Jain, S.K.; Agarwal, P.K. Rainfall-runoff modelling using artificial neural networks: Comparison of network types. *Hydrol. Process.* **2005**, *19*, 1277–1291. [CrossRef]

16. Pang, B.; Guo, S.L.; Xiong, L.H.; Li, C.Q. A nonlinear perturbation model based on artificial neural network. *J. Hydrol.* **2007**, *333*, 504–516. [CrossRef]

17. Rezaeian, Z.M.; Amin, S.; Khalili, D.; Singh, V.P. Daily outflow prediction by multilayer perceptron with logistic sigmoid and tangent sigmoid activation functions. *Water Resour. Manag.* **2010**, *24*, 2673–2688. [CrossRef]

18. Rezaeian, Z.M.; Stein, A.; Tabari, H.; Abghari, H.; Jalalkamali, N.; Hosseinipour, E.Z.; Singh, V.P. Assessment of a conceptual hydrological model and artificial neural networks for daily out-flows forecasting. *Int. J. Environ. Sci. Technol.* **2013**, *10*, 1181–1192. [CrossRef]

19. Shamseldin, A.Y. Artificial neural network model for river flow forecasting in a developing country. *J. Hydroinform.* **2010**, *12*, 22–35. [CrossRef]

20. Wu, J.S.; Han, J.; Annambhotla, S.; Bryant, S. Artificial neural networks for forecasting watershed runoff and stream flows. *J. Hydrol. Eng.* **2005**, *10*, 216–222. [CrossRef]

21. Taormina, R.; Chau, K. Neural network river forecasting with multi-objective fully informed particle swarm optimization. *J. Hydroinform.* **2015**, *17*, 99–113. [CrossRef]

22. Wu, C.L.; Chau, K.W.; Li, Y.S. Methods to improve neural network performance in daily flows prediction. *J. Hydrol.* **2009**, *372*, 80–93. [CrossRef]

23. Nash, J.E.; Brasi, B.I. A hybrid model for flow forecasting on large catchments. *J. Hydrol.* **1983**, *65*, 125–137. [CrossRef]

24. Liang, G.C.; Nash, J.E. Linear models for river flow routing on large catchments. *J. Hydrol.* **1988**, *103*, 157–188. [CrossRef]

25. Sivapragasam, C.; Liong, S.Y.; Pasha, M.F.K. Rainfall and runoff forecasting with SSA-SVM approach. *J. Hydroinform.* **2001**, *3*, 141–152.

26. Marques, C.A.F.; Ferreira, J.; Rocha, A.; Castanheira, J.; Goncalves, P.; Vaz, N.; Dias, J.M. Singular spectral analysis and forecasting of hydrological time series. *Phys. Chem. Earth.* **2006**, *31*, 1172–1179. [CrossRef]

27. Wang, W.S.; Jin, J.L.; Li, Y.Q. Prediction of inflow at Three Gorges Dam in Yangtze River with wavelet network model. *Water Resour. Manage.* **2009**, *23*, 2791–2803. [CrossRef]

28. Wang, Y.; Guo, S.L.; Chen, H.; Zhou, Y.L. Comparative study of monthly inflow prediction methods for the Three Gorges Reservoir. *Stoch. Environ. Res. Risk Assess.* **2014**, *28*, 555–570. [CrossRef]

29. Wu, C.L.; Chau, K.W. Rainfall-runoff modeling using artificial neural network coupled with singular spectrum analysis. *J. Hydrol.* **2011**, *399*, 394–409. [CrossRef]

30. Vautard, R.; Yiou, P.; Ghil, M. Singular-spectrum analysis: A toolkit for short, noisy and chaotic signals. *Physica. D.* **1992**, *58*, 95–126. [CrossRef]

31. Golyandina, N.; Nekrutkin, V.; Zhigljavsky, A. *Analysis of time Series Structure: SSA and the Related Techniques*; CRC Press: Boca Raton, FL, USA, 2001.

32. Toth, E.; Brath, A.; Montanari, A. Comparison of short-term rainfall prediction models for real-time flood forecasting. *J. Hydrol.* **2000**, *239*, 132–147. [CrossRef]

33. Wu, C.L.; Chau, K.W.; Li, Y.S. Predicting monthly streamflow using data-driven models coupled with data-preprocessing techniques. *Water Resour. Res.* **2009**, *45*, 2263–2289. [CrossRef]

water

MDPI

Article

Parameter Automatic Calibration Approach for Neural-Network-Based Cyclonic Precipitation Forecast Models

Der-Chang Lo [1], Chih-Chiang Wei [2],* and En-Ping Tsai [1]

[1] Department of Maritime Information and Technology, National Kaohsiung Marine University, Kaohsiung 80543, Taiwan; loderg@mail.nkmu.edu.tw (D.-C.L.); 1021547104@stu.nkmu.edu.tw (E.-P.T.)
[2] Department of Marine Environmental Informatics, National Taiwan Ocean University, No.2, Beining Rd., Jhongjheng District, Keelung City 20224, Taiwan
* Correspondence: d89521007@ntu.edu.tw; Tel.: +886-2-24622192; Fax: +886-2-24620724

Academic Editor: Kwok-wing Chau
Received: 20 May 2015; Accepted: 14 July 2015; Published: 17 July 2015

Abstract: This paper presents artificial neural network (ANN)-based models for forecasting precipitation, in which the training parameters are adjusted using a parameter automatic calibration (PAC) approach. A classical ANN-based model, the multilayer perceptron (MLP) neural network, was used to verify the utility of the proposed ANN–PAC approach. The MLP-based ANN used the learning rate, momentum, and number of neurons in the hidden layer as its major parameters. The Dawu gauge station in Taitung, Taiwan, was the study site, and observed typhoon characteristics and ground weather data were the study data. The traditional multiple linear regression model was selected as the benchmark for comparing the accuracy of the ANN–PAC model. In addition, two MLP ANN models based on a trial-and-error calibration method, ANN–TRI1 and ANN–TRI2, were realized by manually tuning the parameters. We found the results yielded by the ANN–PAC model were more reliable than those yielded by the ANN–TRI1, ANN–TRI2, and traditional regression models. In addition, the computing efficiency of the ANN–PAC model decreased with an increase in the number of increments within the parameter ranges because of the considerably increased computational time, whereas the prediction errors decreased because of the model's increased capability of identifying optimal solutions.

Keywords: artificial neural network; parameter calibration; hydrology; optimization

1. Introduction

Taiwan is a long and narrow island located between Japan and the Philippines in the Western Pacific and has an area of 35,981 km^2; the Central Mountain Range runs from north to south, and the Tropic of Cancer passes through the south. On average, approximately 80 tropical cyclones, also known as typhoons, form annually worldwide, of which approximately 30 form in the western North Pacific. Most typhoons in Taiwan form between May and November, and, on average, 3.9 typhoons affect Taiwan each year. As soon as a typhoon strikes, it often causes continuous torrential rainfall, leading to severe flooding, landslides, and debris flow [1]. Therefore, an effective and quantitative precipitation forecast model for typhoon periods is necessary.

The concept of artificial neurons was first introduced in 1943 [2]. In the late 1980s, research on artificial neural network (ANN) applications advanced after the introduction of backpropagation training algorithms for feedforward ANNs [3]. ANNs, which simulate the biological nervous system and brain activity, have become the preferred forecasting approach in hydrology and hydrometeorology (e.g., [4–19]). ANNs are advantageous because feedforward networks are universal approximators capable of learning continuous functions with any desired degree of accuracy. Most ANN models have several parameters that users can adjust for realizing different scenarios and objectives, and the results produced by such models are typically distinct, which renders identifying the unique optimal solution difficult [20].

To realize a model that accurately represents the system being modeled, the model parameters must be determined using known system inputs and responses; the process of determining the optimal value of these parameters is termed "calibration." Traditionally, ANN-based models are calibrated using trial-and-error approaches [21]. Maier and Dandy [22] reviewed numerous ANNs and reported that several heuristic calibration approaches have been proposed in which the models dynamically adapt the learning rate and momentum value as training progresses. The majority of these approaches are based on the principle of increasing the step size taken in weight space when successive weight updates reduce the error (or when the steps are in the same direction) and reducing the step size when the error increases in consecutive iterations (or when the steps are in opposite directions) (e.g., [23–33]). For calibrating hidden neurons, Sheela and Deepa [34] reviewed various methods for fixing the number of hidden neurons in ANNs and reported that randomly selecting the number of hidden neurons can result in overfitting or underfitting. Empirical studies have shown that optimizing these parameters is highly problem-dependent [35,36].

Trial-and-error calibration approaches are easy to comprehend but the results are not always satisfactory unless the modeler is experienced. As indicated by Cai *et al.* [20], the parameters are typically separately adjusted during trial-and-error calibration. The adjustment of a parameter is stopped when no further improvement is made in the goodness-of-fit, and the same process is applied to optimize each parameter without considering the effects of the other parameters. Although this method is simple and widely accepted, it can produce unsatisfactory and suboptimal results.

This paper presents the development of ANN-based models for forecasting precipitation in which the training parameters are adjusted using a parameter automatic calibration (PAC) approach. A classical ANN-based multilayer perceptron (MLP) neural network was used to demonstrate the utility of the proposed PAC approach. MLP neural networks are extensively used to model an unknown system with observable inputs and outputs, which is similar to synthesizing an approximation of a set of multidimensional functions, and are widely employed because of their simplicity, flexibility, and ease of use. The developed methodology was used to construct precipitation forecasting models for the Dawu gauge station in Taitung, Taiwan. The performance of the ANN–PAC model in the analysis of historical typhoon events was compared with those of various ANN-based models that employ trial-and-error calibration and traditional linear multiple regressions.

2. Methodology

The MLP ANN is briefly introduced before the methodology of the ANN–PAC algorithm is presented.

2.1. Sketch of MLP ANN

MLPs are feedforward neural networks trained using a standard backpropagation algorithm. They are supervised networks and the desired response must be trained [37]. MLP networks often consist of an input layer, one or more nonlinear hidden layers, and a linear output layer. Each layer may contain one or more nonlinear processing units called neurons or nodes [38]. Figure 1 is a scheme of a typical MLP network featuring three layers: input, hidden, and output layers. Mathematically, a three-layer MLP comprising n_1 input nodes, n_2 hidden nodes, and n_3 output nodes, is expressed as:

$$y_r = f_2 \left(\sum_{q=0}^{n_2} w_{qr}^2 \cdot f_1 \left(\sum_{p=0}^{n_1} w_{pq}^1 \cdot x_p \right) \right) r \in [1, n_3] \tag{1}$$

where p, q, and r are the indices of the input, hidden, and output nodes, respectively; x_p is the input node of the input layer, w_{pq}^1 is the weight set connecting the input and hidden layers, w_{qr}^2 is the weight set connecting the hidden and output layers, y_r denotes the network outputs, $f_1(g)$ is the activity function of the hidden layer, and $f_2(g)$ is the activity function of the output layer.

In a MLP network, the output is generated by passing signals from the input layer to the output layer through the hidden layer. When constructing an MLP structure, the number of neurons in the hidden layer is not constant and must be optimized depending on the characteristics of the application [39]. The inputs to a perceptron are weighted, summed over the inputs, translated, and passed through an activation function. The frequently used activity functions include linear, sigmoidal, and hyperbolic tangents [40]. As the training progresses, the weights are updated systematically using the backpropagation algorithm and the network output is compared with the target output. The learning acquired by the network is stored in its weights in a distributed manner. An MLP comprises major parameters, namely the learning rate, momentum, and number of nodes in the hidden layer. These parameters are typically set on the basis of experience or are adjusted one parameter at a time and their effect on the model observed [20].

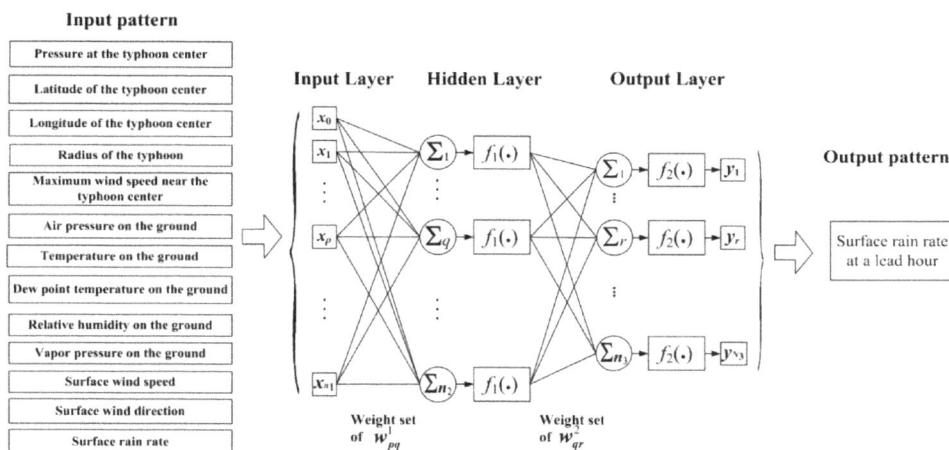

Figure 1. Architecture of the three-layer multilayer perceptron (MLP) neural network.

2.2. Proposed ANN–PAC Model

In this section, a methodology is presented for an ANN–PAC approach in forecasting precipitation during typhoons. Figure 2 illustrates the flowchart of the proposed method, and each step is described as follows.

Phase 1, Data Preprocessing: The collected data contain typhoon characteristics and ground weather data (Section 3.1). Because a traditional training–validation–test procedure is adopted for the optimization of an ANN model, the collected data are classified into training, validation, and testing subsets. The training set is used to build model structures and adjust the connected weights of the constructed models. The validation set is used to validate an optimal parameter set, and the testing set is used to evaluate the performance of the constructed models and confirm their generalizability.

Phase 2, Model Structure and Parameters Setting: The model architecture of the MLP model is fixed, including the number of inputs (attributes) in the input layer, the number of neurons in the hidden layer (considered a decision variable in this study and optimized through automatic calibration), and the output in the output layer. Subsequently, the ranges of three critical parameters in the MLP network—the learning rate, momentum, and number of neurons in the hidden layer—are set. Finally, the number of increments between maximal and minimal parameter values is fixed.

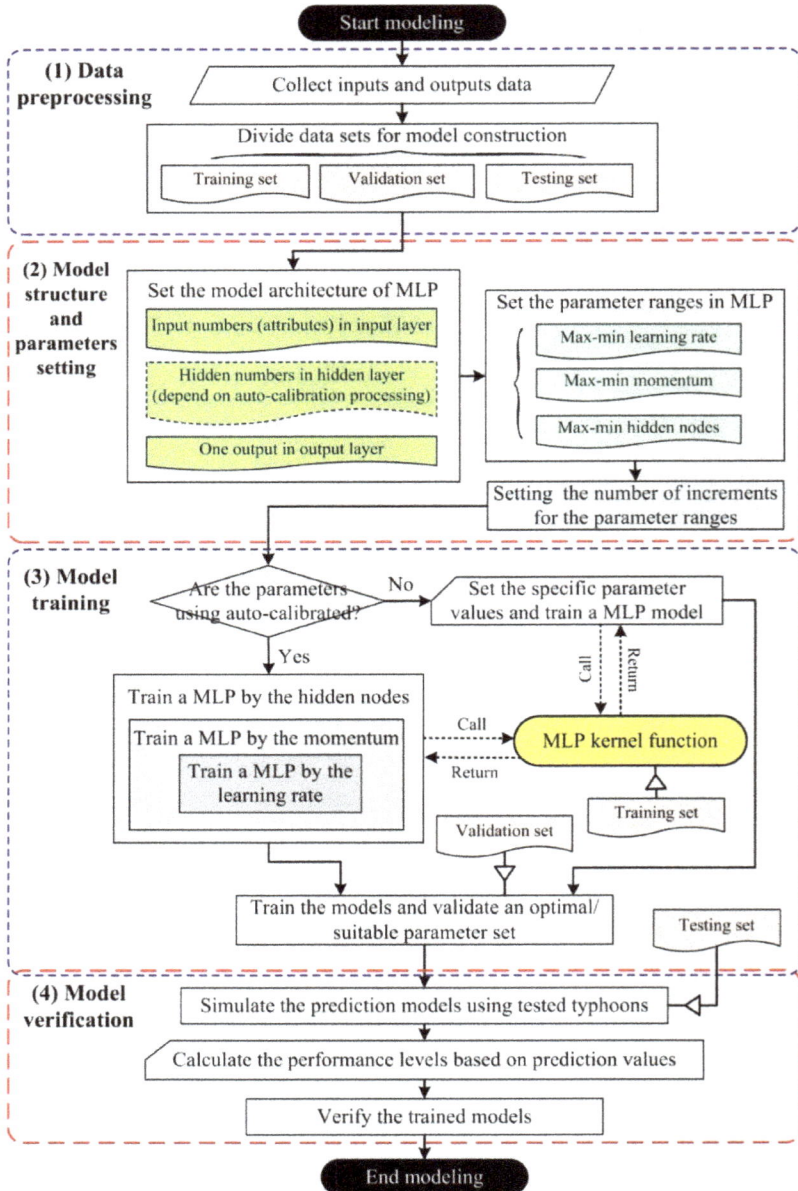

Figure 2. Determining artificial neural network (ANN)-based MLP parameters using an automatic calibration approach.

Phase 3, Model Training: First, a decision condition selects whether the model parameters are calibrated automatically. If "yes", the modeling process proceeds in the three-loop training structure by using the parameter values designed in Phase 2; if "no", the parameter values are set manually (*i.e.*, trial-and-error calibration). The training process is initiated using a training set; the MLP kernel function is repeatedly called and the outputs returned for training the model. The trained models are validated using a validation set. Then, the optimal trained model and their parameter set are identified.

Phase 4, Model Verification: The tested typhoons (*i.e.*, a testing set) are simulated using the optimal trained model, and the forecast results are evaluated according to the performance measures.

In Phase 3, when training the ANN model we performed an early stopping procedure to avoid overfitting caused by an overly close reconstruction of the data in the training set. The stopping procedure is briefly described as follows: first, the backpropagation algorithm is applied on a training set. The performance of the obtained input–output map is then iteratively validated in a validation set. The iteration process is stopped when the performance in the validation set begins to decrease, even if the performance in the training set continues to increase under the desired threshold. Detailed descriptions were provided by Pasini [41] and Prechelt and Orr [42].

3. Experiment

3.1. Study Area and Data

Figure 3 depicts the experimental site at the Dawu gauge station (22°21′27″ N, 120°53′44″ E; elevation 8.1 m) in Taiwan, located along the main path of the Northwestern Pacific tropical typhoons. This study considered 28 typhoon events that affected Dawu station between 2001 and 2012 (Table 1). The climatology of typhoons and the ground weather data of the Dawu station were collected from the Central Weather Bureau of Taiwan. Typhoon characteristics, namely the pressure, latitude, and longitude of the typhoon center; radius of the typhoon; and maximal wind speed near the typhoon center, were collected for analysis. The ground weather data comprised the air pressure, temperature, dew point temperature, relative humidity, and vapor pressure of the ground; surface wind speed and direction; and surface rain rate.

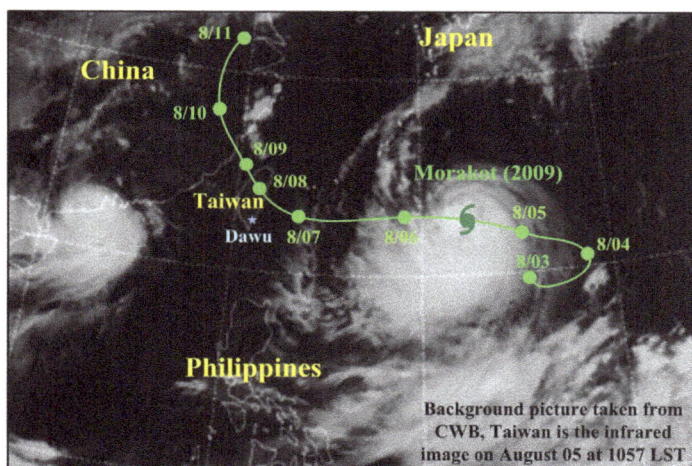

Figure 3. Dawu gauge station and the track of Typhoon Morakot (2009).

Table 1. The 28 typhoon events considered in this study.

Year	Typhoon Name	Year	Typhoon Name
2001	Lekima	2007	Pabuk, Wutip, Sepat, Wipha, Krosa
2002	Nakri	2008	Kalmaegi, Fung-Wong, Sinlaku
2003	Morakot, Dujuan, Melor	2009	Morakot
2004	Mindulle, Aere, Nanmadol	2010	Fanapi
2005	Haitang, Matsa, Talim, Longwang	2011	Nanmadol
2006	Chanchu, Billis, Kaemi, Bopha	2012	Tembin

3.2. Data Division

The typhoon characteristics data comprised 1462 records measured at hourly intervals. Table 2 lists the mean, minimal, and maximal values of the data attributes. To build the ANN–PAC model, the data sets were classified into training and testing sets. The typhoon events that occurred between 2001 and 2008 were used for training. In addition, Typhoons Morakot (2009) and Fanapi (2010) were used as a validation set, and Typhoons Nanmadol (2011) and Tembin (2012) were used as a testing set. Figures 3 and 4 display the historical tracks of these typhoons.

Table 2. Range and average values of data attributes.

Data Attribute	Range	Mean
Pressure at typhoon center (hPa)	912.0–1000.0	964.3
Latitude (°N) of typhoon center (degree)	12.0–27.8	23.2
Longitude (°E) of typhoon center (degree)	115.3–128.1	121.5
Radius of typhoon (km)	0–300.0	207.7
Maximum wind speed near typhoon center ($m\varphi s^{-1}$)	7.0–16.0	11.9
Air pressure on the ground (hPa)	967.2–1011.3	995.0
Temperature on the ground (°C)	23.1–35.8	27.0
Dew point temperature on the ground (°C)	18.1–28.0	24.1
Relative humidity on the ground (%)	40.0–100.0	85.5
Vapor pressure on the ground (hPa)	20.8–37.8	30.2
Surface wind speed ($m \cdot s^{-1}$)	0.0–20.2	3.6
Surface wind direction	0.0–360.0	165.7
Surface rain rate ($mm \cdot h^{-1}$)	0.0–103.0	4.5

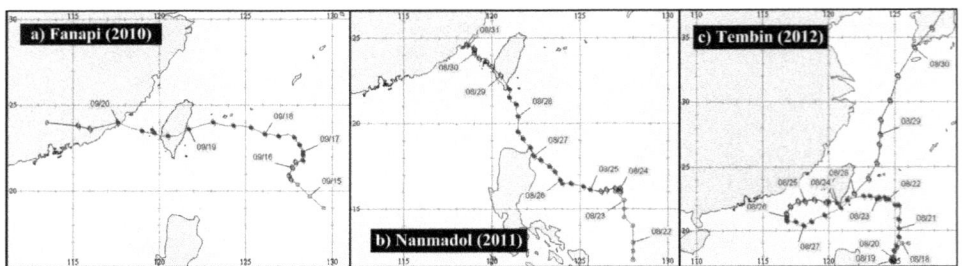

Figure 4. Typhoon tracks of (**a**) Fanapi (2010); (**b**) Nanmadol (2011); and (**c**) Tembin (2012).

3.3. Modeling Using ANN–PAC

This study employed a widely used MLP neural network for forecasting precipitation at the study site. Figure 1 depicts the input–output patterns of the MLP model. The model inputs contained 13 meteorological attributes, and the target output is the amount of rain in the next 1 h. As stated, the MLP ANN comprises the learning rate, momentum, and number of neurons in the hidden layer. To construct the MLP, sigmoid and linear activity functions were used in the hidden and output layers, respectively. The proposed ANN–PAC approach was applied for investigating the optimal parameter combination.

The ranges of the three aforementioned parameters in the MLP network were set. Because the momentum and learning rate are theoretically in the range of [0,1], 0.1 and 1.0 were set as their lower and upper limits. For the number of hidden neurons, we defined the ratio of hidden neurons as the ratio of the number of neurons in the hidden layer to the number of records in a training set. This ratio ranged between 0.01 and 0.1.

In addition, the number of increments between the maximal and minimal values, assumed as 10 equal-sized intervals, is the same for all three calibrated parameters. The effect of the number of increments on the prediction accuracy is evaluated in Section 4.4.

During training, the MLP network was trained using a training set. The model prediction errors, computed using the relative root mean squared error (RRMSE), were then calculated for each iterative process using a validation set:

$$\text{RRMSE} = \sqrt{\frac{1}{N}\sum_{i=1}^{N}\left(O_i^{\text{pre}} - O_i^{\text{obs}}\right)^2} / \overline{O}^{\text{obs}} \qquad (2)$$

where O_i^{pre} and O_i^{obs} are the predicted and observed values at record i, respectively; $\overline{O}^{\text{obs}}$ is the average of the observations and N is the number of records.

The optimal parameter values were obtained after calibrating the parameters using the ANN–PAC approach: the ratio of hidden neurons = 0.02, momentum = 0.2, and learning rate = 0.6. Figure 5 displays the RRMSE results of the ANN–PAC model using a validation set. To three-dimensionally depict the RRMSE variations, one of three parameters was fixed; for example, in Figure 5a, the RRMSE variations were plotted at various learning rate and momentum values and a fixed hidden neurons ratio of 0.02.

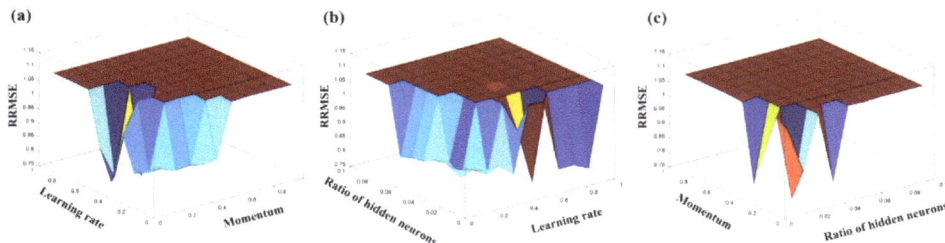

Figure 5. Three-dimensional plots of relative root mean squared error (RRMSE) variations at (**a**) a fixed hidden neurons ratio of 0.02, (**b**) a fixed momentum of 0.2; and (**c**) a fixed learning rate of 0.6.

4. Evaluations and Comparisons

4.1. Results

The traditional multiple linear regression model was selected as the benchmark for comparing the accuracy of the ANN–PAC model. Unlike ANNs, which typically require a trial-and-error or heuristic parameter calibration approach, the coefficients in regression analysis can be efficiently calculated using the matrix algebra regardless of the number of data points and variables. Figure 6a presents the 1-h-ahead rain variations of the observations and predictions obtained using a validation set (*i.e.*, Typhoons Morakot and Fanapi) for the ANN–PAC and regression-based models, and Figure 6b presents the 1-h-ahead rain variations of the observations and predictions obtained using a testing set (*i.e.*, Typhoons Nanmadol and Tembin). The predictions obtained using the ANN–PAC model were highly consistent with the observed data, compared with the regression-based models for both the

Water **2015**, *7*, 3963–3977

validation and testing sets. To evaluate the constructed ANN–PAC models, we designed two model scenarios, as described in the next section.

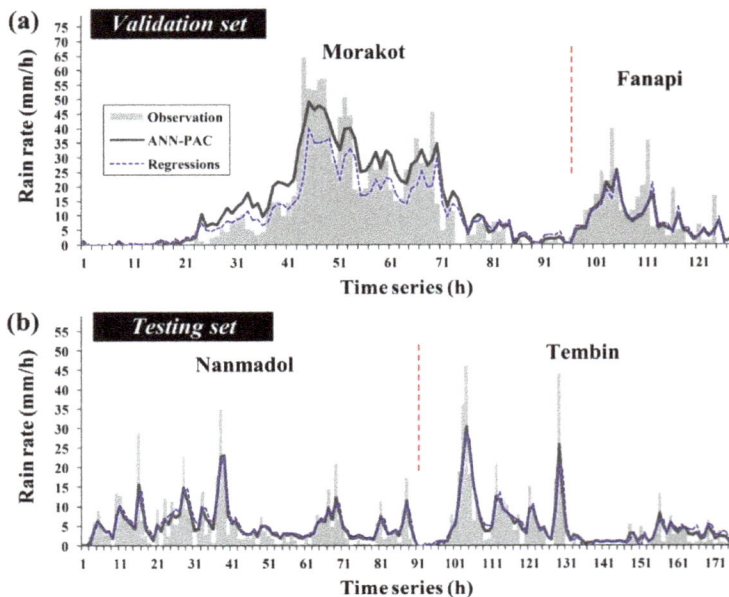

Figure 6. Simulation results of 1-h-ahead predictions for hyetograph using: (a) the validation set and (b) the testing set.

4.2. Model Scenarios

ANN model parameters are typically fixed on the basis of experience. As shown in Figure 2, the parameters of the proposed methodology can be manually tuned using trial-and-error calibration. Herein, the process of calibrating ANN-based MLP parameters by using a validation set is described. As illustrated in Figure 7, the initial momentum and learning rate values were set first. After sensitivity analysis, the "local" optimal ratio of the hidden neurons was calibrated. Subsequently, the local optimal ratio of the hidden neurons and the initial learning rate, which had been calibrated, were fixed, and the local optimal momentum value was calculated through sensitivity analysis. Subsequently, the local optimal ratio of hidden neurons and momentum value were fixed, and the suitable learning rate was calculated through sensitivity analysis.

In this study, two scenarios with differing initial parameters were designed using the aforementioned trial-and-error method. The first scenario, ANN–TRI1, used initial values of 0.02, 0.2, and 0.2 for the ratio of hidden neurons, momentum, and learning rate, respectively. The second scenario, ANN–TRI2, used initial values of 0.05, 0.5 and 0.5, respectively. The ranges of these parameters are the same as those in Section 3.3. Figure 8 plots the sensitivity results of the MLP parameters for the ANN–TRI1 and ANN–TRI2 models. The calibrated values of the three parameters are (0.01, 0.3, 0.5) and (0.03, 0.2, 0.2) for ANN–TRI1 and ANN–TRI2, respectively.

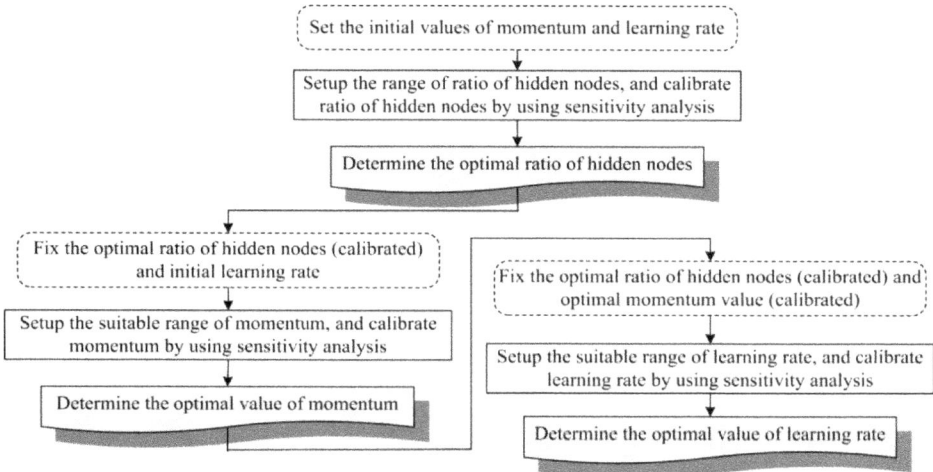

Figure 7. Trial-and-error calibration of ANN parameters.

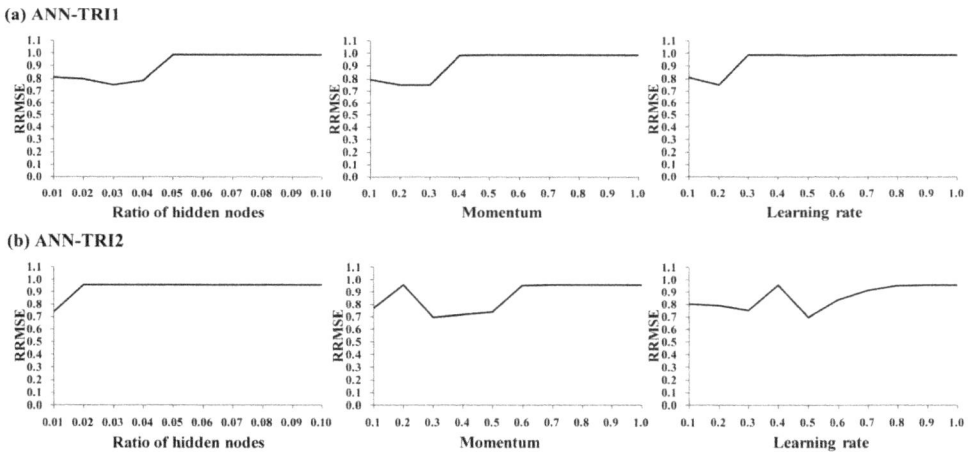

Figure 8. Sensitivity results of MLP parameters by using a validation set for two MLP ANN models based on a trial-and-error calibration method: (**a**) ANN–TRI1; and (**b**) ANN–TRI2.

4.3. Performance Levels and Comparisons

To assess the performance levels from the obtained results, the relative mean absolute error (RMAE), RRMSE, and coefficient of correlation (r) were calculated:

$$\text{RMAE} = \left(\frac{1}{N} \sum_{i=1}^{N} \left| O_i^{\text{pre}} - O_i^{\text{obs}} \right| \right) \Big/ \overline{O}^{\text{obs}} \tag{3}$$

$$r = \frac{\sum\limits_{i=1}^{N} \left(O_i^{\text{obs}} - \overline{O}^{\text{obs}} \right) \left(O_i^{\text{pre}} - \overline{O}^{\text{pre}} \right)}{\sqrt{\sum\limits_{i=1}^{N} \left(O_i^{\text{obs}} - \overline{O}^{\text{obs}} \right)^2 \sum\limits_{i=1}^{N} \left(O_i^{\text{pre}} - \overline{O}^{\text{pre}} \right)^2}} \tag{4}$$

where $\overline{O}^{pre}$ is the average of the predictions. Low RMAE and RRMSE values and high r values typically indicate favorable performance levels. Precise predictions are those whose RMAE, and RRMSE are nearly 0 and r values are nearly 1.

The predictions of the ANN–PAC, ANN–TRI1, ANN–TRI2, and regression models were compared using these performance criteria. Table 3 lists the results for the four models obtained using RMAE, RRMSE, and r performance criteria calculated by the validation and testing sets. The RMAE was computed using a term-by-term comparison of the error in the prediction and the actual value of the variable. Thus, the RMAE is an unbiased statistic for measuring the predictive capability of a model [43]. For the validation and testing sets, the RMAE and RRMSE results for the ANN–PAC model were lower than those for the ANN–TRI1, ANN–TRI2, and regression models, implying that ANN–PAC exhibited relatively few prediction errors and lower bias measures with respect to the actual values, possibly because trial-and-error calibrations cannot be performed for all variables simultaneously but rather separately, which is a time-intensive process. Moreover, because the interaction between parameters cannot be determined, this method cannot obtain global optimal solutions [20]. The r performance levels suggested that the ANN–PAC and regression models successfully exploited the relationship between the observed and predicted rainfalls. In addition, by comparing the ANN–PAC results obtained for the validation and testing sets, we observed that the performance levels obtained using the validation set were slightly higher than those obtained using the testing set. Therefore, we concluded that the generalizability of the constructed ANN–PAC model can be calibrated using the training–validation–testing procedure for applications in precipitation forecasting.

Table 3. Performance levels of the various models assessed by using the validation set Testing sets.

Subset	Model	Performance		
		RMAE	**RRMSE**	**r**
Validation set	ANN-PAC	0.397	0.575	0.886
	ANN-TRI1	0.528	0.750	0.817
	ANN-TRI2	0.482	0.695	0.832
	Regressions	0.441	0.708	0.859
Testing set	ANN-PAC	0.429	0.685	0.824
	ANN-TRI1	0.557	0.901	0.742
	ANN-TRI2	0.555	0.895	0.733
	Regressions	0.581	0.880	0.755

4.4. Effects of the Number of Increments

As stated in Section 3.3, the number of increments between the minimal and maximal values for each parameter was 10. To investigate the effect of the number of increments on the prediction ability and computation efficiency, the number of increments were varied as 5, 8, 10, and 13. Figure 9 illustrates the relationships among RRMSE prediction errors by using a validation set, computational time, and the number of increments. As the number of increments increases, the computing efficiency decreases because of a considerable increase in computational time, whereas the prediction errors decrease because of the increased capability of finding the optimal solution.

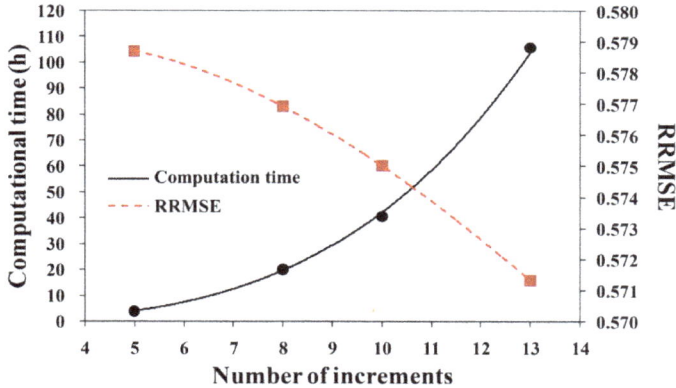

Figure 9. Effect of increment numbers on computational time and prediction errors.

5. Conclusions

ANNs are widely applied in engineering solutions. When constructing ANN-based models, a considerable number of model parameters must be calibrated, and the trial-and-error method is frequently employed for calibration during ANN training. This paper presents ANN models for 1-h-ahead rainfall forecasting, in which the training model parameters are adjusted using the proposed PAC approach. The classical MLP ANN model was used to verify the utility of the proposed approach. The MLP-based ANN comprises three parameters: the learning rate, momentum, and number of nodes in the hidden layer.

Observed typhoon characteristics and ground weather data at the Dawu gauge station in Taitung, Taiwan, were the study data. To compare the accuracy of ANN–PAC, traditional multiple linear regression was selected as the benchmark. In addition, two ANN models based on a trial-and-error calibration method, ANN–TRI1 and ANN–TRI2, were realized by manually tuning the parameters. The results clarify that the ANN–PAC model yielded more reliable results than ANN–TRI1, ANN–TRI2, and the regression models. Moreover, as the number of increments within the parameter ranges increased, the computing efficiency of the ANN–PAC model decreased because of considerable increase in the computational time, whereas the prediction errors of the model decreased because of the model's increased capability of finding the optimal solution. Therefore, a high number of increments within parameter ranges must be used in applications where accuracy is critical, whereas a low number must be used in applications where computing efficiency is essential.

Acknowledgments: The support under grant Nos. MOST103-2221-E-022-014 and MOST103-2622-M-464-001-CC3 by the Ministry of Science and Technology, Taiwan, is sincerely appreciated. The authors acknowledge the Central Weather Bureau (CWB) of Taiwan for the climatologic data.

Author Contributions: Der-Chang Lo and Chih-Chiang Wei devised the experimental strategy and carried out this experiment. Chih-Chiang Wei wrote the manuscript and contributed to the revisions. En-Ping Tsai partially contributed to the experiment and analysis of the data.

Conflicts of Interest: The authors declare no conflict of interest.

References

1. Lee, C.S.; Huang, L.R.; Shen, H.S.; Wang, S.T. A climatology model for forecasting typhoon rainfall in Taiwan. *Nat. Hazards* **2006**, *37*, 87–105. [CrossRef]
2. McCulloch, W.S.; Pitts, W. A logical calculus of the ideas imminent in nervous activity. *Bull. Math. Biophys.* **1943**, *5*, 115–133. [CrossRef]

3.   Rumelhart, D.E.; Hinton, G.E.; Williams, R.J. Learning Internal Representations by Error Propagation. In *Parallel Distributed Processing*; Rumelhart, D.E., McClelland, J.L., Eds.; MIT Press: Cambridge, UK, 1986.

4.   Asklany, S.A.; Elhelow, K.; Youssef, I.K.; El-wahab, M.A. Rainfall events prediction using rule-based fuzzy inference system. *Atmos. Res.* **2011**, *101*, 228–236. [CrossRef]

5.   Babovic, V. Data mining in hydrology. *Hydrol. Process.* **2005**, *19*, 1511–1515. [CrossRef]

6.   Chang, F.J.; Chiang, Y.M.; Tsai, M.J.; Shieh, M.C.; Hsu, K.L.; Sorooshian, S. Watershed rainfall forecasting using neuro-fuzzy networks with the assimilation of multi-sensor information. *J. Hydrol.* **2014**, *508*, 374–384. [CrossRef]

7.   Cheng, C.; Wang, S.; Chau, K.W.; Wu, X. Parallel discrete differential dynamic programming for multireservoir operation. *Environ. Model. Softw.* **2014**, *57*, 152–164. [CrossRef]

8.   Chau, K.W.; Wu, C.L.; Li, Y.S. Comparison of several flood forecasting models in Yangtze River. *J. Hydrol. Eng.* **2005**, *10*, 485–491. [CrossRef]

9.   Kecman, V. *Learning and Soft Computing: Support Vector Machines, Neural Networks, and Fuzzy Logic Models*; MIT Press: Cambridge, UK, 2001.

10. Liu, W.C.; Chung, C.E. Enhancing the predicting accuracy of the water stage using a physical-based model and an artificial neural network-genetic algorithm in a river system. *Water* **2014**, *6*, 1642–1661. [CrossRef]

11. Minns, W.; Hall, M.J. Artificial neural networks as rainfall-runoff models. *Hydrol. Sci. J.* **1996**, *41*, 399–417. [CrossRef]

12. Surridge, B.W.J.; Bizzi, S.; Castelletti, A. A framework for coupling explanation and prediction in hydroecological modelling. *Environ. Model. Softw.* **2014**, *61*, 274–286. [CrossRef]

13. Taormina, R.; Chau, K.W.; Sethi, R. Artificial neural network simulation of hourly groundwater levels in a coastal aquifer system of the Venice lagoon. *Eng. Appl. Artif. Intell.* **2012**, *25*, 1670–1676. [CrossRef]

14. Vojinovic, Z.; Kecman, V.; Babovic, V. Hybrid approach for modeling wet weather response in wastewater systems. *J. Water Resour. Plan. Manag.* **2003**, *129*, 511–521. [CrossRef]

15. Wang, W.C.; Xu, D.M.; Chau, K.W.; Chen, S. Improved annual rainfall-runoff forecasting using PSO–SVM model based on EEMD. *J. Hydroinform.* **2013**, *15*, 1377–1390.

16. Wei, C.C. RBF neural networks combined with principal component analysis applied to quantitative precipitation forecast for a reservoir watershed during typhoon periods. *J. Hydrometeorol.* **2012**, *13*, 722–734. [CrossRef]

17. Wei, C.C. Soft computing techniques in ensemble precipitation nowcast. *Appl. Soft Comput.* **2013**, *13*, 793–805. [CrossRef]

18. Wei, C.C.; Hsu, N.S.; Huang, C.L. Two-Stage pumping control model for flood mitigation in inundated urban drainage basins. *Water Resour. Manag.* **2014**, *28*, 425–444. [CrossRef]

19. Wu, C.L.; Chau, K.W. Prediction of rainfall time series using modular soft computing methods. *Eng. Appl. Artif. Intell.* **2013**, *26*, 997–1007. [CrossRef]

20. Cai, H.; Lye, L.M.; Khan, A. Flood Forecasting on the Humber River using an Artificial Neural Network Approach. In *Proceedings of the 2009 Canadian Society for Civil Engineering Annual Conference*; Canadian Society for Civil Engineering: Montreal, Canada, 2009; Volume 2, pp. 611–620.

21. Dai, H.C.; Macbeth, C. Effects of learning parameters on learning procedure and performance of a BPNN. *Neural Netw.* **1997**, *10*, 1505–1521. [CrossRef]

22. Maier, H.R.; Dandy, G.C. Neural networks for the prediction and forecasting of water resources variables: A review of modelling issues and applications. *Environ. Modell. Softw.* **2000**, *15*, 101–124. [CrossRef]

23. Chen, W.; Chau, K.W. Intelligent manipulation and calibration of parameters for hydrological models. *Int. J. Environ. Pollut.* **2006**, *28*, 432–447. [CrossRef]

24. Dawson, C.W.; Abrahart, R.J.; Shamseldin, A.Y.; Wilby, R.L. Flood estimation at ungauged sites using artificial neural networks. *J. Hydrol.* **2006**, *319*, 391–409. [CrossRef]

25. Jacobs, R.A. Increased rates of convergence through learning rate adaptation. *Neural Netw.* **1988**, *1*, 295–307. [CrossRef]

26. Kamruzzaman, M.; Shahriar, M.S.; Beecham, S. Assessment of short term rainfall and stream flows in South Australia. *Water* **2014**, *6*, 3528–3544. [CrossRef]

27. Lin, G.F.; Jhong, B.C. A real-time forecasting model for the spatial distribution of typhoon rainfall. *J. Hydrol.* **2015**, *521*, 302–313. [CrossRef]

28. Pasini, A.; Pelino, V.; Potestà, S. A neural network model for visibility nowcasting from surface observations: Results and sensitivity to physical input variables. *J. Geophys. Res.* **2001**, *106*, 14951–14959. [CrossRef]

29. Pasini, A.; Langone, R. Attribution of precipitation changes on a regional scale by neural network modeling: A case study. *Water* **2010**, *2*, 321–332. [CrossRef]

30. Pasini, A.; Langone, R. Influence of circulation patterns on temperature behavior at the regional scale: A case study investigated via neural network modeling. *J. Clim.* **2012**, *25*, 2123–2128. [CrossRef]

31. Pasini, A.; Modugno, G. Climatic attribution at the regional scale: A case study on the role of circulation patterns and external forcings. *Atmos. Sci. Lett.* **2013**, *14*, 301–305. [CrossRef]

32. Wei, C.C. Forecasting surface wind speeds over offshore islands near Taiwan during tropical cyclones: Comparisons of data-driven algorithms and parametric wind representations. *J. Geophys. Res. Atmos.* **2015**, *120*, 1826–1847. [CrossRef]

33. Zhang, Y.; Li, G. Long-term evolution of cones of depression in shallow aquifers in the North China Plain. *Water* **2013**, *5*, 677–697. [CrossRef]

34. Sheela, K.G.; Deepa, S.N. Review on methods to fix number of hidden neurons in neural networks. *Math. Probl. Eng.* **2013**, *2013*. [CrossRef]

35. Maier, H.R.; Dandy, G.C. The effect of internal parameters and geometry on the performance of back-propagation neural networks: An empirical study. *Environ. Model. Softw.* **1998**, *13*, 193–209. [CrossRef]

36. Maier, H.R.; Jain, A.; Dandy, G.C.; Sudheer, K. Methods used for the development of neural networks for the prediction of water resource variables in river systems: Current status and future directions. *Environ. Model. Softw.* **2010**, *25*, 891–909. [CrossRef]

37. Panchal, G.; Ganatra, A.; Kosta, Y.P.; Panchal, D. Behaviour analysis of multilayer perceptrons with multiple hidden neurons and hidden layers. *Int. J. Comput. Theor. Eng.* **2011**, *3*, 332–337. [CrossRef]

38. Patra, J.C.; van den Bos, A. Auto-calibration and -compensation of a capacitive pressure sensor using multilayer perceptrons. *ISA Trans.* **2000**, *39*, 175–190. [CrossRef]

39. Kurt, I.; Ture, M.; Kurum, A.T. Comparing performances of logistic regression, classification and regression tree, and neural networks for predicting coronary artery disease. *Expert Syst. Appl.* **2008**, *34*, 366–374. [CrossRef]

40. Imrie, C.E.; Durucan, S.; Korre, A. River flow prediction using artificial neural networks: Generalization beyond the calibration range. *J. Hydrol.* **2000**, *233*, 138–153. [CrossRef]

41. Pasini, A. Artificial neural networks for small dataset analysis. *J. Thorac. Dis.* **2015**, *7*, 953–960. [PubMed]

42. Prechelt, L.; Orr, G.B. Early Stopping—But When? In *Neural Networks: Tricks of the Trade. Lecture Notes in Computer Science*; Montavon, G., Müller, K.R., Eds.; Springer: Berlin, Germany; Heidelberg, Germany, 2012; pp. 53–67.

43. Hu, T.S.; Lam, K.C.; Ng, S.T. River flow time series prediction with a range dependent neural network. *Hydrol. Sci. J.* **2001**, *46*, 729–745. [CrossRef]

water

Article

Spatial Disaggregation of Areal Rainfall Using Two Different Artificial Neural Networks Models

Sungwon Kim [1,*] and Vijay P. Singh [2]

[1]   Department of Railroad and Civil Engineering, Dongyang University, Yeongju 750-711, Korea
[2]   Department of Biological and Agricultural Engineering & Zachry Department of Civil Engineering,
      Texas A & M University, College Station, TX 77843-2117, USA; vsingh@tamu.edu
*   Correspondence: swkim1968@dyu.ac.kr; Tel.: +82-54-630-1241; Fax: +82-54-637-8027

Academic Editor: Kwok-wing Chau
Received: 14 April 2015; Accepted: 26 May 2015; Published: 5 June 2015

Abstract: The objective of this study is to develop artificial neural network (ANN) models, including multilayer perceptron (MLP) and Kohonen self-organizing feature map (KSOFM), for spatial disaggregation of areal rainfall in the Wi-stream catchment, an International Hydrological Program (IHP) representative catchment, in South Korea. A three-layer MLP model, using three training algorithms, was used to estimate areal rainfall. The Levenberg–Marquardt training algorithm was found to be more sensitive to the number of hidden nodes than were the conjugate gradient and quickprop training algorithms using the MLP model. Results showed that the networks structures of 11-5-1 (conjugate gradient and quickprop) and 11-3-1 (Levenberg-Marquardt) were the best for estimating areal rainfall using the MLP model. The networks structures of 1-5-11 (conjugate gradient and quickprop) and 1-3-11 (Levenberg–Marquardt), which are the inverse networks for estimating areal rainfall using the best MLP model, were identified for spatial disaggregation of areal rainfall using the MLP model. The KSOFM model was compared with the MLP model for spatial disaggregation of areal rainfall. The MLP and KSOFM models could disaggregate areal rainfall into individual point rainfall with spatial concepts.

Keywords: areal rainfall; conjugate gradient; Kohonen self-organizing feature map; Levenberg-Marquardt; multilayer perceptron; quickprop; rainfall disaggregation

1. Introduction

Rainfall is a necessary input for the design of hydrologic and hydraulic systems. Rainfall can be either measured or generated using stochastic simulation [1]. The variability of rainfall has been acknowledged as a reason for the uncertainties in hydrologic applications. To minimize uncertainties calls for methods that improve the reliability of rainfall estimation by combining rainfall information from different sources [2].

Areal rainfall is the average rainfall over the region under consideration and is estimated by one of the popular methods, such as arithmetic mean, Thiessen polygon, isohyetal, spline, kriging, and copula amongst others [3–5]. The arithmetic mean method is the simplest one for determining areal rainfall. The Thiessen polygon method assumes a linear variation in rainfall between two neighboring stations and polygons are constructed which are essentially areal weights. This method is considered more accurate than the arithmetic mean method. The isohyetal method involves construction of isohyets using observed depths at rainfall stations and assumes a linear variation between two adjacent isohyets [4,6] The spline method is an interpolation method that divides interpolation intervals into small subintervals and each of these subintervals is interpolated by using the third-degree polynomial [7,8]. The kriging method is an optimal interpolator, based on regression against observed rainfall values of surrounding rainfall points, weighted according to spatial covariance values [5,9].

The copula method can be employed to describe the dependencies on an n dimensional unit cube (uniform) among n random variables. Description of the spatial dependence structure independent of the marginal distribution is one of the most attractive features of copulas [10,11].

Rainfall disaggregation can be both temporal and spatial. Temporal rainfall disaggregation entails disaggregating hourly, daily, or longer duration rainfall into short time rainfall, and many techniques have been proposed [12–25]. Techniques for spatial rainfall disaggregation using various interpolations and global climate models (GCMs) scenarios have been proposed. However, relatively limited research has been reported on spatial rainfall disaggregation as compared with temporal rainfall disaggregation [26–29].

Artificial neural networks (ANNs) are a robust computational method that has been primarily used for pattern recognition, classification, and prediction [30]. The main advantage of the ANNs as an alternative of the physical and conventional methods is that we do not need an explicit description in mathematical terms for the complex processes of the system under consideration [31–33]. Therefore, ANNs can generalize the strong nonlinear patterns of natural phenomena, including aggregation and disaggregation of rainfall with stabilization.

During the past decades, a variety of ANNs have been developed and applied for temporal rainfall disaggregation [1,34,35]. In this study, two ANN models, including multilayer perceptron (MLP) and Kohonen self-organizing feature map (KSOFM), have been applied to estimate spatial disaggregation of areal rainfall in the Wi-stream catchment. MLP and KSOFM have been used effectively to model and forecast hydrologic time series. Recently, outstanding results using the MLP and KSOFM models in the fields of modeling and forecasting, including evapotranspiration, pan evaporation, river flood, precipitation downscaling, dew point temperature, soil temperature, and water level and so on, have been obtained [31,36–47]. In this study, areal rainfall is the average rainfall over the region under consideration and is estimated using the kriging method. Spatial disaggregation of areal rainfall, therefore, refers to the process of estimating point rainfall corresponding to individual rainfall stations. Although there have been many investigations using ANNs, their application for spatial disaggregation of areal rainfall has been limited. The mathematical formulas based on the spatial disaggregation of areal rainfall on the catchment cannot be derived or developed using conventional methods, including simple regression analysis. Therefore, the strong nonlinear behavior in nature, such as spatial disaggregation of areal rainfall, can be overcome using the ANNs successfully in this study.

The objective of this study therefore is to develop and apply two ANN models, including multilayer perceptron (MLP) and Kohonen self-organizing feature map (KSOFM), for spatial disaggregation of areal rainfall in the Wi-stream catchment, an IHP representative catchment, in South Korea. The paper is organized as follows: The second part describes ANNs, including MLP and KSOFM. The third part describes a case study, including data used and study area. The forth part presents application and results. Conclusions are presented in the last part of the paper.

2. Artificial Neural Networks

2.1. Multilayer Perceptron (MLP) Model

The MLP model has an input layer, an output layer, and one or more hidden layers between input and output layers. The nodes in one layer are connected only to the nodes of the immediate next layer. The strength of signal passing from one node to the other depends on the connection weights of interconnections. The hidden layers enhance the network's ability to model complex functions.

The MLP model is trained using many kinds of backpropagation algorithms. Training is a process of adjusting the connection weights and biases, which calculate the error committed by the networks simply by taking the difference between the desired and actual responses, so that its output can match the desired output best [30,48]. Detailed information for the MLP model can be found in Tsoukalas and Uhrig [49] and Kim *et al.* [38–40].

2.2. Kohonen Self-Organizing Feature Map (KSOFM) Model

The KSOFM consists of four layers, that is, the input layer, Kohonen layer, hidden layer, and output layer. The input layer is composed of n input nodes, each connected to all nodes of the Kohonen layer [50–54]. The Kohonen layer consists of $[n_1$-by-$n_1]$ matrices. The KSOFM model is a simple yet powerful learning process and an effective clustering method, and uses a neighborhood function to preserve the topological properties of the input space. It can transform high dimensional input patterns into the responses of two-dimensional arrays of neurons and perform this transformation adaptively in a topologically ordered fashion based on similarity. Detailed information on the KSOFM model can be found in Kohonen [55,56], Principe *et al.* [57], and Hsu *et al.* [58].

3. Case Study

The data derived from the Wi-stream catchment were employed to train, cross-validate, and test ANNs models. The Wi-stream catchment, shown in Figure 1, is located in 36°10′ N to 36°14′ N in latitude and in 128°33′ E to 128°54′ E in longitude. The catchment is in Kunwi-gun County, which is located in the center of Gyeongsangbuk-do province. The catchment, 472.53 km^2 in area, represents 77.1% of the total area, 612.86 km^2, of Kunwi-gun county. The Wi-stream catchment is narrow from south to north and long from east to west. The central part of the Wi-stream catchment is quite flat and suffers from storm and flood damages every year. There are six river stage stations, six groundwater stations, 11 rainfall stations, and 11 evaporation stations in the Wi-stream catchment. The stream network consists of one main stream and one tributary [59]. The hydrological data of the Wi-stream catchment, such as rainfall, river stage, discharge, and groundwater table, have been recorded since 1982.

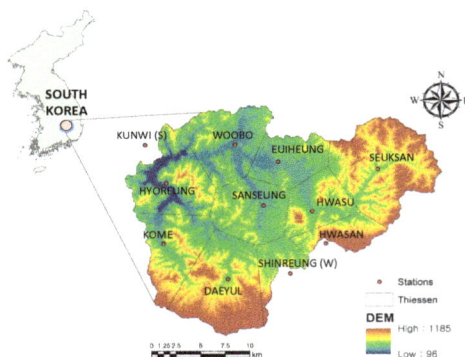

Figure 1. Schematic diagram of the Wi-stream catchment.

To estimate areal rainfall using the kriging method in the Wi-stream catchment, hourly rainfall data from 11 rainfall stations, including Kunwi (S) (No.1), Hyoreung (No.2), Daeyul (No.3), Kome (No.4), Woobo (No.5), Sanseung (No.6), Shinreung (No.7), Euiheung (No.8), Hwasu (No.9), Hwasan (No.10), and Seuksan (No.11), were used. In order for ANNs to make accurate generalizations about rainfall, sufficient rainfall data should be available [31]. Rainfall must be recorded for more than 24 h, including non-rainfall hour, and non-rainfall period must be within 3 h in order to prevent overfitting when ANN models are trained for this study. Fourteen rainfall events (Cases 1–14) were chosen from the mid-1980s to the mid-1990s to meet this condition. For estimating areal rainfall using the MLP model, input nodes consist of point rainfall values from individual rainfall stations including Kunwi (S) (No.1), Hyoreung (No.2), Daeyul (No.3), Kome (No.4), Woobo (No.5), Sanseung (No.6), Shinreung (No.7), Euiheung (No.8), Hwasu (No.9), Hwasan (No.10), and Seuksan (No.11) stations. Output node consists of areal rainfall values using the kriging method from individual rainfall stations and *vice versa* for spatial disaggregation of areal rainfall using the MLP and KSOFM models.

For ANNs model, data were split into training, cross-validation, and testing sets. The training data were used for optimizing the connection weights and bias of ANNs model. In general, one of the problems that weaken the training performances is overfitting. If the overfitting problem occurs, the convergence process over the mean square error of the testing data will not decrease but will increase as the training data are still trained [31]. It usually occurs when an ANN model has memorized the training data and has not learned to generalize to new situations. To minimize the effect of overfitting, cross-validation data was used through an early stopping technique where an ANN model performance for the cross-validation data was monitored, and training performance was stopped when error on the cross-validation data began to rise. Once the ANN model was trained, the generalization and modeling ability of the ANN model was evaluated using a completely new testing data [60,61]. In all of these applications, 67% of data (Cases 1, 2, 3, 4, 5, 6, 7, 9 and 10, *N* = 338 h) was applied for training, 15% of data (Cases 8 and 11, *N* = 77 h) for cross-validation, and 18% of data (Cases 12, 13, and 14, *N* = 91 days) for testing.

Table 1 shows a summary of statistical indices of data used. In Table 1, X_{mean}, X_{max}, X_{min}, S_x, C_v, C_{sx}, and SE denote, respectively, the mean, maximum, minimum, standard deviation, coefficient of variation, skewness coefficient and standard error values of training, cross-validation, and testing data. The estimated values were compared with observed values using four different performance evaluation criteria: the Nash-Sutcliffe efficiency [62] (NS), root mean square error (RMSE), mean absolute error (MAE), and average performance error (APE). As a measure of the accuracy of any hydrologic model, NS is one of the most widely used criteria for calibration and evaluation of hydrological models [63]. It has been shown that NS alone cannot define which model is better than others. The various evaluation criteria (e.g., RMSE, MAE, and APE) must be used to define the model performance. The NS, RMSE, MAE, and APE evaluation criteria quantify the efficiency of a model in capturing extremely complex, dynamic, nonlinear, and fragmented relationships. A model, which is efficient in capturing the complex relationship among the various input and output variables involved in a particular problem, must be considered [64]. Table 2 shows mathematical expressions of performance evaluation criteria.

Table 1. Statistical indices of areal rainfall data using the kriging method.

Division	Number of Data	Statistical Indices of Areal Rainfall						
		X_{mean}	X_{max}	X_{min}	S_x	C_v	C_{sx}	SE
Training	338	3.26	27.76	0.00	4.21	1.12	2.32	0.21
Cross-validation	77	2.10	16.68	0.00	3.12	1.32	2.62	0.34
Testing	91	3.62	19.56	0.00	4.13	1.13	1.46	0.42

Table 2. Mathematical expressions of performance evaluation criteria.

Evaluation Criteria	Equation
NS	$1 - \dfrac{\sum_{i=1}^{n} [y_i(x) - \hat{y}_i(x)]^2}{\sum_{i=1}^{n} [y_i(x) - u_y]^2}$
RMSE	$\sqrt{\dfrac{1}{n}\sum_{i=1}^{n} [y_i(x) - \hat{y}_i(x)]^2}$
MAE	$\dfrac{1}{n}\sum_{i=1}^{n} |y_i(x) - \hat{y}_i(x)|$
APE	$\dfrac{\sum_{i=1}^{n} |y_i(x) - \hat{y}_i(x)|}{\sum_{i=1}^{n} y_i(x)} \times 100$

Notes: $y_i(x)$ = the observed hourly rainfall (mm); $y_i(x)$ = the estimated hourly rainfall (mm); u_v = the mean of observed hourly rainfall (mm); and *n* = the total number of hourly rainfall values considered.

4. Applications and Results

4.1. Selection of Optimal MLP Models for Estimating Areal Rainfall

Selection of an appropriate structure is important, because the network structure of ANNs directly affects the computational complexity and generalization capability [65]. Currently, there is no reliable and established method for selecting an appropriate network structure before completion of training [66]. A three-layer ANN, with a single hidden layer, has been usually sufficient for approximating conventional hydrological processes [67]. The training performance of ANNs is iterated until the training error is reached to the training tolerance [38–40]. In this study, the training tolerance where the mean square error converged to a certain value was fixed at 0.001. The training performances of MLP and KSOFM models were stopped after 10,000 iterations. Results of training were slightly different from each completion of training performance, because the values of initial weights for each layer were set as random values. Therefore, optimal parameters were determined when the results of training showed the best categories [31]. A three-layer MLP, with a single hidden layer, was used to estimate areal rainfall. Since the kriging method includes considerable variables to estimate the areal rainfall compared with the Thiessen polygon and spline methods, areal rainfall estimated using the kriging method was assumed as the observed areal rainfall. Based on the training data, the MLP model adopted three training algorithms, conjugate gradient [68,69], Levenberg–Marquardt [70,71], and quickprop [72], using different numbers of hidden nodes ranging from 1 to 10. Three training algorithms, including conjugate gradient, Levenberg–Marquardt, and quickprop, were used for the MLP model from the previous literatures. Outstanding results using the three training algorithms have been reported previously [37–44,61]. To overcome problems associated with extreme values, the data were normalized and scaled between 0 and 1. Another important reason for data normalization is that different data sets represent observed values in different units. The similarity effect of data was also eliminated [73,74].

Figure 2 shows the influence of the number of hidden nodes on the performance evaluation criteria (NS, RMSE, MAE, and APE) for three training algorithms during the test period. The Levenberg-Marquardt training algorithm was more sensitive to the number of hidden nodes than were conjugate gradient and quickprop training algorithms, as seen from large fluctuations with respect to the number of hidden nodes. This result is consistent with that reported by [61]. The best values of NS, RMSE, MAE, and APE for 11-5-1 networks were, respectively, 0.996, 0.242, 0.072, and 2.014 for the conjugate gradient training algorithm. The best values of NS, RMSE, MAE, and APE for 11-3-1 networks were, respectively, 0.992, 0.398, 0.258, and 7.401 for the Levenberg-Marquardt training algorithm. The best values of NS, RMSE, MAE, and APE for 11-5-1 networks were, respectively, 0.984, 0.514, 0.317, and 9.029 for quickprop training algorithm. It is clear from Figure 2a–d that 11-5-1 networks was the best for conjugate gradient and quickprop training algorithms, and 11-3-1 networks was the best for Levenberg-Marquardt training algorithm. The inverse networks of 11-5-1 and 11-3-1 structures, 1-5-11 (conjugate gradient and quickprop) and 1-3-11 (Levenberg-Marquardt), were identified for spatial disaggregation of areal rainfall using the MLP model. In this study, results of the MLP output layer with a 11-5-1 structure can be written as:

$$R_a = \Phi_2 \left(\sum_{k=1}^{1} W_{kj} \cdot \Phi_1 \left(\sum_{j=1}^{5} W_{ji} \cdot X(t) + B_1 \right) + B_2 \right) \tag{1}$$

where i, j, k = the input, hidden, and output layers, respectively; R_a = the areal rainfall (mm); $\Phi_1(\cdot)$ = the linear sigmoid transfer function of hidden layer; $\Phi_2(\cdot)$ = the linear sigmoid transfer function of output layer; W_{kj} = the connection weights between the hidden and output layers; W_{ji} = the connection weights between the input and hidden layers; X(t) = the time series data of input variables; B_1 = the bias in hidden layer; and B_2 = the bias in output layer. Figure 3 shows the structure of MLP (11-5-1) developed for estimating areal rainfall in this study.

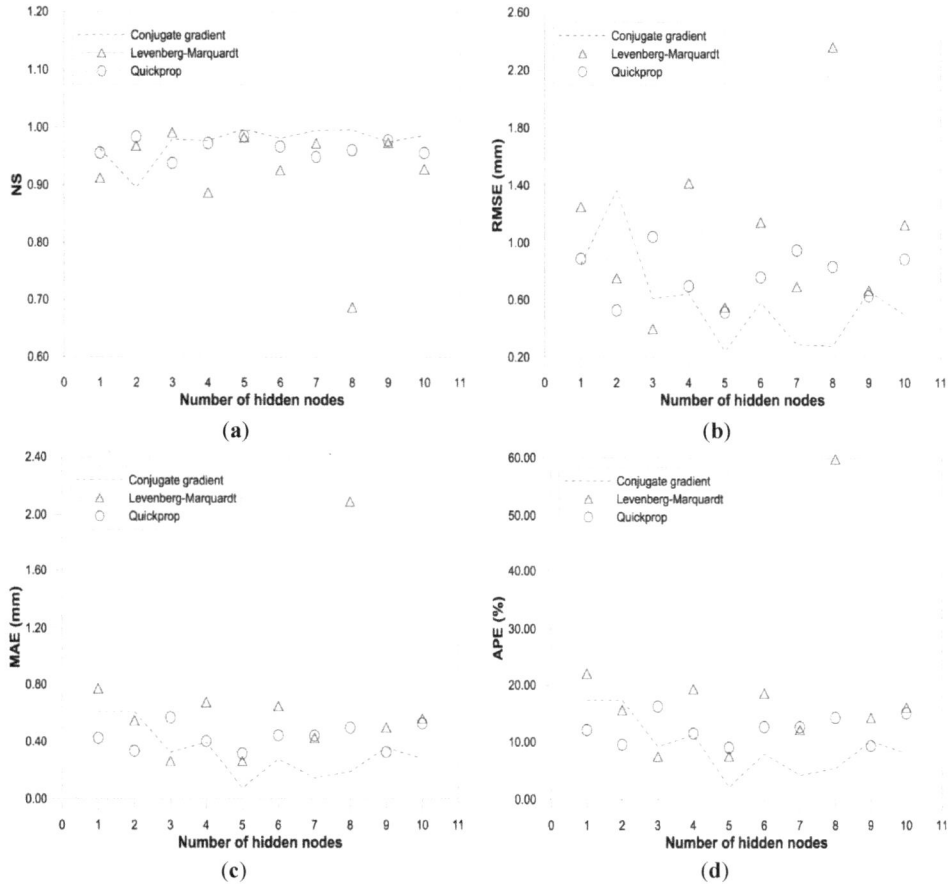

Figure 2. Influence of the number of hidden nodes for three training algorithms (test period). (**a**) NS; (**b**) MAF; (**c**) RMSE; (**d**) APE.

Before the chosen structures, such as 11-5-1 and 11-3-1, for three training algorithms were used for the spatial disaggregation of areal rainfall, homogeneity between observed (kriging method) and estimated (MLP model) areal rainfall values was analyzed. The Mann-Whitney U test, one of the tests for homogeneity, was used to compare observed and estimated areal rainfall values to evaluate the confidence level of MLP model. It is a nonparametric alternative to the two-sample t-test for two independent samples and can be used to test whether two independent samples have been taken from the same population [75–78]. The critical value of z statistic (z_α) was computed for the specific level of significance. If the computed value of z statistic is greater than the critical value of z statistic (z_α), the null hypothesis, that the two independent samples are from the same population, should be rejected and the alternative hypothesis should be accepted.

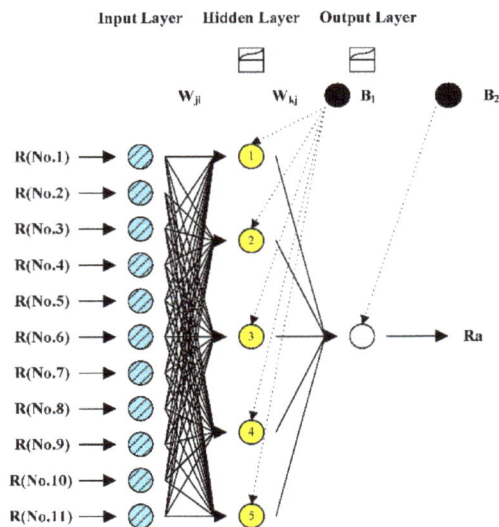

Figure 3. Structure of MLP (11-5-1) developed for estimating areal rainfall.

Table 3 shows results of the Mann-Whitney U test between observed and estimated areal rainfall values for the testing data. The critical value of z statistic (z_α), $z_{0.05} = 1.960$, was computed for the five percent level of significance. Since the computed values of z statistic for both stations were not significant, the null hypothesis was accepted for areal rainfall using the MLP model.

Table 3. Results of the Mann-Whitney U test.

Model	Networks	Training Algorithms	Level of Significance	Mann-Whitney U test		
				Critical z Statistic	Computed z Statistic	Null Hypothesis
	11-5-1	Conjugate gradient	0.05	1.960	−0.287	Accept
MLP	11-3-1	Levenberg–Marquardt	0.05	1.960	−0.617	Accept
	11-5-1	Quickprop	0.05	1.960	−0.515	Accept

4.2. Evaluation for Spatial Disaggregation of Areal Rainfall Using MLP Model

Three different MLP models, including 1-5-11 (conjugate gradient), 1-3-11 (Levenberg–Marquardt), and 1-5-11 (quickprop), were used for spatial disaggregation of areal rainfall. Figure 4 shows the developed structure of MLP (1-5-11) for spatial disaggregation of areal rainfall.

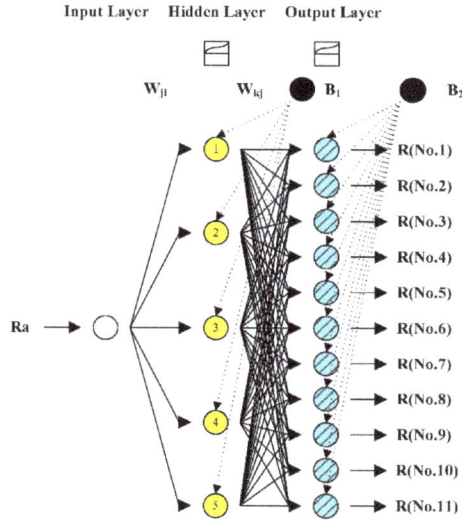

Figure 4. Structure of MLP (1-5-11) developed for spatial disaggregation of areal rainfall.

Figure 5 shows the influence of individual rainfall station on the performance evaluation criteria (NS, RMSE, MAE, and APE) for three training algorithms during the test period. The three training algorithms were generally sensitive to individual rainfall station, as seen from large fluctuations with respect to the individual rainfall station. The spatial disaggregated rainfall using three training algorithms yielded similar values on the performance evaluation criteria (NS, RMSE, MAE, and APE) for individual rainfall station. For Euiheung (No.8) station, the values of NS, RMSE, MAE, and APE were 0.870, 1.480, 0.849, and 25.335, respectively, for 1-5-11 structure (conjugate gradient); were 0.886, 1.385, 0.732, and 21.863, respectively, for 1-3-11 structure (Levenberg–Marquardt); and were 0.869, 1.481, 0.723, and 21.553, respectively, for 1-5-11 structure (quickprop). Figure 5a–d shows that spatial disaggregated rainfall at Euiheung (No.8) station yielded the best results among the 11 rainfall stations for the MLP model. For Hwasu (No.9) station, the values of NS, RMSE, MAE, and APE were 0.378, 3.515, 1.817, and 52.021, respectively, for 1-5-11 structure (conjugate gradient); were 0.388, 3.492, 1.795, and 51.431, respectively, for 1-3-11 structure (Levenberg–Marquardt); and were 0.373, 3.531, 1.805, and 51.680, respectively, for 1-5-11 structure (quickprop). Figure 5a–d shows that spatial disaggregated rainfall at Hwasu (No.9) station yielded the worst results among the 11 rainfall stations for the MLP model. In this study, the MLP model is capable of disaggregating areal rainfall into individual point rainfall.

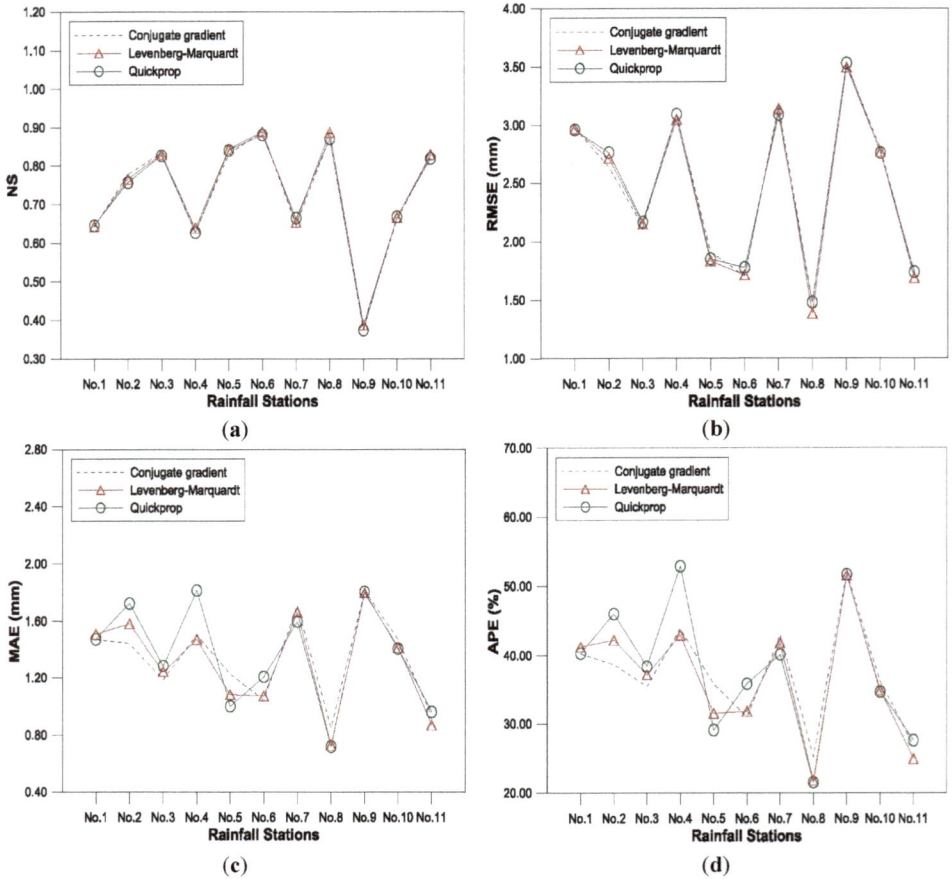

Figure 5. Influence of individual rainfall stations for three training algorithms of MLP (test period). (a) NS; (b) MAF; (c) RMSE; (d) APE.

4.3. Evaluation for Spatial Disaggregation of Areal Rainfall Using KSOFM Model

The KSOFM model was used and compared with the MLP model for spatial disaggregation of areal rainfall. The KSOFM model classifies each input node and determines as to which node in the hidden layer it must be routed for spatial disaggregation of areal rainfall for the output layer. Six different KSOFM models, including (1) [5-by-5] and [7-by-7] matrices in the Kohonen layer; and (2) 11-5-1 (conjugate gradient), 11-3-1 (Levenberg–Marquardt), and 11-5-1 (quickprop) in the hidden layer, were used for spatial disaggregation of areal rainfall. Figure 6 shows the developed structure of the KSOFM (1-[5-by-5]-5-11) for spatial disaggregation of areal rainfall. Results of the KSOFM output layer with 1-[5-by-5]-5-11 structure can be written as:

$$R_d = \Phi_2 \left(\sum_{l=1}^{11} W_{lk} \cdot \Phi_1 \left(\sum_{k=1}^{5} W_{kj} \cdot S_j + B_1 \right) + B_2 \right) \qquad (2)$$

where i, j, k, l = the input, Kohonen, hidden, and output layers, respectively; R_d = the disaggregated rainfall (mm) for individual rainfall station; W_{kj} = the connection weights between the Kohonen and hidden layers; S_j = the results calculated from the Euclidean distance (d_j) and the Kohonen layer; $\Phi_1(\cdot)$ = the linear sigmoid transfer function of hidden layer; $\Phi_2(\cdot)$ = the linear sigmoid transfer function of output layer; B_1 = the bias in hidden layer; B_2 = the bias in output layer; and W_{lk} = the connection weights between the hidden and output layers. The Euclidean distance between the input and Kohonen nodes can be written as:

$$d_j = \sqrt{\sum_{i=1}^{n} (x_i - W_{ji})^2} \tag{3}$$

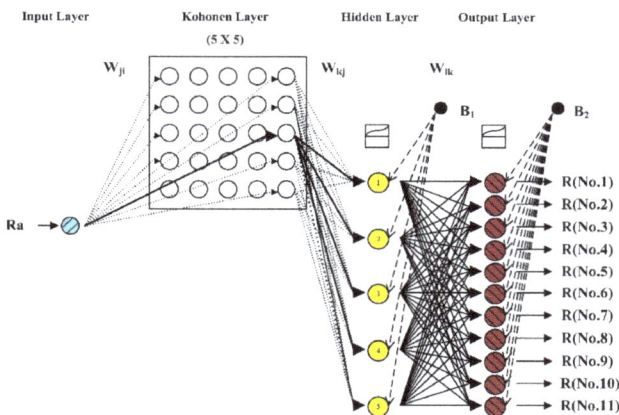

Figure 6. Structure of KSOFM (1-[5 X 5]-5-11) developed for spatial disaggregation of areal rainfall.

Figure 7 shows the influence of individual rainfall station on the performance evaluation criteria (NS, RMSE, MAE, and APE) for the three training algorithms of the KSOFM model based on [5-by-5] matrice (KSOFM1) during the test period. The three training algorithms were generally sensitive to individual rainfall station, as seen from large fluctuations with respect to the individual rainfall station. The spatial disaggregated rainfall using the three training algorithms yielded similar values on the performance evaluation criteria (NS, RMSE, MAE, and APE) for individual rainfall station. For Euiheung (No.8) station, the values of NS, RMSE, MAE, and APE were 0.847, 1.615, 1.174, and 35.129, respectively, for 1-5-11 structure (conjugate gradient); were 0.885, 1.402, 0.884, and 26.462, respectively, for 1-3-11 structure (Levenberg–Marquardt); and were 0.877, 1.436, 0.738, and 22.035, respectively, for 1-5-11 structure (quickprop). Figure 7 shows that spatial disaggregated rainfall at Euiheung (No.8) station yielded the best results among the 11 rainfall stations for KSOFM1 model. For Hwasu (No.9) station, the values of NS, RMSE, MAE, and APE were 0.358, 3.573, 1.885, and 53.953, respectively, for 1-5-11 structure (conjugate gradient); were 0.408, 3.432, 1.778, and 50.907, respectively, for 1-3-11 structure (Levenberg–Marquardt); and were 0.388, 3.492, 1.736, and 49.732, respectively, for 1-5-11 structure (quickprop). Figure 7 shows that spatial disaggregated rainfall at Hwasu (No.9) station yielded the worst results among the 11 rainfall stations for KSOFM1 model.

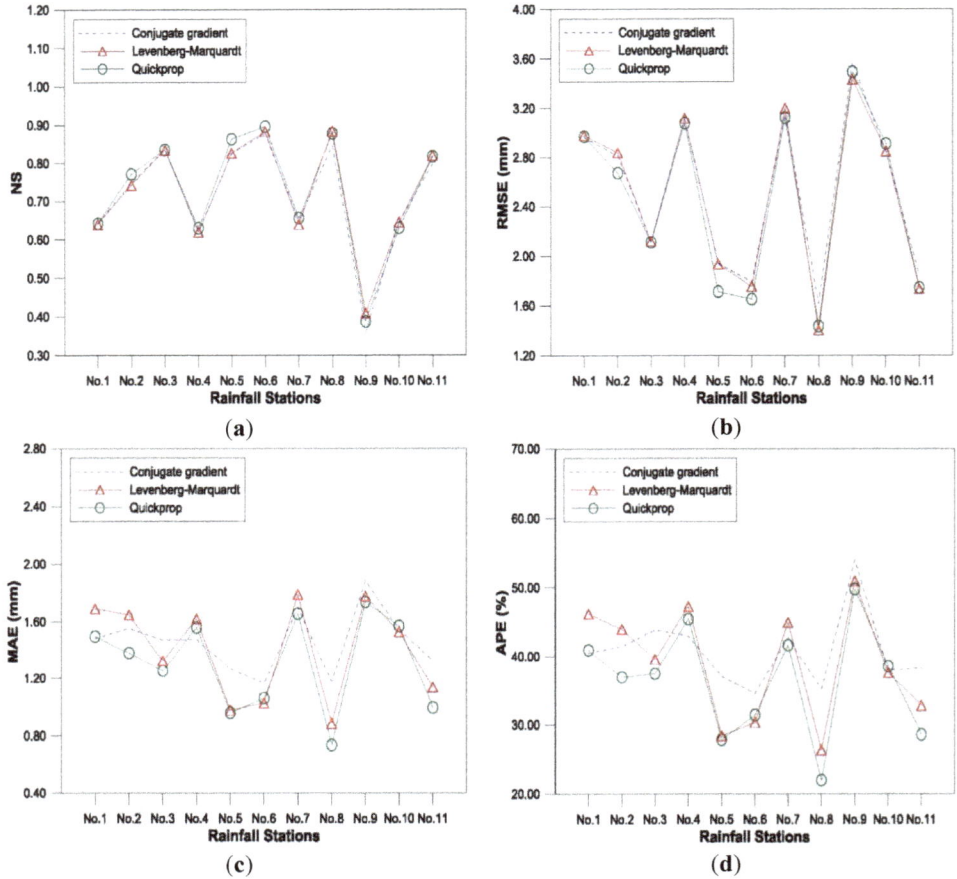

Figure 7. Influence of individual rainfall stations for three training algorithms of KSOFM1 (test period). (a) NS; (b) MAF; (c) RMSE; (d) APE.

Figure 8 shows the influence of individual rainfall station on the performance evaluation criteria (NS, RMSE, MAE, and APE) for the three training algorithms of the KSOFM model based on [7-by-7] matrice (KSOFM2) during the test period. The three training algorithms were generally sensitive to individual rainfall station, as seen from large fluctuations with respect to the individual rainfall station. The spatial disaggregated rainfall using three training algorithms yielded similar values on performance evaluation criteria (NS, RMSE, MAE, and APE) for individual rainfall station. For Euiheung (No.8) station, the values of NS, RMSE, MAE, and APE were 0.845, 1.622, 1.130, and 33.806, respectively, for 1-5-11 structure (conjugate gradient); were 0.895, 1.334, 0.791, and 23.680, respectively, for 1-3-11 structure (Levenberg–Marquardt); and were 0.888, 1.371, 0.715, and 21.354, respectively, for 1-5-11 structure (quickprop). Figure 8 shows that spatial disaggregated rainfall at Euiheung (No.8) station yielded the best results among the 11 rainfall stations for the KSOFM2 model. For Hwasu (No.9) station, the values of NS, RMSE, MAE, and APE were 0.317, 3.687, 2.176, and 62.290, respectively, for 1-5-11 structure (conjugate gradient); were 0.427, 3.378, 1.702, and 48.680, respectively, for 1-3-11 structure (Levenberg–Marquardt); and were 0.385, 3.496, 1.726, and 49.398, respectively, for 1-5-11 structure (quickprop). Figure 8 shows that spatial disaggregated rainfall at Hwasu (No.9) station yielded the worst results among the 11 rainfall stations for the KSOFM2 model. In this study, the KSOFM1 and KSOFM2 models were capable of disaggregating areal rainfall into individual point rainfall. However, because of strong nonlinearity of rainfall, it is difficult to conclude with confidence which model is superior to other models. The specific rainfall stations did not generally show the satisfactory results in the evaluation criteria for the three training algorithms of the MLP, KSOFM1, and KSOFM2 performances. It can be found that the spatial distribution of rainfall stations can affect the performance of ANNs models from this observation.

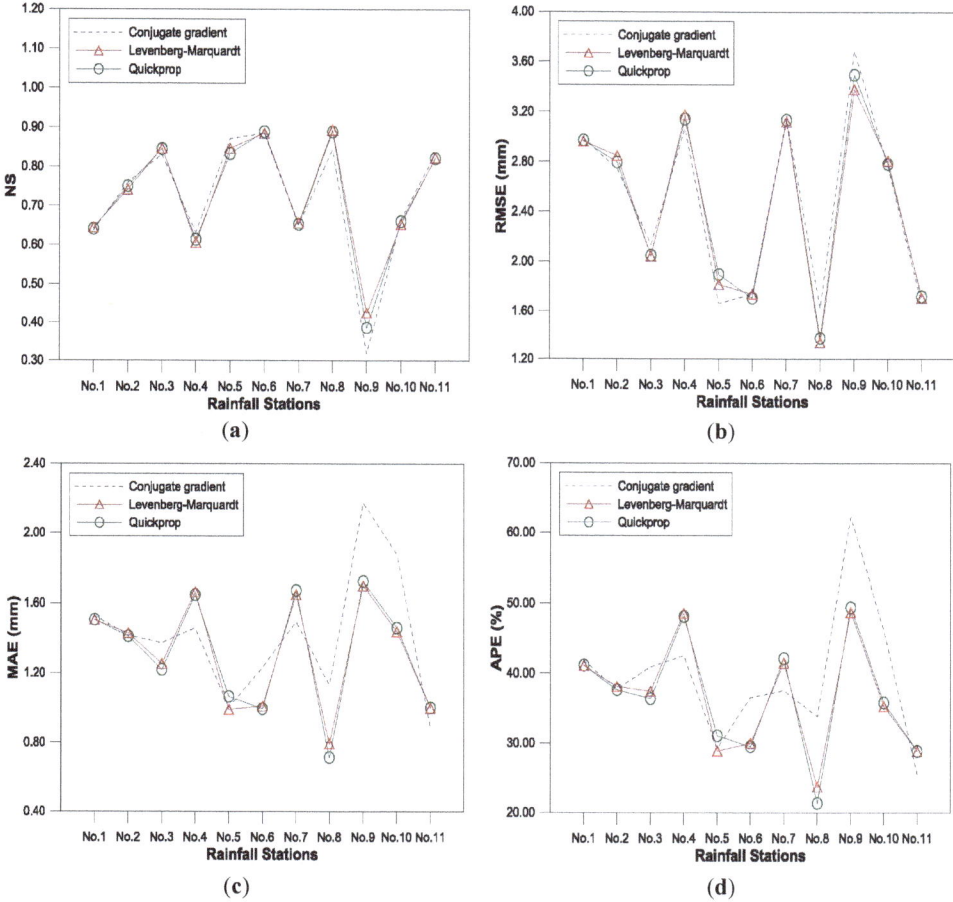

Figure 8. Influence of individual rainfall stations for three training algorithms of KSOFM2 (test period). (**a**) NS; (**b**) MAF; (**c**) RMSE; (**d**) APE.

Figures 9 and 10 show the box plots for spatial disaggregated rainfall during the test period at Euiheung (No.8) and Hwasu (No.9) stations. The box plots show the distributions of basic statistics for performances of MLP, KSOFM1, and KSOFM2 with three training algorithms. Figures 9 and 10 show the centerline (median) dividing the rectangular box defined by 25th and 75th percentiles, and lines extend from maximum to minimum data point at Euiheung (No.8) and Hwasu (No.9) stations. The basic statistics of spatial disaggregated rainfall for performances of the MLP, KSOFM1, and KSOFM2 models yielded similar behaviors compared with observed rainfall at Euiheung (No.8) and Hwasu (No.9) stations except for the maximum rainfall values.

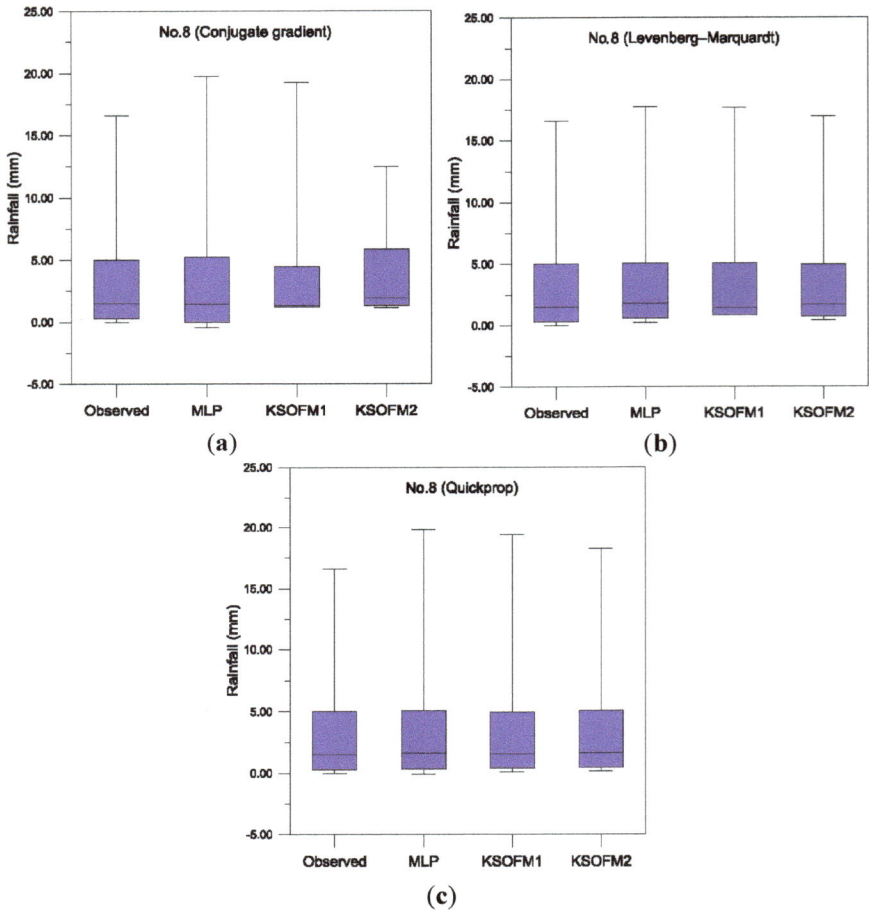

Figure 9. Rainfall box plots for Euiheung (No.8) station (test period). (**a**) Conjugate gradient; (**b**) Levenberg–Marquardt; (**c**) Quickprop.

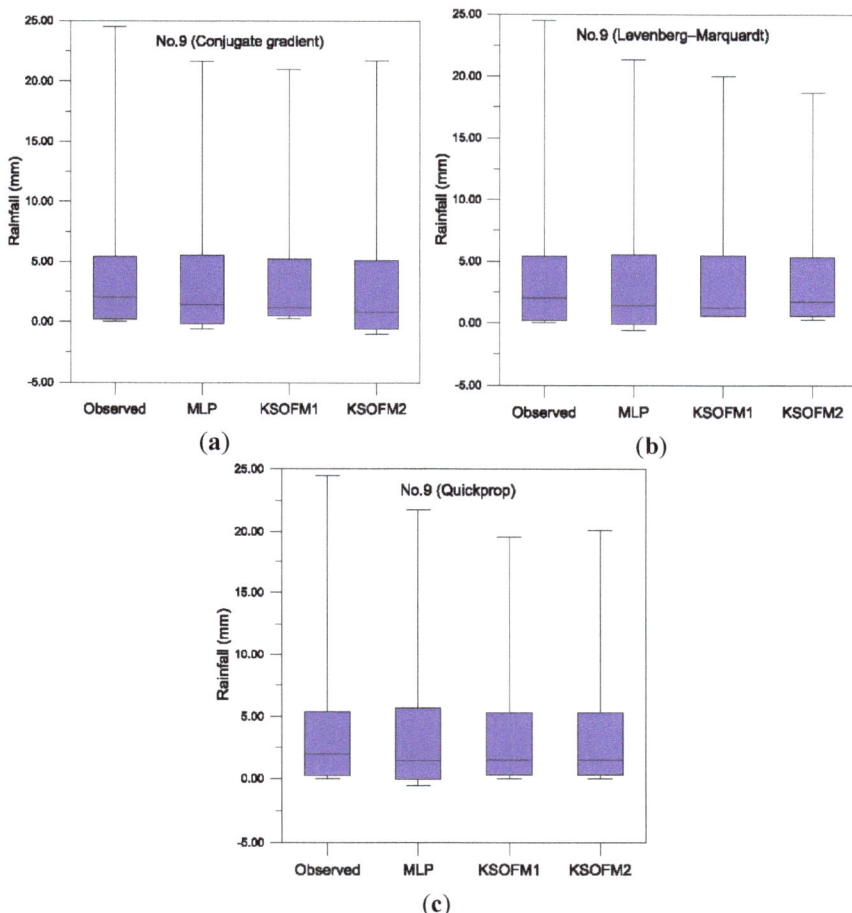

Figure 10. Rainfall box plots for Hwasu (No.9) station (test period). (a) Conjugate gradient; (b) Levenberg–Marquardt; (c) Quickprop.

5. Conclusions

This study develops and evaluates artificial neural network (ANN) models for spatial disaggregation of areal rainfall in the Wi-stream catchment, an IHP representative catchment, in South Korea. A three-layer MLP is used to estimate areal rainfall. Areal rainfall estimated using the kriging method is assumed as observed areal rainfall. Based on training data, the MLP models employ three training algorithms, conjugate gradient, Levenberg–Marquardt, and quickprop.

The influence of number of hidden nodes for the three training algorithms is evaluated to estimate areal rainfall using the MLP model. The Levenberg-Marquardt training algorithm is more sensitive to the number of hidden nodes than are the conjugate gradient and quickprop training algorithms. It is seen from large fluctuations with respect to the number of hidden nodes. The Mann-Whitney U test is performed to compare observed and estimated areal rainfall values to evaluate the confidence level of the MLP model. The null hypothesis is accepted for areal rainfall using the MLP model. The structures of 1-5-11 (conjugate gradient and quickprop) and 1-3-11 (Levenberg–Marquardt) are identified for spatial disaggregation of areal rainfall using the MLP model.

Three different MLP models are employed for spatial disaggregation of areal rainfall. The influence of individual rainfall station to disaggregate areal rainfall using the MLP model is evaluated. Three training algorithms are generally sensitive to individual rainfall station, as seen from large fluctuations with respect to the individual rainfall station. The spatial disaggregated rainfall using the three training algorithms yields similar values for individual rainfall station. The spatial disaggregated rainfall at Euiheung (No.8) station yields the best results, whereas spatial disaggregated rainfall at Hwasu (No.9) station yields the worst results among the 11 rainfall stations using the MLP model.

The KSOFM model is compared with the MLP model for spatial disaggregation of areal rainfall. Six different KSOFM models are employed for spatial disaggregation of areal rainfall. The spatial disaggregated rainfall at Euiheung (No.8) station yields the best results, whereas spatial disaggregated rainfall at Hwasu (No.9) station yields the worst results among the 11 rainfall stations using the KSOFM1 and KSOFM2 models, respectively.

It can be found that the MLP, KSOFM1, and KSOFM2 models can disaggregate areal rainfall into individual point rainfall. However, because of strong nonlinearity of rainfall, it is difficult to conclude with confidence as to which model is superior. Continuing studies, including data extension and new model application, are needed for aggregation and disaggregation of rainfall.

Author Contributions: All authors contributed extensively to the work presented in this paper. Sungwon Kim contributed to the subject of the research, literature review, manuscripts preparation, modeling, statistical analysis, and finalized the manuscripts. Vijay P. Singh contributed to the conceptualization, manuscripts revision and review, and supervised the research.

Conflicts of Interest: The authors declare no conflict of interest.

References

1. Burian, S.J.; Durrans, S.R.; Tomić, S.; Pimmel, R.L.; Wai, C.N. Rainfall disaggregation using artificial neural networks. *J. Hydrol. Eng. ASCE* **2000**, *5*, 299–307. [CrossRef]
2. Boushaki, F.I.; Hsu, K.L.; Sorooshian, S.; Park, G.H.; Mahani, S.; Shi, W. Bias adjustment of satellite precipitation estimation using ground-based measurement: A case study evaluation over the southwestern United States. *J. Hydrometeor.* **2009**, *10*, 1231–1242. [CrossRef]
3. AghaKouchak, A.; Bárdossy, A.; Habib, E. Conditional simulation of remotely sensed rainfall data using a non-Gaussian v-transformed copula. *Adv. Water Resour.* **2010**, *33*, 624–634. [CrossRef]
4. Chow, V.T.; Maidment, D.R.; Mays, L.W. *Applied Hydrology*; McGraw-Hill: New York, NY, USA, 1988.
5. Goovaerts, P. Geostatistical approaches for incorporating elevation into the spatial interpolation of rainfall. *J. Hydrol.* **2000**, *228*, 113–129. [CrossRef]
6. Singh, V.P. *Elementary Hydrology*; Prentice Hall: Englewood Cliffs, NJ, USA, 1992.
7. Apaydin, H.; Sonmez, F.K.; Yildirim, Y.E. Spatial interpolation techniques for climate data in the GAP region in Turkey. *Clim. Res.* **2004**, *28*, 31–40. [CrossRef]
8. Tait, A.; Henderson, R.; Turner, R.; Zheng, X. Thin plate smoothing spline interpolation of daily rainfall for New Zealand using a climatological rainfall surface. *Int. J. Climatol.* **2006**, *26*, 2097–2115. [CrossRef]
9. Ly, S.; Charles, C.; Degré, A. Geostatistical interpolation of daily rainfall at catchment scale: The use of several variogram models in the Ourthe and Ambleve catchments, Belgium. *Hydrol. Earth Syst. Sci.* **2011**, *15*, 2259–2274. [CrossRef]
10. Genest, C.; Favre, A.; Béliveau, J.; Jacques, C. Metaelliptical copulas and their use in frequency analysis of multivariate hydrological data. *Water Resour. Res.* **2007**, *43*, W09401:1–W09401:12. [CrossRef]
11. Zhang, L.; Singh, V.P. Bivariate rainfall frequency distributions using Archimedean copulas. *J. Hydrol.* **2007**, *332*, 93–109. [CrossRef]
12. Choi, J.; Socolofsky, S.; Olivera, F. Hourly disaggregation of daily rainfall in Texas using measured hourly precipitation at other locations. *J. Hydrol. Eng. ASCE* **2008**, *13*, 476–487. [CrossRef]
13. Connolly, R.D.; Schirmer, J.; Dunn, P.K. A daily rainfall disaggregation model. *Agric. For. Meteorol.* **1998**, *92*, 105–117. [CrossRef]
14. Durrans, S.; Burian, S.J.; Nix, S.J.; Hajji, A.; Pitt, R.E.; Fan, C.Y.; Field, R. Polynomial-based disaggregation of hourly rainfall for continuous hydrologic simulation. *J. Am. Water Resour. Assoc.* **1999**, *35*, 1213–1221.

15. Hershenhorn, J.; Woolhiser, D.A. Disaggregation of daily rainfall. *J. Hydrol.* **1987**, *95*, 299–322. [CrossRef]

16. Glasbey, C.A.; Cooper, G.; McGechan, M.B. Disaggregation of daily rainfall by conditional simulation from a point process model. *J. Hydrol.* **1995**, *165*, 1–9. [CrossRef]

17. Gyasi-Agyei, Y. Stochastic disaggregation of daily rainfall into one-hour time scale. *J. Hydrol.* **2005**, *309*, 178–190. [CrossRef]

18. Knoesen, D.; Smithers, J. The development and assessment of a daily rainfall disaggregation model for South Africa. *Hydrol. Sci. J.* **2009**, *54*, 217–233. [CrossRef]

19. Koutsoyiannis, D.; Xanthopoulos, T. A dynamic model for short-scale rainfall disaggregation. *Hydrol. Sci. J.* **1990**, *35*, 303–322. [CrossRef]

20. Olsson, J. Evaluation of a scaling cascade model for temporal rainfall disaggregation. *Hydrol. Earth Syst. Sci.* **1998**, *2*, 19–30. [CrossRef]

21. Olsson, J.; Berndtsson, R. Temporal rainfall disaggregation based on scaling properties. *Water Sci. Technol.* **1998**, *37*, 73–79. [CrossRef]

22. Ormsbee, L. Rainfall disaggregation model for continuous hydrologic modeling. *J. Hydraul. Eng. ASCE* **1989**, *115*, 507–525. [CrossRef]

23. Sivakumar, B.; Sorooshian, S.; Gupta, H.V.; Gao, X. A chaotic approach to rainfall disaggregation. *Water Resour. Res.* **2001**, *37*, 61–72. [CrossRef]

24. Socolofsky, S.; Adams, E.; Entekhabi, D. Disaggregation of daily rainfall for continuous watershed modeling. *J. Hydrol. Eng. ASCE* **2001**, *6*, 300–309. [CrossRef]

25. Zhang, J.; Murch, R.; Ross, M.; Ganguly, A.; Nachabe, M. Evaluation of statistical rainfall disaggregation methods using rain-gauge information for West-Central Florida. *J. Hydrol. Eng. ASCE* **2008**, *13*, 1158–1169. [CrossRef]

26. Perica, S.; Foufoula-Georgiou, E. Model for multiscale disaggregation of spatial rainfall based on coupling meteorological and scaling descriptions. *J. Geophys. Res.* **1996**, *101*, 26347–26361. [CrossRef]

27. Sharma, D.; das Gupta, A.; Babel, M.S. Spatial disaggregation of bias-corrected GCM precipitation for improved hydrologic simulation: Ping River Basin, Thailand. *Hydrol. Earth Syst. Sci.* **2007**, *11*, 1373–1390. [CrossRef]

28. Tsangaratos, P.; Rozos, D.; Benardos, A. Use of artificial neural network for spatial rainfall analysis. *J. Earth Syst. Sci.* **2014**, *123*, 457–465.

29. Venugopal, V.; Foufoula-Georgiou, E.; Sapozhnikov, V. A space-time downscaling model for rainfall. *J. Geophys. Res.* **1999**, *104*, 19705–19721. [CrossRef]

30. Haykin, S. *Neural Networks and Learning Machines*, 3rd ed.; Prentice Hall: New York, NJ, USA, 2009.

31. Kim, S.; Kim, H.S. Uncertainty reduction of the flood stage forecasting using neural networks model. *J. Am. Water Resour. Assoc.* **2008**, *44*, 148–165. [CrossRef]

32. Taormina, R.; Chau, K.W. Neural network river forecasting with multi-objective fully informed particle swarm optimization. *J. Hydroinform.* **2015**, *17*, 99–113. [CrossRef]

33. Wu, C.L.; Chau, K.W.; Li, Y.S. River stage prediction based on a distributed support vector regression. *J. Hydrol.* **2008**, *358*, 96–111. [CrossRef]

34. Burian, S.J.; Durrans, S.R.; Nix, S.J.; Pitt, R.E. Training artificial neural networks to perform rainfall disaggregation. *J. Hydrol. Eng. ASCE* **2001**, *6*, 43–51. [CrossRef]

35. Burian, S.J.; Durrans, S.R. Evaluation of an artificial neural network rainfall disaggregation model. *Water Sci. Technol.* **2002**, *45*, 99–104. [PubMed]

36. Kim, S. Modeling of precipitation downscaling using MLP-NNM and SVM-NNM approach. *Disaster Adv.* **2010**, *3*, 14–24.

37. Kim, S.; Kim, J.H.; Park, K.B. Neural networks models for the flood forecasting and disaster prevention system in the small catchment. *Disaster Adv.* **2009**, *2*, 51–63.

38. Kim, S.; Park, K.B.; Seo, Y. Estimation of pan evaporation using neural networks and climate-based models. *Disaster Adv.* **2012**, *5*, 34–43.

39. Kim, S.; Shiri, J.; Kisi, O. Pan evaporation modeling using neural computing approach for different climatic zones. *Water Resour. Manag.* **2012**, *26*, 3231–3249. [CrossRef]

40. Kim, S.; Shiri, J.; Kisi, O.; Singh, V.P. Estimating daily pan evaporation using different data-driven methods and lag-time patterns. *Water Resour. Manag.* **2013**, *27*, 2267–2286. [CrossRef]

41. Kim, S.; Singh, V.P. Flood forecasting using neural computing techniques and conceptual class segregation. *J. Am. Water Resour. Assoc.* **2013**, *49*, 1421–1435. [CrossRef]

42. Kim, S.; Singh, V.P. Modeling daily soil temperature using data-driven models and spatial distribution concepts. *Theor. Appl. Climatol.* **2014**, *118*, 465–479. [CrossRef]

43. Kim, S.; Singh, V.P.; Lee, C.J.; Seo, Y. Modeling the physical dynamics of daily dew point temperature using soft computing techniques. *KSCE J. Civ. Eng.* **2015**. [CrossRef]

44. Kim, S.; Singh, V.P.; Seo, Y. Evaluation of pan evaporation modeling with two different neural networks and weather station data. *Theor. Appl. Climatol.* **2014**, *117*, 1–13. [CrossRef]

45. Seo, Y.; Kim, S.; Kisi, O.; Singh, V.P. Daily water level forecasting using wavelet decomposition and artificial intelligence techniques. *J. Hydrol.* **2015**, *520*, 224–243. [CrossRef]

46. Seo, Y.; Kim, S.; Singh, V.P. Estimating spatial precipitation using regression kriging and artificial neural network residual kriging (RKNNRK) hybrid approach. *Water Resour. Manag.* **2015**, *29*, 2189–2204. [CrossRef]

47. Seo, Y.; Kim, S.; Singh, V.P. Multistep-ahead flood forecasting using wavelet and data-driven methods. *KSCE J. Civ. Eng.* **2015**, *19*, 401–417. [CrossRef]

48. Simpson, P.K. *Artificial Neural Systems: Foundations, Paradigms, Applications and Implementations*; Pergamon: New York, NY, USA, 1990.

49. Tsoukalas, L.H.; Uhrig, R.E. *Fuzzy and Neural Approaches in Engineering*; John Wiley & Sons Inc.: New York, NY, USA, 1997.

50. Chang, F.J.; Chang, L.C.; Wang, Y.S. Enforced self-organizing map neural networks for river flood forecasting. *Hydrol. Process.* **2007**, *21*, 741–749. [CrossRef]

51. Lin, G.F.; Chen, L.H. Time series forecasting by combining the radial basis function network and the self-organizing map. *Hydrol. Process.* **2005**, *19*, 1925–1937. [CrossRef]

52. Lin, G.F.; Chen, L.H. Identification of homogeneous regions for regional frequency analysis using self-organizing map. *J. Hydrol.* **2006**, *324*, 1–9. [CrossRef]

53. Lin, G.F.; Wu, M.C. A SOM-based approach to estimating design hyetographs of ungaged sites. *J. Hydrol.* **2007**, *339*, 216–226. [CrossRef]

54. Lin, G.F.; Wu, M.C. A hybrid neural network model for typhoon-rainfall forecasting. *J. Hydrol.* **2009**, *375*, 450–458. [CrossRef]

55. Kohonen, T. The self-organizing map. *Proc. IEEE* **1990**, *78*, 1464–1480. [CrossRef]

56. Kohonen, T. *Self-Organizing Maps*; Springer-Verlag: New York, NY, USA, 2001.

57. Principe, J.C.; Euliano, N.R.; Lefebvre, W.C. *Neural and Adaptive Systems: Fundamentals through Simulation*; Wiley, John & Sons: New York, NY, USA, 2000.

58. Hsu, K.; Gupta, V.H.; Gao, X.; Sorooshian, S.; Imam, B. Self-Organizing linear output map (SOLO): An artificial neural network suitable for hydrologic modeling and analysis. *Water Resour. Res.* **2002**, *38*, 1302. [CrossRef]

59. Ministry of Construction and Transportation. *Collection and Fundamental Analysis of Hydrologic Data of the Representative Basin*; International Hydrological Program (IHP): Seoul, Korea; pp. 1982–2007.

60. Dawson, C.W.; Wilby, R.L. Hydrological modelling using artificial neural networks. *Prog. Phys. Geogr.* **2001**, *25*, 80–108. [CrossRef]

61. Izadifar, Z.; Elshorbagy, A. Prediction of hourly actual evapotranspiration using neural networks, genetic programming, and statistical models. *Hydrol. Process.* **2010**, *24*, 3413–3425. [CrossRef]

62. Nash, J.; Sutcliffe, J.V. River flow forecasting through conceptual models part I—A discussion of principles. *J. Hydrol.* **1970**, *10*, 282–290. [CrossRef]

63. Gupta, H.V.; Kling, H.; Yilmaz, K.K.; Martinez, G.F. Decomposition of the mean squared error and NSE performance criteria: Implications for improving hydrological modeling. *J. Hydrol.* **2009**, *377*, 80–91. [CrossRef]

64. Jain, A.; Srinivasulu, S. Integrated approach to model decomposed flow hydrograph using artificial neural network and conceptual techniques. *J. Hydrol.* **2006**, *317*, 291–306. [CrossRef]

65. Jain, S.K.; Nayak, P.C.; Suhheer, K.P. Models for estimating evapotranspiration using artificial neural networks, and their physical interpretation. *Hydrol. Process.* **2008**, *22*, 2225–2234. [CrossRef]

66. Coulibaly, P.; Anctil, F.; Aravena, R.; Bobée, B. Artificial neural network modeling of water table depth fluctuations. *Water Resour. Res.* **2001**, *37*, 885–896. [CrossRef]

67. Maier, H.R.; Dandy, G.C. Neural networks for the prediction and forecasting of water resources variables: A review of modelling issues and applications. *Environ. Modell. Softw.* **2000**, *15*, 101–124. [CrossRef]

68. Adeli, H.; Hung, S.L. *Machine Learning Neural Networks, Genetic Algorithms, and Fuzzy Systems*; John Wiley & Sons Inc.: New York, NY, USA, 1995.

69. Fletcher, R.; Reeves, C.M. Function minimization by conjugate gradients. *Comput. J.* **1964**, *7*, 149–153. [CrossRef]

70. Levenberg, K. A method for the solution of certain problems in least squares. *Quart. Appl. Math.* **1944**, *2*, 164–168.

71. Marquardt, D. An algorithm for least squares estimation of nonlinear parameters. *J. Soc. Ind. Appl. Math.* **1963**, *11*, 431–441. [CrossRef]

72. Fahlman, S.E. Faster-Learning variations on back-propagation: An empirical study. In Proceedings of the 1988 Connectionist Models Summer School; Morgan Kaufmann: San Mateo, CA, USA, 1988.

73. Sudheer, K.P.; Gosain, A.K.; Ramasastri, K.S. Estimating actual evapotranspiration from limited climatic data using neural computing technique. *J. Irrig. Drain. Eng. ASCE* **2003**, *129*, 214–218. [CrossRef]

74. Sudheer, K.P.; Gosain, A.K.; Rangan, D.M.; Saheb, S.M. Modeling evaporation using an artificial neural network algorithm. *Hydrol. Process.* **2002**, *16*, 3189–3202. [CrossRef]

75. Ayyub, B.M.; McCuen, R.H. *Probability, Statistics, and Reliability for Engineers and Scientists*, 2nd ed.; Taylor & Francis: Boca Raton, FL, USA, 2003.

76. Kottegoda, N.T.; Rosso, R. *Statistics, Probability, and Reliability for Civil and Environmental Engineers*; McGraw-Hill: Singapore, 1997.

77. McCuen, R.H. *Microcomputer Applications in Statistical Hydrology*; Prentice Hall: Englewood Cliffs, NJ, USA, 1993.

78. Singh, V.P.; Jain, S.K.; Tyagi, A. *Risk and Reliability Analysis: A Handbook for Civil and Environmental Engineers*; ASCE Press: Reston, VA, USA, 2007.

water

MDPI

Article

Subgrid Parameterization of the Soil Moisture Storage Capacity for a Distributed Rainfall-Runoff Model

Weijian Guo [1,2,*], Chuanhai Wang [1,2], Xianmin Zeng [1,2], Tengfei Ma [1,2] and Hai Yang [1,2]

[1] State Key Laboratory of Hydrology-Water Resources and Hydraulic Engineering, Hohai University, Nanjing 210098, China; wangchuanhai@vip.sina.com (C.W.); zxmhhu@qq.com (X.Z.); matengfei863@gmail.com (T.M.); yhasan@hhu.edu.cn (H.Y.)
[2] College of Hydrology and Water Resources, Hohai University, Nanjing 210098, China
* Correspondence: gjjsher@126.com; Tel.: +86-139-5164-8814

Academic Editor: Kwok-wing Chau
Received: 9 March 2015; Accepted: 21 May 2015; Published: 29 May 2015

Abstract: Spatial variability plays an important role in nonlinear hydrologic processes. Due to the limitation of computational efficiency and data resolution, subgrid variability is usually assumed to be uniform for most grid-based rainfall-runoff models, which leads to the scale-dependence of model performances. In this paper, the scale effect on the Grid-Xinanjiang model was examined. The bias of the estimation of precipitation, runoff, evapotranspiration and soil moisture at the different grid scales, along with the scale-dependence of the effective parameters, highlights the importance of well representing the subgrid variability. This paper presents a subgrid parameterization method to incorporate the subgrid variability of the soil storage capacity, which is a key variable that controls runoff generation and partitioning in the Grid-Xinanjiang model. In light of the similar spatial pattern and physical basis, the soil storage capacity is correlated with the topographic index, whose spatial distribution can more readily be measured. A beta distribution is introduced to represent the spatial distribution of the soil storage capacity within the grid. The results derived from the Yanduhe Basin show that the proposed subgrid parameterization method can effectively correct the watershed soil storage capacity curve. Compared to the original Grid-Xinanjiang model, the model performances are quite consistent at the different grid scales when the subgrid variability is incorporated. This subgrid parameterization method reduces the recalibration necessity when the Digital Elevation Model (DEM) resolution is changed. Moreover, it improves the potential for the application of the distributed model in the ungauged basin.

Keywords: Grid-Xinanjiang model; scale effect; scale-invariant hydrologic response; subgrid parameterization

1. Introduction

For the last few decades, the development of numerous distributed rainfall-runoff models enables the spatial variations to be represented by a network of grid elements. Advances in geographic information systems (GIS), remote sensing (RS) and computational technology have also offered the potential to build complex distributed hydrologic models and improve the accuracy of hydrologic prediction in time and space [1–3].

However, many recent studies have suggested that distributed modelling approaches may not always provide improved simulations at the outlet compared to lumped conceptual models [4]. One of the underlying reasons is that most models do not represent the spatial variability well [5,6]. Limited by the resolution of available data and the computational efficiency, most grid-based distributed models do not take into account the subgrid variability of model input, parameters and model state [7–9].

With the assumption of the uniform subgrid, the high frequency information of hydrologic variables and parameters will be lost as the large sampling dimensions act as a filter [10,11].

Because of the nonlinearity of hydrologic processes, model simulations of hydrologic responses are inherently sensitive to the spatial variability of input forcing and watershed characteristics [12]. There is a growing awareness of the sensitivity of small scale variability in hydrologic systems modelling. For example, Wood *et al.* [13] introduced the concept of the Representative Elementary Area (REA). The REA is defined as a critical threshold at which the implicit continuum assumption can be used without knowledge of the patterns when building the catchment modelling. Arora *et al.* [14] compared the performances of land surface simulations with and without incorporating the subgrid variability of precipitation intensity and soil moisture. The results indicated that the inclusion of subgrid variability results in significant changes of magnitude, time and frequency of surface runoff generation and partitioning. Ghan *et al.* [15] assessed the relative influence of the subgrid variability of meteorology, vegetation characteristics, soil properties on surface runoff with a land surface model. They found that neglecting subgrid variability leads to the underestimation of runoff and overestimation of evaporation. Vázquez *et al.* [16] illustrated the scale-dependence of model effective parameters. They noted that the effective parameters need a recalibration when the grid resolution is changed. The scale-dependence of the model performances and effective parameters makes it a challenge to determine the scale at which the spatial variability can be replaced by grid-averaged characteristics. In order to reduce the necessity of recalibration, it is required to provide a well representation of subgrid variability.

The Grid-Xinanjiang model is an improved version of the Xinanjiang model, which is widely used for flood forecasting in humid and semi-humid area of China [17,18]. The soil storage capacity is a key variable in the Grid-Xinanjiang model, which controls runoff generation and partitioning. Due to the relative short spatial structure, the soil storage capacity is more sensitive to the uniform grid assumption. The bias of estimation of soil storage capacity will introduce the uncertainty of hydrologic simulation, especially for application in the ungauged basin. Therefore, a good representation of subgrid variability of soil storage capacity is necessary for a scale-invariant hydrologic response in the Grid-Xinanjiang model. In this paper, based on the analysis of the model performances of the original Grid-Xinanjiang model at different grid scales, a subgrid parameterization method is presented to account for the subgrid variability of the soil storage capacity.

The rest of paper is organized as follows: in the next section, we provide a description of the study area; a brief description of the Grid-Xinanjiang model and the subgrid parameterization method are presented in the model description section; the following section includes a set of numerical experiments conducted in the Yanduhe Basin to compare the model performance with and without incorporating the subgrid variability; and the final section provides conclusions and perspectives.

2. Study Area

The Yanduhe Basin is located in central China with a catchment area of about 601 km^2. The Yanduhe River, the main river of the Yanduhe Basin, originating from south of Shennongjia Mountain, flowing into the Yangtze River at 31°14′ N, 110°18′ E, is 60.6 km in length, with a mean slope of 9.5‰. More than 70% of the area is covered by vegetation. The watershed climate is humid, and the average annual precipitation is approximately 1300–1700 mm. Dominated by a monsoon climate, most rainfall occurs during the wet season between April and September.

As shown in Figure 1, the hourly rainfall is monitored at five rainfall gauging stations located in Duizi, Xiagu, Banqiao, Songziyuan and Yanduhe. Hourly streamflow and evaporation data are recorded at the outlet of the watershed. The morphology of the basin is described by the Digital Elevation Model (DEM) with 30 m resolution from the National Aeronautics and Space Administration (NASA). The elevation of the Yanduhe Basin ranges from 130 to 3031 m.

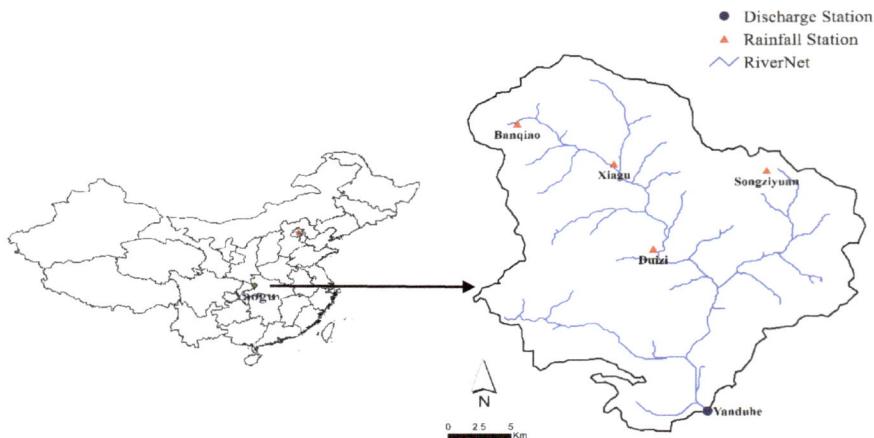

Figure 1. Location and gauging stations of the study area.

3. Method

3.1. The Grid-Xinanjiang Model

DEMs are the primary computational elements for rainfall-runoff modeling in the Grid-Xinanjiang model. In each grid cell, canopy interception, direct channel precipitation, evapotranspiration, runoff generation and partitioning are simulated. A simple storage based equation is adopted to calculate the cumulative interception during rainfall events. The precipitation that falls on the channel can be treated as the direct runoff without loss. The evapotranspiration is simulated as a function of moisture content of the vertical soil profile. The soil profile is divided into three layers (upper, lower and deeper layers) in each grid cell to account for the uneven vertical distribution of the soil moisture content. The Grid-Xinanjiang model employs the saturation excess mechanism, and adopts the concept of soil storage capacity to partition the rainfall into runoff and infiltration. Depending on the free water capacity, the runoff is further subdivided into surface runoff, interflow and groundwater runoff.

For the daily simulation, the surface runoff directly routes to the channel as the fast component. The interflow and groundwater runoff represent the slow component that routes to the outlet of the corresponding subcatchment by two linear reservoirs with different lag times. The subcatchments are connected by the channel network. The outflow of each subcatchment is routed to the watershed outlet by the multiple-reach Muskingum method. More details are available in Yao *et al.* [17] and Liu *et al.* [19].

3.2. Subgrid Scale Parameterization of the Soil Storage Capacity

In the original Xinanjiang model, the spatially uneven distribution of the soil storage capacity is depicted by a power function [20]:

$$\frac{f}{F} = 1 - \left(1 - \frac{WM}{WMM}\right)^{B} \tag{1}$$

where *WM* is the soil storage capacity, *WMM* is maximum watershed soil storage capacity, f/F is fraction of basin with the soil storage capacity less than *WM*, *B* is exponent of the curve.

A similar method is also adopted in the ARNO [21] and the Variable Infiltration Capacity (VIC) models [22]. The power function provides an analytical solution of runoff generation but lacks definite physical interpretation. Following the work of Williams *et al.* [23] and Anderson *et al.* [24], Yao *et al.* [25]

utilized the soil texture and the land cover attributes to estimate the spatial distribution of the soil storage capacity. However, limited by resolution of soil property, the small-scale variability information is not readily available. Therefore, the uniform grid assumption is usually adopted. However, the high frequency information will be smoothed as the uniform grid acts as a filter. Especially for the soil storage capacity, due to the relative short spatial correlation structure, the spatial distribution of the soil storage capacity is more easily affected by the smoothing effect [26–28], which may further lead to the scale-dependence of the model performance. Therefore, it is necessary to take into account the subgrid variability of the soil storage capacity in the Grid-Xinanjiang model.

By analyzing the spatial organization of soil moisture and different terrain attributes (slope, mean curvature, topographic index, specific area, *etc.*), Western *et al.* [29] demonstrated that the topographic index (*TI*) can better explain the spatial variability at all scales from 10 m up to the catchment scales. Shi *et al.* [30] also found a similar spatial pattern between the soil storage capacity and the topographic index. On one hand, topography is an important control of the soil moisture distribution [31,32]. The areas that have large topographic indices usually correspond to the riparian areas, where it is easier to reach saturation because of the relatively small water deficit, and vice versa. On the other hand, the high resolutions of topographic indices are more readily obtained than the soil properties. Shi *et al.* [30] suggested the topographic index as an auxiliary variable to correlate with the soil storage capacity as following:

$$\frac{WM}{WMM} = \exp\left\{-\left[\frac{\ln(TI - TI_{min} + 1)}{a}\right]^b\right\} \tag{2}$$

where TI_{min} is the minimum topographic index, a and b are two shape parameters. The topographic index TI is defined as $\ln(a/\tan\beta)$, in which a is the cumulative area per unit length of contour line and β is the slope.

As discussed by Pradhan *et al.* [33], a distinct shift of the value of the topographic index occurs as the DEM resolution becomes coarser. As a function of the topographic index, the soil storage capacity curve also changes correspondingly. Therefore, it is necessary to correct the grid-averaged soil storage capacity. By integrating the soil storage capacity in each grid, we can estimate the total watershed soil storage capacity at each grid scale. The deviation of the total watershed soil storage capacity between the finest grid and other grids can be used to correct the mean value of the soil storage capacity within the grid cell:

$$WM_c = WM\frac{WMM_t}{WMM_c} \tag{3}$$

where WM_c is the soil storage capacity in each grid after correction, WMM_t is the total watershed soil storage capacity at the finest resolution and WMM_c is the total watershed soil storage capacity at the modelling scale.

As suggested by Li and Avissar [34], here we use a beta distribution to describe the subgrid variability of the soil storage capacity. Compared to the other commonly used probability distribution (gamma, lognormal, *etc.*), the bounded character of beta distribution is more suitable for the description of soil property. It is defined as following:

$$f(WM) = \frac{\Gamma(\alpha + \beta)}{\Gamma(\alpha)\Gamma(\beta)}WM^{\alpha-1}(1 - WM)^{\beta-1} \tag{4}$$

where $\Gamma()$ is the gamma function, and α and β are two shape parameters.

The parameters of the beta distribution can be estimated by the mean and variance values of the soil storage capacity within the grid. We can obtain the mean value of the soil storage capacity of the grid cell by Equations (2) and (3). The variance indicates the fluctuation range of the soil storage capacity within grid which can be derived by spatial aggregation from the finest resolution. Due to the uneven distribution of *WM* within the grid, part of the effective rainfall (P_e) is partitioned into the runoff (R), and the other part is stored in the soil (ΔW). As shown in Figure 2, the runoff R in a grid can be expressed as:

$$R = \int_{A}^{A+P_e} P_e I_{WM} dWM \tag{5}$$

where A is the soil storage capacity corresponding to the soil content and W_0; I_{WM} is the cumulative density function of WM.

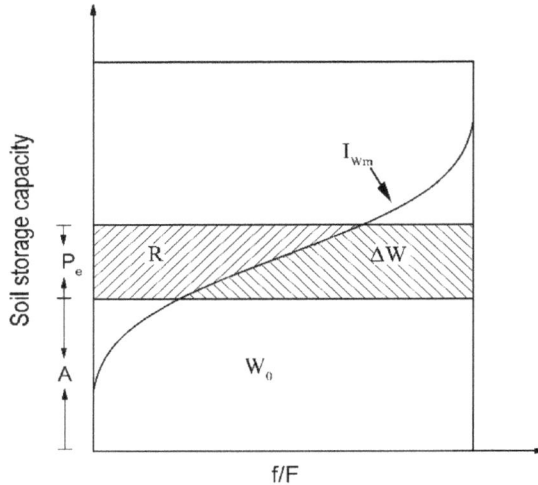

Figure 2. Schematic representation of runoff generation within a grid.

4. Results and Discussion

4.1. Model Validation

The proposed subgrid parameterization method is validated against the observed data from 1981 to 1986 using a daily time step. The model parameters are calibrated at 30 m resolution with the observations from 1981 to 1984. The rainfall data at five gauging stations is interpolated to each grid using the inverse distance weighting method. Adopting the seeding technology [35], the Yanduhe Basin is subdivided into 58 subcatchments with a threshold of 5 km^2. We ran a drainage experiment presented by Vivoni [36] to obtain a reasonable spatial distribution of the initial soil moisture. The watershed is assumed to drain from a full saturation status without rainfall and evapotranspiration, until the watershed soil moisture content reaches the condition that we choose. The annual runoff deviation (ARD) and the Nash-Sutcliffe coefficient (NSC) are used as two criteria for the model evaluation. The ARD provides a general sense of the water balance, and the NSC is used to assess the goodness of fit between the simulated and the observed discharge. The ARD and NSC are calculated as follows:

$$ARD = \frac{R_{sim} - R_{obs}}{R_{obs}} \times 100\% \tag{6}$$

$$NSC = 1 - \frac{\sum\limits_{n}(Q_{sim}^t - Q_{obs}^t)^2}{\sum\limits_{n}(Q_{obs}^t - \overline{Q}_{obs})^2} \tag{7}$$

where R_{sim} is the annual simulated runoff; R_{obs} is the annual observed runoff; Q^t_{sim} is the simulated discharge at time step t; Q^t_{obs} is the observed discharge at time step t; and $\overline{Q}_{obs}$ is the mean value of the observed discharge, n is the total number of values in the time period.

The simulated results at the Yanduhe Station are summarized in Table 1. The averaged ARD and NSC are 9% and 0.81 respectively in the calibration periods. In the validation period, the ARD and NSC also reach 10% and 0.76. Figure 3 shows an illustration of the simulated hydrograph against the observed data at the Yanduhe Station from April to October in 1986. The results demonstrate consistency between the simulation and observation. Further analysis is also based on the observed data in 1986.

Table 1. Performance of the Grid-Xinanjiang model for the calibration and validation periods.

Period	Year	ARD (%)	NSC
Calibration	1981	13	0.74
	1982	4	0.90
	1983	7	0.81
	1984	11	0.79
Validation	1985	14	0.65
	1986	6	0.87

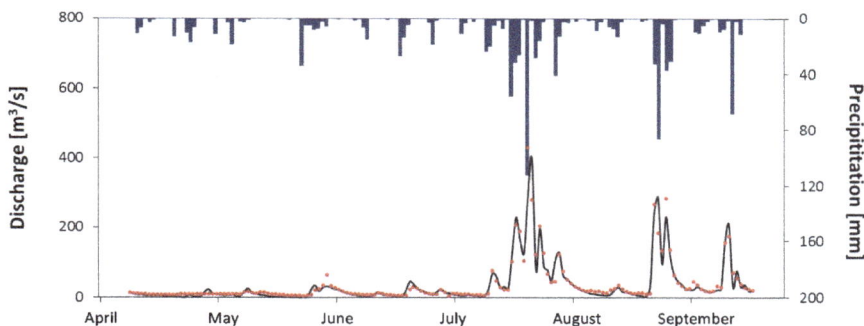

Figure 3. An illustration of the model performance of the Grid-Xinanjiang model with the subgrid parameterization in the Yanduhe Basin in 1986. Red dot, observed discharge; black line, simulated discharge; blue bar, precipitation.

4.2. The Scale-Dependence of the Grid-Xinanjiang Model with a Uniform Grid

The scale-dependence of model performance is the reason that we propose the subgrid parameterization method. Before evaluating the reasonability of the subgrid parameterization, we are also interested in, to what extent, the hydrologic responses of the original Grid-Xinanjiang model depend on the grid scale. Figure 4 depicts the probability density functions of the soil storage capacity from four different grid scales (50 m, 100 m, 500 m and 1000 m) in the Yanduhe Basin. A distinct shift is observed as the grid scale increases. The mean value of the watershed soil storage capacity increases from 30 to 57 mm when the grid scale aggregates from 50 to 1000 m. In addition, the peak of the density function also moves towards a high value. As a key variable in the Grid-Xinanjiang model, the bias indicates that for the coarse grid, more rainfall can be stored in the soil, and the runoff process will be more sensitive to the higher rainfall intensity.

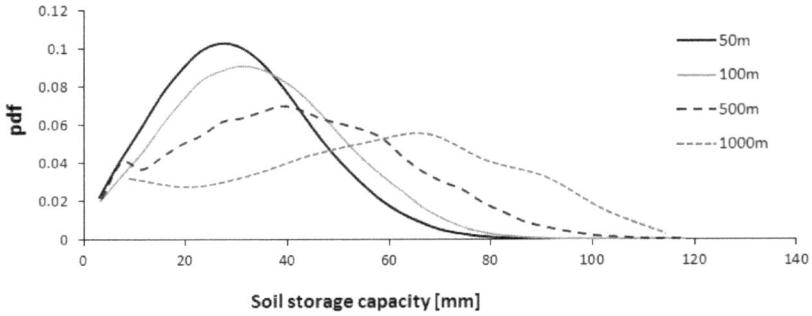

Figure 4. Effect of the grid resolution on the density function of the soil storage capacity.

The hydrologic responses of the original Grid-Xinanjiang model were evaluated with the observed data from April to October in 1986 in the Yanduhe Basin. Figure 5 shows the processes of the average monthly precipitation, evapotranspiration, runoff and soil moisture at the different resolutions. For comparison, the soil moisture content θ is normalized to the relative soil moisture: $\theta^* = (\theta - \theta_r)/(\theta_s - \theta_r)$. θ_s and θ_r are the saturation and the residual soil moisture, respectively, the values of which relate to the soil texture [37]. The calibrated parameters at the 30 m resolution are directly adopted without recalibration at each grid scale. As can be seen in Figure 5, all these processes show an obvious scale-dependence. The spatially averaged precipitation reduces with the increasing grid scale. The bias of the precipitation mainly concentrates before March and after August, when the amount of rainfall is relatively low. The maximum margin of the monthly rainfall volume between 50 and 1000 m grids reaches the peak of 8% in September. For the relatively large rainfall volume, such as during June and July, the bias is only approximately 2%. This can be interpreted by the different spatial characteristics of rainfall types. As discussed by Ciach and Krajewski [38], rainfall fields are less variable for higher rainfall intensity. It is obvious that the smoothing effect will be more significant for the storm with higher variability. Compared to the precipitation, the runoff is more sensitive to the change of the grid scale. The bias of the estimation of precipitation, combined with the bias of totally watershed soil storage capacity, results in the inconsistencies of runoff at the different grid scales. For the coarse grid, the precipitation is underestimated. In addition, large soil storage capacity also allows more rainfall stored in the soil, rather than converting into runoff. The averaged bias of runoff between 50 and 1000 m resolution is approximately 28%. The bias of runoff reaches the peak around August. The runoff derived from 50 m is almost three times that from 1000 m. Since more rainfall infiltrates into the soil, the relative soil moisture increases with the grid scale. Therefore, as a function of moisture content of soil profile, the evapotranspiration is correspondingly higher for the coarse grid. The evapotranspiration and the relative soil moisture processes exhibit marked differences between March and August. This is because the evapotranspiration is more intensive during this period. The averaged bias of evapotranspiration and relative soil moisture caused by the spatial aggregation from 50 to 1000 m are 13% and 14%, respectively. Due to the decline of the measured evaporation, only slight differences occur in September and October.

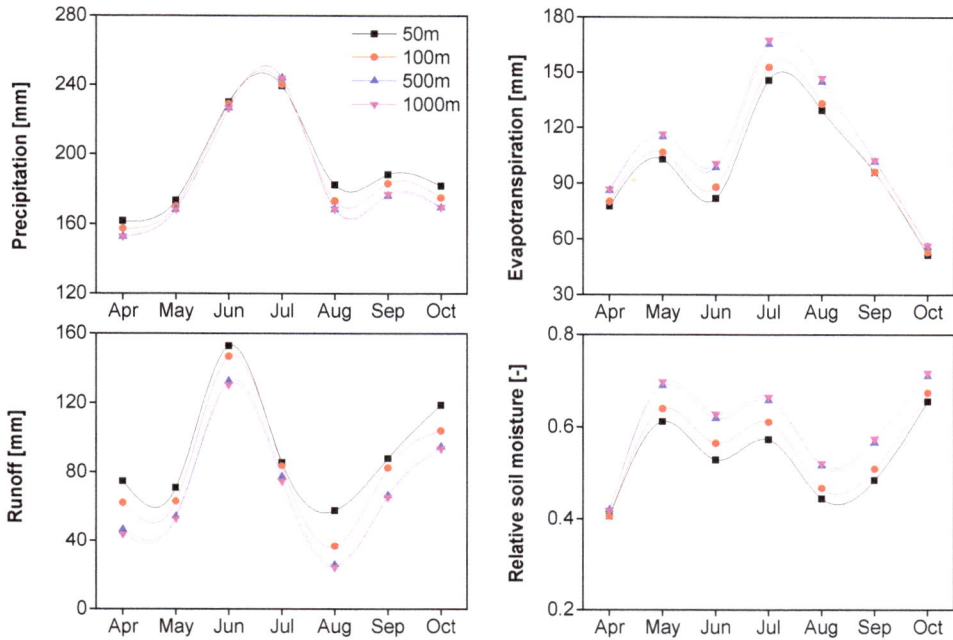

Figure 5. The monthly precipitation, evapotranspiration, runoff and relative soil moisture processes.

To evaluate the scale effect on the effective parameters, the model parameters require a recalibration at the different grid scales. To avoid the subjectivity of parameter estimation, automated calibration methods are needed. There has been a great deal of work on the research of automated calibration methods [39–41]. In this study, the eleven model parameters are auto-calibrated based on the SCE-UA (Shuffled Complex Evolution method developed at the University of Arizona) algorithm, which has been found to be consistent, effective, and efficient in searching the globally optimum parameters [42,43]. The initial parameters are referred to in Yao *et al.* [17]. The Nash-Sutcliffe coefficient is used as an objective function. The iteration of SCE-UA algorithm will stop when the objective function cannot improve 0.1% over five iterations or the number of iteration exceeds 10,000. Table 2 lists the value of the effective parameters at four different grid resolutions. It is clear that the model parameters vary with grid scale in varying degrees. The ratio of the potential evapotranspiration to pen evaporation (*K*), the maximum watershed soil storage capacity (*WMM*) and the recession constant of the interflow storage (*C_i*) are relatively sensitive. The ratio of the potential evapotranspiration to pen evaporation decreases from 1.0 to 0.93 when the grid resolution increases from 50 to 1000 m. The maximum watershed soil storage capacity also decrease from 124 to 112. No significant changes were observed for the recession constant of groundwater storage (*C_g*) and two parameters in the Muskingum routing method (*X*,*V*).

Table 2. Model parameters and calibrated values at 4 different grid resolutions.

Parameter	Description	Range	Calibrated value			
			50 m	100 m	500 m	1000 m
K	Ratio of potential evapotranspiration to pan evaporation	0–2	1.0	0.98	0.94	0.93
WMM	Maximum watershed soil storage capacity (mm)	60–300	124	118	114	112
α	Shape parameter	0–20	1.1	1.0	0.9	0.9
β	Shape parameter	0–20	1.5	1.5	1.5	1.4
SM	Free water storage capacity (mm)	0–100	12	11	10	10
K_i	Outflow coefficient of free water storage to interflow	0–0.7	0.42	0.40	0.41	0.40
K_g	Outflow coefficient of free water storage to Groundwater	0–0.7	0.28	0.26	0.26	0.25
C_i	Recession constant of interflow storage	0.3–0.8	0.58	0.57	0.54	0.53
C_g	Recession constant of groundwater storage	0.8–0.995	0.85	0.86	0.85	0.84
X	A weight factor of Muskingum method	0.1–0.5	0.33	0.33	0.32	0.32
V	Flow velocity in channel (m/s)	0.5–2	1.3	1.3	1.3	1.3

4.3. Evaluation of the Subgrid Parameterization

As discussed above, the bias of the soil storage capacity at the different grid scales is an important reason for the scale-dependence of the model performances and the effective parameters. Therefore, a good representation of soil moisture capacity at the subgrid scale is necessary for a scale-invariant hydrologic response in the Grid-Xinanjiang model. Following the subgrid parameterization described in Section 3, Table 3 compares the annual water budget with and without the subgrid variability. The total annual evapotranspiration (E_p), runoff (R), surface runoff (R_S), interflow (R_I) and groundwater runoff (R_G) at four different resolutions are calculated with the same parameters. As seen in Table 3, with the uniform grid, the annual evapotranspiration increases with the grid scale. The bias of the annual evapotranspiration between 50 and 1000 m resolution can reach 48 mm. The total runoff is significantly underestimated for the coarse grid. The annual total runoff at the 50 m resolution is 852 mm, and 763 mm at the 1000 m resolution. Note that the differences of interflow and groundwater runoff are quite small, and the bias of runoff mainly originates from surface runoff. This is because the runoff is partitioned into different components by the free water capacity, which is relatively small. The impact of the change of the free water capacity on the partitioning of interflow and groundwater runoff is limited. The runoff in excess of the free water capacity converts into surface runoff. Thus, the decrease in the total runoff from fine to coarse grid firstly leads to a change of the surface runoff. However, when the subgrid variability of the soil storage capacity is incorporated, the bias of the annual evapotranspiration between 50 and 1000 m significantly reduces to 3 mm. For the 1000 m resolution, the bias of evapotranspiration with and without the subgrid parameterization are considerably large, accounting for almost 22% of the annual evapotranspiration. For the non-uniform subgrid, the runoff increases by 23 mm and 101 mm for the 50 m and 1000 m resolutions, respectively. Compared to the uniform subgrid, both interflow and groundwater runoff increase marginally after incorporating the subgrid variability, and the differences at different resolutions are almost negligible.

In Figure 6, the Nash-Sutcliffe coefficient is used as the criteria to evaluate the model performances of two subgrid schemes at the different grid scale. Because there is no measured data available for the actual evapotranspiration and soil moisture, the simulated results at the 30 m resolution are taken as the true values. In Figure 6, the dash-dot line is obtained from the original Grid-Xinanjiang model, and the solid line represents the model performance after incorporating the subgrid variability. With the uniform grid, the *NSC* of runoff process ranges between 0.93 and 0.98. The difference is more apparent for evapotranspiration and soil moisture processes. With the same parameters, the *NSC* of the evapotranspiration and the relative soil moisture decline to 0.88 and 0.82 at 1000 m from 0.98 and

0.97 at 50 m. However, when the subgrid variability is taken into account, the model performances at the different resolutions are quite consistent. The improvement of the model performance is significant, especially at the larger grid scales. The increases of the *NSC* for the three processes at 1000 m resolution reach 4%, 5% and 12%, respectively. It can be concluded that the subgrid parameterization can partly eliminate the scale-dependence of the model. Not only the total water budget, but also the performance at each time step is quite consistent at each resolution when the subgrid variability is taken into account, but it needs to be pointed out that the proposed subgrid parameterization only depicts the subgrid variability of soil storage capacity, and the variability of precipitation, evapotranspiration or flow routing velocity at the subgrid scale may still cause the inconsistency of model performances at the different grid scales.

Table 3. Performance of the Grid-Xinanjiang model with and without the subgrid parameterization.

Process	Uniform Subgrid				Non-uniform Subgrid			
	50 m	100 m	500 m	1000 m	50 m	100 m	500 m	1000 m
E_p(mm)	472	487	516	520	430	430	427	427
R (mm)	852	819	768	763	876	875	862	864
R_S (mm)	244	208	154	147	253	253	242	243
R_I (mm)	374	376	378	379	383	383	382	383
R_G (mm)	234	235	236	237	239	239	239	239

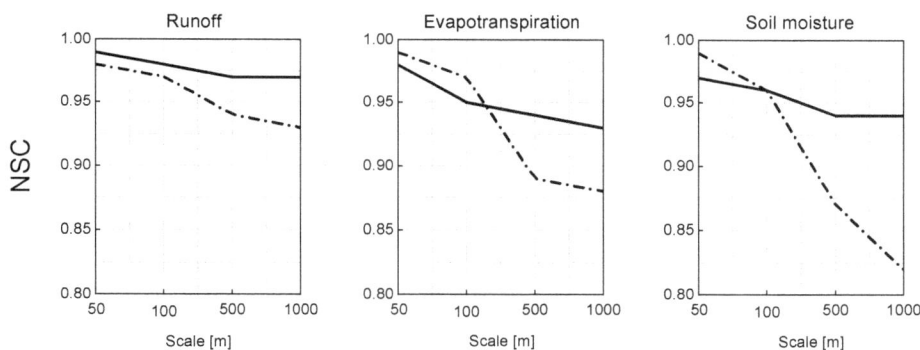

Figure 6. Model performances with and without subgrid parameterization. The solid line represents the *NSC* from the Grid-Xinanjiang model with uniform grid, and the dash-dot line represents the *NSC* after incorporating the subgrid variability.

To further investigate the effect of subgrid parameterization, Figure 7 plots the simulated discharge at the outlet from the original Grid-Xinanjiang model versus the discharge after incorporating the subgrid variability at 50 m, 100 m, 500 m and 1000 m grid resolutions. It seems that the model tends to underestimate the discharge if the subgrid variability of soil storage capacity is neglected. The gap between the two schemes increases with grid scale. For the 50 m grid resolution, the discharge is closely fit to the 1:1 line. While for the 1000 m resolution, the discharge increases by an average of 6% after incorporating the subgrid variability. The bias of the discharge with and without subgrid variability can be as high as 40 m³/s. The large bias between the two schemes mainly occurs when the discharge is less than 100 m³/s. Even for small discharge, the gap is also evident. However, no significant change is observed for large discharge. It is because, for the saturation excess mechanism employed by the Grid-Xinanjiang model, large discharge is usually associated with relatively high soil content and intense rainfall. Once the watershed is fully saturated, all of the effective rainfall will directly convert into the runoff without loss. In this case, the effect of the spatial variability on runoff will no longer exist. It demonstrates that the subgrid variability is more necessary for the relatively dry period. This conclusion not only works for the Grid-Xinanjiang model, but also for the other saturation excess dominated hydrologic model.

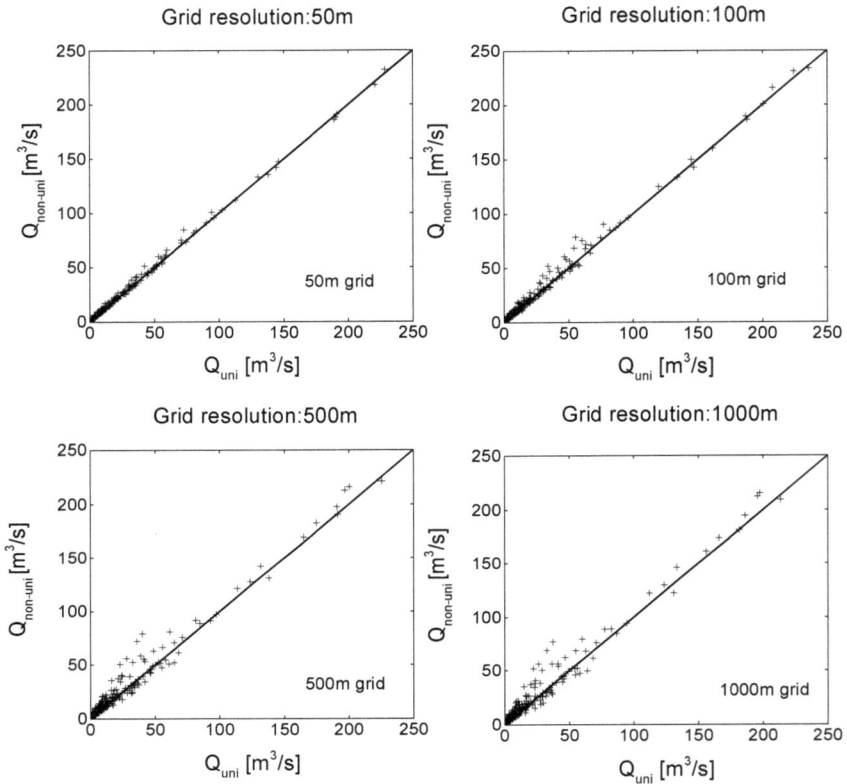

Figure 7. Discharge from the original Grid-Xinanjiang model (Q_{uni}) versus runoff after incorporating the subgrid variability ($Q_{non-uni}$).

5. Conclusions

Spatial variability is known to increase with scale. With the assumption of a uniform grid, the spatial averaging operation leads to the scale-dependence of model performance. In this study, we take the Grid-Xinanjiang model as an example to investigate the effect of subgrid variability on the hydrologic response. The processes of precipitation, runoff, evapotranspiration and soil moisture at four different grid scales (50 m, 100 m, 500 m and 1000 m) are compared. The calibrated parameters based on 30 m resolution are used for each simulation without recalibration. The results derived from the Yanduhe Basin show that the model performances vary with grid scales. As a key variable in the Grid-Xinanjiang model, the total watershed soil storage capacity increases from 30 to 57 mm when the grid resolution spatially aggregates from 50 to 1000 m. Depending on the different rainfall structure, the precipitation is underestimated for coarse grid. The bias of precipitation process and watershed soil storage capacity leads to the inconsistency of the hydrologic responses across scales. Calibrated by the SCE-UA method against the observed data, the model effective parameters also vary with grid scale in varying degrees.

Water **2015**, 7, 2691–2706

Therefore, for a scale-invariant hydrologic response, the subgrid variability is required to be taken into account. In light of the sensitivity of the Grid-Xinanjiang model to the soil storage capacity, this study presents a subgrid parameterization method to incorporate the subgrid variability of the soil storage capacity. The topographic index is adopted as an auxiliary variable to correlate the soil storage capacity. On one hand, the topographic index and the soil storage capacity have similar spatial distributions and physical basis. On the other hand, the high resolution topographic index is more readily obtained than the soil property information. A beta distribution is introduced to represent the spatial distribution of the soil storage capacity within grid cell. Compared to the original Grid-Xinanjiang model, the simulated runoff, evapotranspiration and soil moisture processes are quite consistent at different grid scales when the subgrid variability is incorporated. The inclusion of the subgrid variability results in a significant increase of runoff and a decrease of evapotranspiration. For the annual water budget, the differences of runoff and evapotranspiration with and without incorporating the subgrid variability can reach 101 mm and 93 mm respectively at the 1000 m resolution. Due to the saturation excess mechanism employed by the Grid-Xinanjiang model, the correction of hydrologic responses resulting from subgrid parameterization is more obvious for relatively small rainfall event or dry conditions. The subgrid parameterization method benefits to reduce the necessity of recalibration when DEM resolution is changed, but it also needs to be noted that the proposed parameterization method only partly eliminates the scale-dependence of the runoff generation. Further research deserves more attention on the scale effect on flow routing.

Acknowledgments: This research is funded by the graduate students scientific research innovation plan of Jiangsu Province (1043-B1203332), China Scholarship Council (201306710013), the state major project of water pollution control and management (2014ZX07101-011) and National Non Profit Research Program of China (201301075).

Author Contributions: Weijian Guo contributed to the experiment design, manuscript preparation and editing; Chuanhai Wang contributed to the experiment design and manuscript review; Xianmin Zeng contributed to the data analysis and manuscript review; Tengfei Ma contributed to the data analysis and manuscript review; Hai Yang contributed to the manuscript review.

References

1. Paniconi, C.; Wood, E.F. A detailed model for simulation of catchment scale subsurface hydrologic processes. *Water Resour. Res.* **1993**, *29*, 1601–1620. [CrossRef]
2. Abbott, M.B.; Bathurst, J.C.; Cunge, J.A.; O'Connell, P.E.; Rasmussen, J. An introduction to the European Hydrological System—Systeme Hydrologique Europeen, "SHE", 1: History and philosophy of a physically-based, distributed modelling system. *J. Hydrol.* **1986**, *87*, 45–59. [CrossRef]
3. Blöschl, G.; Reszler, C.; Komma, J. A spatially distributed flash flood forecasting model. *Environ. Model. Softw.* **2008**, *23*, 464–478. [CrossRef]
4. Reed, S.; Koren, V.; Smith, M.; Zhang, Z.; Moreda, F.; Seo, D.-J.; Dmip Participants. Overall distributed model intercomparison project results. *J. Hydrol.* **2004**, *298*, 27–60. [CrossRef]
5. Carpenter, T.M.; Georgakakos, K.P. Impacts of parametric and radar rainfall uncertainty on the ensemble streamflow simulations of a distributed hydrologic model. *J. Hydrol.* **2004**, *298*, 202–221. [CrossRef]
6. Smith, M.B.; Koren, V.I.; Zhang, Z.; Reed, S.M.; Pan, J.-J.; Moreda, F. Runoff response to spatial variability in precipitation: An analysis of observed data. *J. Hydrol.* **2004**, *298*, 267–286. [CrossRef]
7. Ciarapica, L.; Todini, E. TOPKAPI: A model for the representation of the rainfall-runoff process at different scales. *Hydrol. Process.* **2002**, *16*, 207–229. [CrossRef]
8. Beven, K.; Freer, J. A dynamic TOPMODEL. *Hydrol. Process.* **2001**, *15*, 1993–2011. [CrossRef]
9. Dehotin, J.; Braud, I. Which spatial discretization for distributed hydrological models? Proposition of a methodology and illustration for medium to large-scale catchments. *Hydrol. Earth Syst. Sci.* **2008**, *12*, 769–796. [CrossRef]
10. Band, L.E.; Moore, I.D. Scale: Landscape attributes and geographical information systems. *Hydrol. Process.* **1995**, *9*, 401–422. [CrossRef]

11. Kavvas, M.L. On the coarse-graining of hydrologic processes with increasing scales. *J. Hydrol.* **1999**, *217*, 191–202. [CrossRef]

12. Beven, K. How far can we go in distributed hydrological modelling? *Hydrol. Earth Syst. Sci.* **1999**, *5*, 1–12. [CrossRef]

13. Wood, E.F.; Sivapalan, M.; Beven, K.; Band, L. Effects of spatial variability and scale with implications to hydrologic modeling. *J. Hydrol.* **1988**, *102*, 29–47. [CrossRef]

14. Arora, V.K.; Chiew, F.H.S.; Grayson, R.B. Effect of sub-grid-scale variability of soil moisture and precipitation intensity on surface runoff and streamflow. *J. Geophys. Res.* **2001**, *106*, 17073–17091. [CrossRef]

15. Ghan, S.J.; Liljegren, J.C.; Shaw, W.J.; Hubbe, J.H.; Doran, J.C. Influence of Subgrid Variability on Surface Hydrology. *J. Clim.* **1997**, *10*, 3157–3166. [CrossRef]

16. Vázquez, R.F.; Feyen, L.; Feyen, J.; Refsgaard, J.C. Effect of grid size on effective parameters and model performance of the MIKE-SHE code. *Hydrol. Process.* **2002**, *16*, 355–372. [CrossRef]

17. Yao, C.; Li, Z.; Bao, H.; Yu, Z. Application of a Developed Grid-Xinanjiang Model to Chinese Watersheds for Flood Forecasting Purpose. *J. Hydrol. Eng.* **2009**, *14*, 923–934. [CrossRef]

18. Zhao, R.; Liu, X. The Xinanjiang model. In *Computer Models of Watershed Hydrology*; Singh, V., Ed.; Water Resources Publications: Littleton, CO, USA, 1995; pp. 215–232.

19. Liu, J.; Chen, X.; Zhang, J.; Flury, M. Coupling the Xinanjiang model to a kinematic flow model based on digital drainage networks for flood forecasting. *Hydrol. Process.* **2009**, *23*, 1337–1348. [CrossRef]

20. Zhao, R. The Xinanjiang model applied in China. *J. Hydrol.* **1992**, *135*, 371–381.

21. Todini, E. The ARNO rainfall—Runoff model. *J. Hydrol.* **1996**, *175*, 339–382. [CrossRef]

22. Wood, E.F.; Lettenmaier, D.P.; Zartarian, V.G. A land-surface hydrology parameterization with subgrid variability for general circulation models. *J. Geophys. Res.* **1992**, *97*, 2717–2728. [CrossRef]

23. Williams, J.; Ouyang, Y.; Chen, J.-S.; Ravi, V.; Jewett, D.S.B.D.G. *Estimation of Infiltration Rate in Vadose Zone: Application of Selected Mathematical Models*; Office of Research and Development, United States Environmental Protection Agency: Washington, DC, USA, 1998.

24. Anderson, R.M.; Koren, V.I.; Reed, S.M. Using SSURGO data to improve Sacramento Model a priori parameter estimates. *J. Hydrol.* **2006**, *320*, 103–116. [CrossRef]

25. Yao, C.; Li, Z.; Yu, Z.; Zhang, K. A priori parameter estimates for a distributed, grid-based Xinanjiang model using geographically based information. *J. Hydrol.* **2012**, *468–469*, 47–62. [CrossRef]

26. Famiglietti, J.S.; Ryu, D.; Berg, A.A.; Rodell, M.; Jackson, T.J. Field observations of soil moisture variability across scales. *Water Resour. Res.* **2008**. [CrossRef]

27. Western, A.W.; Blöschl, G.; Grayson, R.B. Geostatistical characterisation of soil moisture patterns in the Tarrawarra catchment. *J. Hydrol.* **1998**, *205*, 20–37. [CrossRef]

28. Western, A.W.; Zhou, S.-L.; Grayson, R.B.; McMahon, T.A.; Blöschl, G.; Wilson, D.J. Spatial correlation of soil moisture in small catchments and its relationship to dominant spatial hydrological processes. *J. Hydrol.* **2004**, *286*, 113–134. [CrossRef]

29. Western, A.W.; Grayson, R.B.; Blöschl, G.; Willgoose, G.R.; McMahon, T.A. Observed spatial organization of soil moisture and its relation to terrain indices. *Water Resour. Res.* **1999**, *35*, 797–810. [CrossRef]

30. Shi, P.; Rui, X.; Qu, S.; Chen, X. Development and application of a grid-based distributed hydrological model. *Dv. In Water Sci.* **2008**, *19*, 662–670.

31. Woods, R.A.; Sivapalan, M.; Robinson, J.S. Modeling the spatial variability of subsurface runoff using a topographic index. *Water Resour. Res.* **1997**, *33*, 1061–1073. [CrossRef]

32. Hjerdt, K.N.; McDonnell, J.J.; Seibert, J.; Rodhe, A. A new topographic index to quantify downslope controls on local drainage. *Water Resour. Res.* **2004**, *40*. [CrossRef]

33. Pradhan, N.R.; Tachikawa, Y.; Takara, K. A downscaling method of topographic index distribution for matching the scales of model application and parameter identification. *Hydrol. Process.* **2006**, *20*, 1385–1405. [CrossRef]

34. Li, B.; Avissar, R. The Impact of Spatial Variability of Land-Surface Characteristics on Land-Surface Heat Fluxes. *J. Clim.* **1994**, *7*, 527–537. [CrossRef]

35. Jenson, S.K.; Domingue, J.O. Extracting topographic structure from digital elevation data for geographic information system analysis. *Photogramm. Eng. Remote Sens.* **1988**, *54*, 1593–1600.

36. Vivoni, E.R.; Entekhabi, D.; Bras, R.L.; Ivanov, V.Y. Controls on runoff generation and scale-dependence in a distributed hydrologic model. *Hydrol. Earth Syst. Sci. Discuss.* **2007**, *11*, 1683–1701.

37. Rawls, W.; Brakensiek, D.; Miller, N. Green-ampt Infiltration Parameters from Soils Data. *J. Hydraul. Eng.* **1983**, *109*, 62–70. [CrossRef]

38. Ciach, G.J.; Krajewski, W.F. Analysis and modeling of spatial correlation structure in small-scale rainfall in Central Oklahoma. *Adv. Water Resour.* **2006**, *29*, 1450–1463. [CrossRef]

39. Chen, W.; Chau, K. Intelligent manipulation and calibration of parameters for hydrological models. *Int. J. Environ. Pollut.* **2006**, *28*, 432–447. [CrossRef]

40. Gupta, V.; Sorooshian, S. Calibration of conceptual hydrologic models: Past, present and future. In *Trends in Hydrology. Research Trends*; Council of Scientific Research Integration: Trivandrum, India, 1994; pp. 329–346.

41. Taormina, R.; Chau, K.-W. Neural network river forecasting with multi-objective fully informed particle swarm optimization. *J. Hydroinform.* **2015**, *17*, 99–113. [CrossRef]

42. Duan, Q.; Sorooshian, S.; Gupta, V.K. Optimal use of the SCE-UA global optimization method for calibrating watershed models. *J. Hydrol.* **1994**, *158*, 265–284. [CrossRef]

43. Duan, Q.Y.; Gupta, V.K.; Sorooshian, S. Shuffled complex evolution approach for effective and efficient global minimization. *J. Optim. Theory Appl.* **1993**, *76*, 501–521. [CrossRef]

water

MDPI

Article

Grey Forecast Rainfall with Flow Updating Algorithm for Real-Time Flood Forecasting

Jui-Yi Ho [1] and Kwan Tun Lee [1,2,*]

[1] Hydrotech Division, Taiwan Typhoon and Flood Research Institute, National Applied Research Laboratories, 11F., No. 97, Sec. 1, Roosevelt Rd., Taipei City 10093, Taiwan; juiyiho@narlabs.org.tw
[2] Department of River and Harbor Engineering, National Taiwan Ocean University, No 2, Beining Rd., Keelung City 20224, Taiwan
* Correspondence: ktlee@ntou.edu.tw; Tel.: +886-2-2462-2192 (ext. 6121); Fax: +886-2-2463-4122

Academic Editor: Kwok-wing Chau
Received: 17 March 2015; Accepted: 17 April 2015; Published: 27 April 2015

Abstract: The dynamic relationship between watershed characteristics and rainfall-runoff has been widely studied in recent decades. Since watershed rainfall-runoff is a non-stationary process, most deterministic flood forecasting approaches are ineffective without the assistance of adaptive algorithms. The purpose of this paper is to propose an effective flow forecasting system that integrates a rainfall forecasting model, watershed runoff model, and real-time updating algorithm. This study adopted a grey rainfall forecasting technique, based on existing hourly rainfall data. A geomorphology-based runoff model can be used for simulating impacts of the changing geo-climatic conditions on the hydrologic response of unsteady and non-linear watershed system, and flow updating algorithm were combined to estimate watershed runoff according to measured flow data. The proposed flood forecasting system was applied to three watersheds; one in the United States and two in Northern Taiwan. Four sets of rainfall-runoff simulations were performed to test the accuracy of the proposed flow forecasting technique. The results indicated that the forecast and observed hydrographs are in good agreement for all three watersheds. The proposed flow forecasting system could assist authorities in minimizing loss of life and property during flood events.

Keywords: rainfall forecasting; flow forecasting; grey theory; geomorphology-based runoff model; flow updating algorithm

1. Introduction

Flood forecasting systems are nonstructural methods for reducing flood damage. An efficient forecasting system can assist with mitigating imminent disasters by providing information that can be disseminated rapidly to the flood-threatened areas. Standard practices in flood forecasting systems include hydrometeorological data transmission, database management, rainfall prediction, runoff estimation, and forecast information dissemination.

Brath *et al.* [1] indicated that quantitative rainfall forecasting plays a primary role in extending the lead time of river flow forecasting, which can improve the timeliness of flood control mechanisms. Because of improvements in the accuracy of weather radar systems, radar-based rainfall forecasting systems have superseded traditional rain gauges that provide measurements at only several locations for flood forecasting [2–4]. Toth *et al.* [5] indicated that radar detection is particularly difficult in mountainous regions because of the effect of ground occultation and altitude. Consequently, radar-based measurement techniques are limited under topographic conditions where radar reflectivity is poor [6,7]. Thus, hydrologists typically use probabilistic and stochastic methods for rainfall forecasting based on current and past rainfall measurements (e.g., [8–13]). Because these methods typically require large volumes of rainfall data for calibrating and training the model parameters,

Deng [14] proposed a grey system theory-based model for future data prediction. Moreover, grey theory-based models require relatively few observations to predict outcomes [15–17]; thus, they are suitable for rainfall forecasting.

Rainfall forecasts are inputted into rainfall-runoff models to provide flood warning information for authorities. In recent decades, artificial neural networks (ANNs) have become a well-known tool for hydrologic forecasting [18–29]. However, ANNs require a large amount of hydrologic data to determine the adaptive weights, which are inadequate to be applied to data-sparse areas. Although fully distributed grid-based routing models can provide detailed information on flood wave transports, they may be unsuitable for real-time flood forecasting systems because the simulation process is typically time-consuming [30]. Hence, lumped and semi-distributed hydrological models are acceptable practical alternatives. For example, the Sacramento model was adopted by the National Weather Service River Forecast System in the United States [31,32], the tank model has been widely applied for runoff forecasting in Japan [33], the Hydrologiska Byråns Vattenbalansavdelning (HBV) model was adopted in Europe [34], and the Xinanjiang model was introduced in China [35]. To further minimize the requirement of observed flow data to develop semi-distributed models, hydrologists have adopted geomorphology-based runoff models [36–40].

Rodriguez-Iturbe and Valdes [35] proposed the geomorphologic instantaneous unit hydrograph (GIUH) model, which can be employed to derive the instantaneous unit hydrograph (IUH) of a watershed based on information from a topographic map or digital elevation data set. Subsequent studies have modified the GIUH model by incorporating kinematic-wave approximation, thereby providing reasonable estimations of flow velocity, which augments rainfall-runoff simulation used in both gauged and ungauged sites [41–43].

It is necessary to implement the effective data assimilation in the forecast process to bridge the immense gap between the theory and operational practice [44]. Comprehensive reviews of data assimilation approaches in operational hydrologic forecasting were presented by Liu *et al.* [45]. Since uncertainty is an inherent characteristic of watershed hydrodynamics, an ideal flood forecasting system should incorporate a real-time updating algorithm that revises the model state to improve the forecasting accuracy. Refsgaard [46] reported that techniques for updating real-time forecasting can be classified into the following four categories: (1) updating input variables; (2) updating state variables; (3) updating model parameters; and (4) updating output variables (*i.e.*, error prediction). Previous studies have developed updating techniques based on time-series analysis [47,48], statistical methods [17,49], multiple regression analysis [50], dimensional variational algorithms [51,52], and the filter approaches [53–58]. Selection of an appropriate updating algorithm depends on the availability of real-time feedback data and the structure of the rainfall-runoff model employed for flow forecasting.

The purpose of this study is to develop an effective flood forecasting system for midsize rural watersheds. We adopted the grey rainfall forecasting technique based on existing hourly rainfall data to avoid poor radar reflectivity in mountainous watersheds. In performing the watershed runoff simulation, a geomorphology-based runoff model which can account different geomorphologic and hydrological characteristics of the watershed was used in this study. Furthermore, a flow updating algorithm was linked to the runoff model to estimate watershed runoff in the next three hours. The proposed flow forecasting system can operate with high efficiency to meet the requirements of real-time flow forecasting. The system was applied to three watersheds; one in the United States (Goodwin Creek) and two in Northern Taiwan (Heng-Chi and San-Hsia). The results of the flood forecasting were compared with official records to confirm the validity of the proposed system. In the following sections, Section 2 describes the analytical methods including the short-term rainfall forecasting and the geomorphology-based runoff model with an updating algorithm. The application of the proposed methods and the forecast results are presented in Section 3. Section 4 summarizes the conclusions of this study.

2. Analytical Methods

The framework of the proposed flood forecasting system incorporates a grey rainfall forecasting model [14], kinematic-wave-based GIUH (KW-GIUH) model [36], and flow updating algorithm that is linked to the KW-GIUH model to improve the flow forecasting accuracy.

2.1. Short-Term Rainfall Forecasting

The grey rainfall forecasting is adopted herein for two reasons: (1) a short-term rainstorm system is too complex to be simulated by using deterministic approaches; (2) the grey system provides an efficient way for rainfall prediction using only small amount of past observed rainfall data. Consequently, the grey model proposed by Deng [14] is appropriate for the present system for rainfall forecasting.

Although hydrological time-series data typically exhibit random forms, a systematic trend can be observed after a repeatedly accumulated generating operations (AGO). According to the AGO concept, Deng [14] developed an effective method for predicting future data based on a limited number of observations. A series of raw rainfall data can be expressed as follows:

$$R^{(0)}(t) = \left[r^{(0)}(1),\ r^{(0)}(2),\ ...,r^{(0)}(k),...,\ r^{(0)}(n) \right] \tag{1}$$

where $R^{(0)}(t)$ denotes the raw time-series rainfall data set, and $r^{(0)}(k)$ is the kth observed rainfall. The first-order AGO series can be defined as [14]:

$$R^{(1)}(t) = \sum_{k=1}^{t} r^{(0)}(k)\ ;\ \ t = 1,\ 2,\ 3,\ ...,n \tag{2}$$

where $R^{(1)}(t)$ is the first-order AGO rainfall time series, and $r^{(1)}(t)$ is the first-order AGO observed rainfall data at time t. A first-order differential equation is employed to fit the cumulative rainfall data, which can be expressed as:

$$\frac{dR^{(1)}(t)}{dt} + aR^{(1)}(t) = b \tag{3}$$

where a and b are the grey system model parameters. Deng [14] indicated that the whitening of the grey derivatives of discrete data with unit time intervals can be expressed as:

$$\left. \frac{dR^{(1)}(t)}{dt} \right|_{t=k} = r^{(1)}(k) - r^{(1)}(k-1) = R^{(0)}(k) \tag{4}$$

The whitening value of $\left. R^{(1)}(t) \right|_{t=k}$ is defined as:

$$Z^{(1)}(k) = \left. R^{(1)}(t) \right|_{t=k} \cong \frac{1}{2}\left(r^{(1)}(k) + r^{(1)}(k-1) \right),\ \ \ \ \forall k = 2,\ 3,\ ...\ ,\ t \tag{5}$$

where $Z^{(1)}(k)$ denotes the whitening value of $\left. R^{(1)}(t) \right|_{t=k}$. Next, Equations (4) and (5) are substituted into Equation (3) to obtain a grey discrete differential form as:

$$R^{(0)}(k) + a \cdot Z^{(1)}(k) = b \tag{6}$$

The grey parameters a and b can be estimated using the least square method. Thus, the solution of Equation (6) is expressed as:

$$\hat{r}^{(1)}(k + \Delta t) = \left(r^{(0)}(k) - \frac{b}{a} \right) e^{-ak} + \frac{b}{a} \tag{7}$$

where $\hat{r}^{(1)}(k+1)$ is the forecast value of the first-order AGO series. Consequently, the rainfall depth at the subsequent time step can be obtained from the equation:

$$\hat{r}^{(0)}(k+\Delta t) = \hat{r}^{(1)}(k+\Delta t) - \hat{r}^{(1)}(k), \quad \forall k = 1,\ 2,\ 3,\ \dots,\ n \in N \tag{8}$$

where $\hat{r}^{(0)}(k+\Delta t)$ is the forecast rainfall depth at time $k+\Delta t$. The grey parameters in Equation (7) are updated when the new observed rainfall data are obtained. Yu *et al.* [17] indicated that the accuracy of rainfall forecasting decreases when the lead time is increased because the forecast error is cumulated from previous lead-time forecasting. Consequently, an algorithm called single-time-step forecasting proposed by Yu *et al.* [17] was used to overcome the shortcoming.

Several studies have successfully applied the first-order grey model for hydrological forecasting [14–17]. Because forecast errors are cumulative, grey forecasting models become less reliable as the forecast lead time increases. However, when a grey rainfall forecasting model is combined with a watershed rainfall-runoff model, the forecast lead time can be extended because of the time lag in the transporting of a flood wave from upstream to downstream.

This study adopted four criteria to evaluate the performance of the grey rainfall forecasting model. First, the error of total cumulative rainfall (*ETCR*) is defined as:

$$ETCR = \frac{\left| \sum_{t=1}^{n} r_t - \sum_{t=1}^{n} \hat{r}_t \right|}{\sum_{t=1}^{n} r_t} \tag{9}$$

where $\hat{r}_t$ is the forecast rainfall at time t; r_t denotes the observed rainfall at time t; and n represents the number of time steps to be estimated. A more accurate forecast can be obtained when *ETCR* is approximately zero. Second, the relative root mean square error (*RMSE*) is defined as:

$$RMSE = \sqrt{\frac{\sum_{t=1}^{n} \left[(R_t - \hat{R}_t)/R_t \right]^2}{n}} \tag{10}$$

where R_t denotes the observed cumulative rainfall at time t; $\hat{R}_t$ is the forecast cumulative rainfall at time t. A more accurate forecast can be obtained when *RMSE* is approximately zero. Third, the coefficient of efficiency (*CE*) is defined as [56]:

$$CE = 1 - \frac{\sum_{t=1}^{n} (R_t - \hat{R}_t)^2}{\sum_{t=1}^{n} (R_t - \overline{R})^2} \tag{11}$$

$\overline{R}$ represents the mean of the observed cumulative rainfall. A more accurate fit between the forecast rainfall and the observed rainfall can be obtained when *CE* is approximately one. Moreover, the coefficient of correlation (*CC*) is defined as:

$$CC = \frac{\sum_{t=1}^{n} (R_t - \hat{R}_t)\left(\hat{R}_t - \widetilde{R} \right)}{\sqrt{\sum_{t=1}^{n} (R_t - \overline{R})^2 \cdot \sum_{t=1}^{n} \left(\hat{R}_t - \widetilde{R} \right)^2}} \tag{12}$$

where $\widetilde{R}$ is the mean of the forecast cumulative rainfall at time t. A more accurate forecast can be obtained when the value of *CC* is approximately one. The *ETCR* and *RMSE* represent a quantitative judgment of model performance. The *CE* is used to measure the similarity between the predicted and observed accumulated rainfall. The CC is used to measure the correlative relationship between the predicted and observed accumulative rainfall.

2.2. Geomorphology-Based Runoff Model with an Updating Algorithm

This study adopted an IUH model to provide an efficient method for estimating watershed runoff. The KW-GIUH model [36] was used because the IUH can be derived only by using watershed geomorphologic information obtained from a topographic map or digital elevation dataset. The hydrological response function of the watershed can be expressed analytically as follows [35]:

$$u(t) = \sum_{w \in W} \left[f_{x_{0_i}}(t) * f_{x_i}(t) * f_{x_j}(t) * \dots * f_{x_\Omega}(t) \right]_w \cdot P(w) \tag{13}$$

where $u(t)$ is the IUH of the watershed; W is the flow path space, which is expressed as $W = \langle x_{0_i}, x_i, x_j, \dots, x_\Omega \rangle$; $f_{x_{0_i}}(t)$ denotes the travel time probability density function in state x_j with a mean value of T_{x_j}; $*$ denotes a convolution integral; and $P(w)$ represents the probability of a raindrop adopting a flow path w.

Kinematic-wave approximation can be employed to express the runoff travel time for the ith-order surface flow region as follows [59]:

$$T_{x_{0_i}} = \left(\frac{n_o \overline{L}_{0_i}}{\overline{S}_{0_i}^{1/2} i_e^{m-1}} \right)^{\frac{1}{m}} \tag{14}$$

where n_o is the overland-flow roughness coefficient; $\overline{L}_{0_i}$ denotes the mean ith-order overland length; $\overline{S}_{0_i}$ is the mean ith-order overland slope; i_e represents the effective rainfall intensity; and m is an exponent recognized as 5/3 in Manning's formula. The runoff travel time for the ith-other channel is expressed as follows [36]:

$$T_{x_i} = \frac{B_i}{2 i_e \overline{L}_{0_i}} \left[\left(h_{co_i}^m + \frac{2 i_e n_c \overline{L}_{0_i} \overline{L}_{c_i}}{\overline{S}_{c_i}^{1/2} B_i} \right)^{\frac{1}{m}} - h_{co_i} \right] \tag{15}$$

where B_i is the ith-order channel width; n_c represents the channel roughness coefficient; $\overline{L}_{c_i}$ is the mean ith-order channel length; $\overline{S}_{c_i}$ denotes the mean ith-order channel slope; and h_{co_i} is the inflow depth of the ith-order channel caused by water transporting from upstream reaches. Hence, the runoff travel times for different orders of overland-flow paths and channels can be estimated, and the watershed IUH can then be derived by using Equation (13). Consequently, the watershed runoff simulated by using KW-GIUH model can be expressed as:

$$Q_{sim,t} = \int_0^\tau i(\tau) u(t - \tau) d\tau \tag{16}$$

where $Q_{sim,t}$ is the simulated direct runoff at time t; $i(\tau)$ is the rainfall intensity; and $u(t - \tau)$ is the unit impulse response function derived from the KW-GIUH model.

Uncertainty is an inherent hydrodynamic characteristic of watershed; therefore, this study adopted a real-time updating algorithm to improve the accuracy of flow forecasting. The change in measured discharge between time t and $t + \Delta t$ can be expressed as:

$$\Delta Q_{rec} = Q_{rec,t+\Delta t} - Q_{rec,t} \tag{17}$$

where $Q_{rec,t}$ and $Q_{rec,t+\Delta t}$ denote the measured discharges at time t and $t + \Delta t$, respectively; and ΔQ_{rec} represents the change in measured discharge between time t and $t + \Delta t$. Assuming that a reliable runoff model is used and short-term rainfall forecasting data (*i.e.*, with a lead time of several hours) are available, the value of ΔQ_{rec} in Equation (17) is assumed equal to the change in simulated discharge between time t and $t + \Delta t$; this is illustrated as follows:

$$\Delta Q_{rec} = \Delta Q_{sim} = Q_{sim,t+\Delta t} - Q_{sim,t} \qquad (18)$$

where $Q_{sim,t}$ and $Q_{sim,t+\Delta t}$ denote the simulated discharges at time t and $t + \Delta t$, respectively; and ΔQ_{sim} represents the change in simulated discharge between time t and $t + \Delta t$. Consequently, the forecast discharge at time t can be approximated by:

$$\begin{aligned} Q_{fore,t+\Delta t} &= Q_{rec,t} + \Delta Q_{rec} \\ &\cong Q_{rec,t} + \Delta Q_{sim} \end{aligned} \qquad (19)$$

where $Q_{fore,t+\Delta t}$ is the forecast discharge at time $t + \Delta t$ and ΔQ_{sim} is obtained from Equation (18). The schematic of the updating algorithm is shown in Figure 1. In the case that the real-time measured discharge $Q_{rec,t}$ cannot be transmitted successfully through the telemetric system during the rainstorm, the forecast discharge at time $t + \Delta t$ ($Q_{fore,t+\Delta t}$) is replaced by the model generated runoff discharge ($Q_{sim,t+\Delta t}$) without using the updating techniques. Although the proposed updating algorithm is simple, it is an efficient method for watershed runoff forecasting.

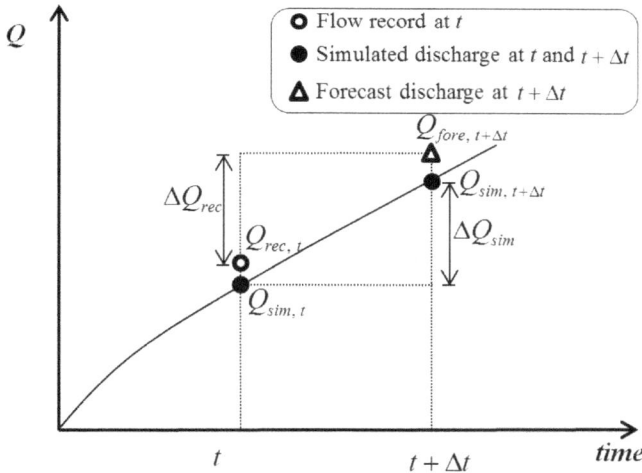

Figure 1. Schematic of the updating algorithm.

To evaluate the suitability of the KW-GIUH model, two criteria were chosen to determine the goodness-of-fit between the observed and simulated flow hydrographs. The coefficient of efficiency CE_Q is defined as follows [60]:

$$CE_Q = 1 - \frac{\sum\limits_{t=1}^{n} \left(Q_{rec}(t) - Q_{fore}(t) \right)^2}{\sum\limits_{t=1}^{n} \left(Q_{rec}(t) - \overline{Q}_{rec} \right)^2} \qquad (20)$$

where $Q_{rec}(t)$ and $Q_{fore}(t)$ denote the recorded and forecast discharges at time t, respectively; $\overline{Q}_{rec}$ is the mean recorded discharge during a storm event, and n is the number of discharge records during the storm event. The CE_Q is used to measure the similarity between the predicted and observed discharge hydrographs. A more accurate fit is obtained when the value of CE_Q is approximately one. The peak discharge error is defined as follows:

$$EQ_P(\%) = \frac{\left|(Q_P)_{fore} - (Q_P)_{rec}\right|}{(Q_P)_{rec}} \times 100 \tag{21}$$

where $(Q_P)_{fore}$ is the forecast peak discharge, and $(Q_P)_{rec}$ denotes the recorded peak discharge. The EQ_p is used to measure the error of peak discharge directly. The error of time to peak discharge, ET_P, is defined as:

$$ET_P = (T_P)_{fore} - (T_P)_{rec} \tag{22}$$

where $(T_P)_{fore}$ and $(T_P)_{rec}$ are the forecast and recorded time to peak discharge, respectively.

3. Model Applications

3.1. Description of Study Watersheds

Three watersheds were selected to investigate the applicability of the proposed model; one in the United States (Goodwin Creek) and two in Northern Taiwan (Heng-Chi and San-Hsia). Goodwin Creek is a tributary of Long Creek that flows into the Yocona River, which is one of the main rivers of the Yazoo River Basin. Figure 2a shows the watershed stream network and locations of hydrological gauging stations. The terrain elevation of the Goodwin Creek watershed ranges from 71 to 128 m above sea level (mean). The land area is composed of cultivated land (13.79%), forests (26.00%), pastures (59.80%), and water (0.41%). The climate of the Goodwin Creek watershed is humid with hot temperatures during summer and mild temperatures during winter. The mean annual temperature and rainfall are approximately 17 °C and 1399 mm, respectively. Most of the rainfall occurs during winter and spring. Hydrological data were obtained from the Agricultural Research Service of the United States Department of Agriculture. Among the 32 rain-gauging stations in the area, this study obtained rainfall records from nine stations. The Thiessen polygons method [61] was employed to calculate the hourly spatial-average rainfall intensities. Fourteen flow gauging stations were set up in the Goodwin Creek watershed area. The control areas of the flow gauging stations ranged from 0.06 to 21.39 km². In this study, Flow-gauging Station No.1 (STA01), which has a drainage area of 21.39 km², was selected as the test site to verify the model.

The Heng-Chi and San-Hsia watersheds are subwatersheds in Ta-Han Creek, which is one of the main rivers of the Tam-Sui River Basin in Northern Taiwan. Figure 2b shows the watershed stream networks and locations of the hydrological gauging stations. The elevation of the Heng-Chi (San-Hsia) watershed ranges from 20 to 970 m (30 to 1770 m), and the land is composed of 70% (75%) forest, 25% (20%) cultivated land, and 5% (5%) buildings/road. The mean annual precipitation in these areas is approximately 3000 mm. Most of the severe storm events are from typhoon activity between May and October, and intense rainfall (>50 mm/h) occurs every year.

The geomorphologic factors were obtained from a digital elevation model [62] based on datasets of the Goodwin Creek watershed (30-m resolution) and the Heng-Chi and San-Hsia watersheds (40-m resolution). Table 1 shows the geomorphologic factors of the watersheds used in the KW-GIUH model.

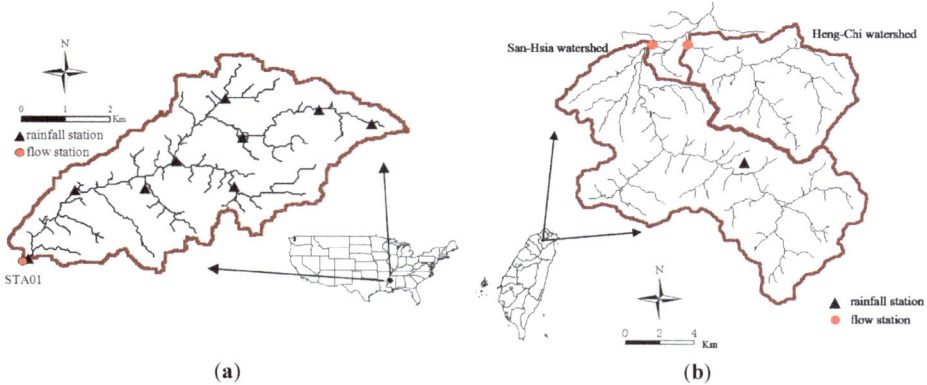

(a)   **(b)**

Figure 2. Watershed boundary and channel network of the study watersheds: (a) Goodwin Creek watershed; (b) Heng-Chi and San-Hsia watershed.

Table 1. Geomorphologic factors of the study watersheds.

Watershed	i	N_i	$\bar{A}_i$ (km²)	$\bar{L}_{c_i}$ (km²)	$\bar{S}_{c_i}$ (m/m)	$\bar{S}_{o_i}$ (m/m)
Goodwin (STA01)	1	76	0.18	0.40	0.0128	0.0228
	2	16	0.75	0.76	0.0090	0.0257
	3	4	3.08	1.56	0.0060	0.0260
	4	1	21.38	7.53	0.0019	0.0213
Heng-Chi	1	29	1.07	0.80	0.1304	0.3028
	2	6	6.91	3.13	0.0580	0.2957
	3	2	19.81	1.79	0.0105	0.2468
	4	1	53.15	4.98	0.0078	0.1977
San-Hsia	1	69	1.15	0.92	0.1613	0.3138
	2	16	4.99	2.08	0.0924	0.3016
	3	3	18.15	3.88	0.0372	0.3644
	4	1	125.88	17.83	0.0131	0.2918

Notes: N_i is the number of ith-order streams; $\bar{A}_i$ is the mean ith-order subwatershed area; $\bar{L}_{c_i}$ is the mean ith-order channel length; $\bar{S}_{c_i}$ is the mean ith-order channel slope; $\bar{S}_{o_i}$ is the mean ith-order hillslope slope.

3.2. Rainfall Forecasting

Table 2 shows the details of storm events that occurred in the study watersheds; these details were used for parameter calibration and model verification. In performing the grey rainfall model, parameters a and b (Equation (7)) can be estimated by using a least square method only based on small amount of past observed rainfall data. The watershed geomorphological factors in performing the KW-GIUH model are shown in Table 1, which can be obtained by applying a digital elevation model. The calibrated model parameters of the KW-GIUH model for the Heng-Chi and San-Hsia watersheds are $n_o = 0.6$ and $n_c = 0.05$, and $n_o = 0.2$ and $n_c = 0.02$ for the Goodwin watershed. The values of model parameters were stable for the test storms in the watersheds. Sensitivity analysis for the model parameters of KW-GIUH can be found in Lee and Yen [42].

Table 2. Storm records analyzed in this study.

Watershed (Rain Station)	Event Date	Rainfall Peak (mm/h)	Total Rainfall (mm)	Rainfall Duration (h)	Flow Peak (m^3/s)
Goodwin (STA01)	10/07/1989	11.13	92	48	29.7
	02/03/1991	16.80	62	18	21.1
	14/02/1992	4.66	30	11	9.1
	04/08/1995	13.29	113	28	16.7
	29/11/1996	6.95	44	29	10.2
	23/12/1997	7.17	45	13	19.6
	15/02/1998	10.20	62	48	27.3
	13/03/1999	11.92	95	52	31.0
	01/04/2000	24.09	152	63	32.9
	17/01/2001	7.26	78	60	10.3
Heng-Chi (Ta-Pao)	17/08/1984	36.00	372	51	169.0
	16/09/1985	69.00	348	25	620.0
	17/09/1986	46.00	420	61	457.0
	27/07/1987	32.00	114	18	164.0
	08/09/1987	59.00	261	45	329.0
	18/08/1990	48.00	342	48	492.0
	05/06/1993	54.00	146	18	179.0
	10/07/1994	22.00	150	31	58.2
	30/07/1996	31.00	450	42	243.0
	31/10/2000	33.00	508	38	317.0
12125San-Hsia (Ta-Pao)	17/08/1984	36.00	372	51	214.0
	16/09/1985	69.00	348	25	620.0
	17/09/1986	46.00	420	61	404.0
	27/07/1987	32.00	114	18	349.0
	08/09/1987	59.00	261	45	379.0
	18/08/1990	48.00	342	48	1060.0
	05/06/1993	54.00	146	18	339.0
	10/07/1994	22.00	150	31	257.0
	30/07/1996	31.00	450	42	720.0
	31/10/2000	33.00	508	38	435.0

Table 3 and Figure 3 show the performance of the grey rainfall forecasting model for the three watersheds. The *ETCR* and RMSE from Equations (9) and (10) represent the quantitative evaluation of the model performance, and *CE* from Equation (11) indicates the performance of the model based on cumulative rainfall. The performance of the model was assessed qualitatively based on the value of *CC* (Equation (12)) relative to the correlation between the forecast and observed cumulative rainfall. The results showed that *ETCR* is less than 0.24, *RMSE* is less than 0.38, *CE* is greater than 0.85, and *CC* is greater than 0.90, indicating that the forecast and recorded hyetographs are in good agreement. The forecast and recorded hyetographs in Figures 4 and 5 show the performance of the grey rainfall forecasting model based on lead times ranging from 1 to 3 h. Although the accuracy of the forecast rainfall decreases as the lead time increased, the results indicate that the proposed grey model is suitable for rainfall forecasting.

Table 3. Results of grey forecast rainfall.

Watershed	Event Date	ETCR			RMSE			CE			CC		
		1-h Ahead	2-h Ahead	3-h Ahead	1-h Ahead	2-h Ahead	3-h Ahead	1-h Ahead	2-h Ahead	3-h Ahead	1-h Ahead	2-h Ahead	3-h Ahead
Goodwin Creek	10/07/1989	0.03	0.18	0.22	0.03	0.08	0.17	0.99	0.98	0.92	0.99	0.95	0.88
	02/03/1991	0.05	0.16	0.20	0.08	0.17	0.29	0.96	0.93	0.88	0.99	0.95	0.88
	14/02/1992	0.01	0.03	0.08	0.02	0.14	0.27	1.00	0.98	0.95	0.99	0.96	0.90
	04/08/1995	0.06	0.11	0.16	0.04	0.17	0.24	0.97	0.90	0.87	0.99	0.98	0.92
	29/11/1996	0.03	0.09	0.10	0.08	0.24	0.31	0.97	0.90	0.85	0.99	0.98	0.96
	23/12/1997	0.06	0.15	0.21	0.03	0.19	0.25	0.98	0.91	0.88	0.99	0.99	0.97
	15/02/1998	0.04	0.07	0.16	0.06	0.11	0.19	1.00	0.94	0.88	1.00	0.96	0.97
	13/03/1999	0.09	0.14	0.20	0.06	0.18	0.21	0.99	0.95	0.89	1.00	0.98	0.90
	01/04/2000	0.03	0.08	0.15	0.03	0.12	0.16	0.99	0.96	0.91	1.00	1.00	0.98
	17/01/2001	0.07	0.11	0.19	0.07	0.11	0.16	0.98	0.91	0.88	0.98	0.94	0.91
Heng-Chi and San-Hsia	17/08/1984	0.05	0.08	0.16	0.11	0.18	0.27	0.99	0.98	0.94	1.00	0.98	0.96
	16/09/1985	0.06	0.12	0.24	0.09	0.22	0.31	0.96	0.93	0.86	0.99	0.95	0.88
	17/09/1986	0.01	0.03	0.05	0.05	0.18	0.21	1.00	0.98	0.95	1.00	1.00	0.99
	27/07/1987	0.09	0.18	0.22	0.03	0.11	0.18	0.97	0.91	0.88	0.98	0.93	0.91
	08/09/1987	0.01	0.09	0.10	0.14	0.26	0.38	0.89	0.83	0.80	1.00	0.98	0.96
	18/08/1990	0.03	0.09	0.12	0.08	0.17	0.24	0.95	0.85	0.81	1.00	0.99	0.97
	05/06/1993	0.05	0.08	0.11	0.01	0.04	0.19	1.00	0.94	0.87	0.99	0.96	0.97
	10/07/1994	0.09	0.11	0.18	0.02	0.13	0.20	0.98	0.99	0.96	0.99	0.98	0.90
	30/07/1996	0.04	0.07	0.11	0.05	0.15	0.22	0.99	0.95	0.83	1.00	1.00	0.98
	31/10/2000	0.04	0.05	0.17	0.08	0.09	0.13	0.99	0.97	0.93	1.00	1.00	0.99
Average		0.05	0.10	0.16	0.06	0.16	0.23	0.98	0.93	0.89	1.00	0.98	0.94

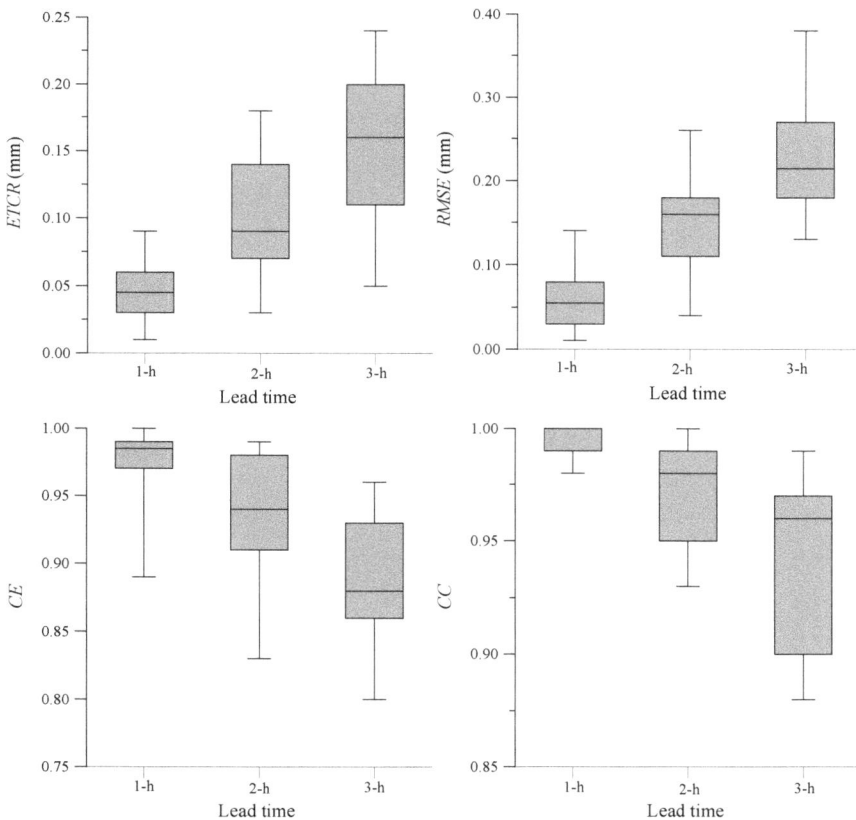

Figure 3. Results of evaluated criteria for grey forecast rainfall.

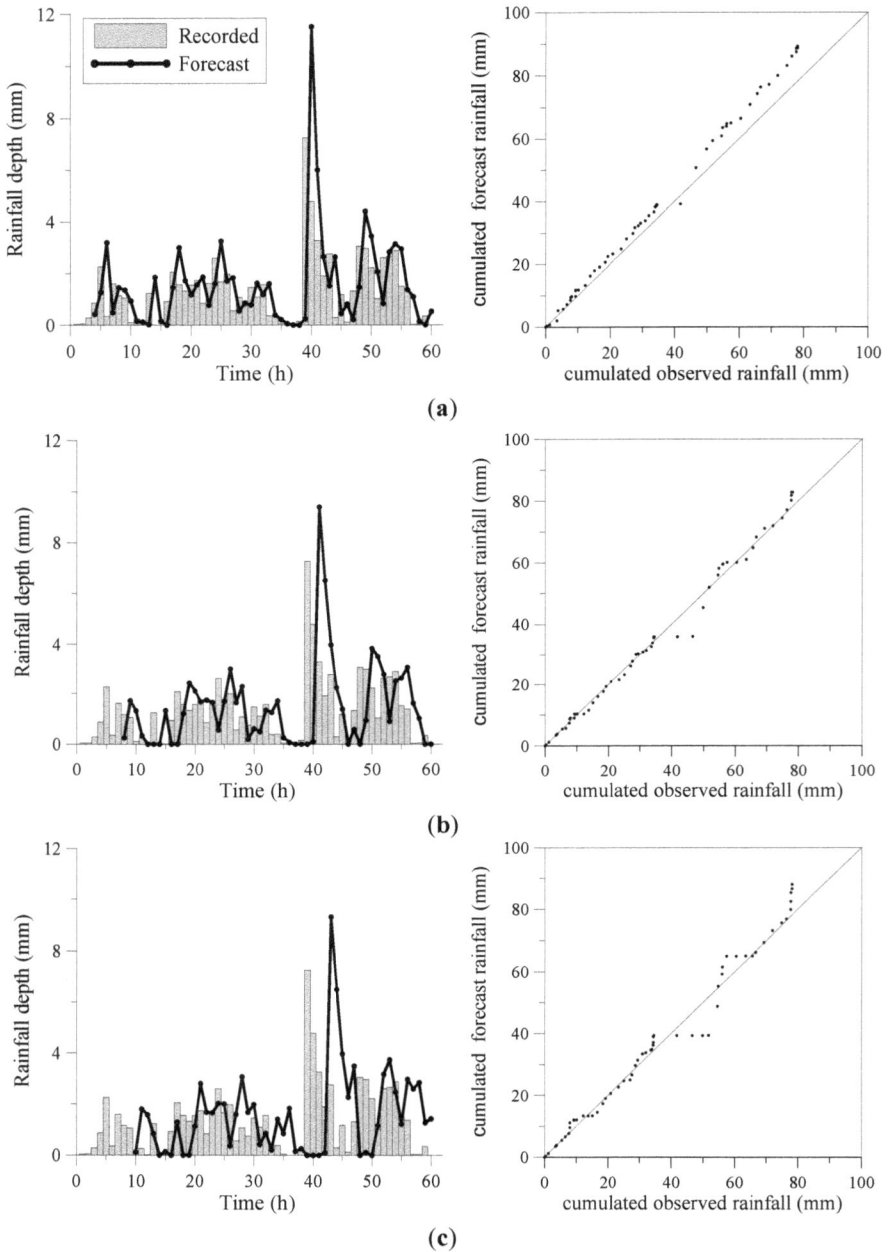

Figure 4. Grey model for rainfall forecasting in Goodwin Creek watershed: (**a**) 1-h ahead; (**b**) 2-h ahead; (**c**) 3-h ahead.

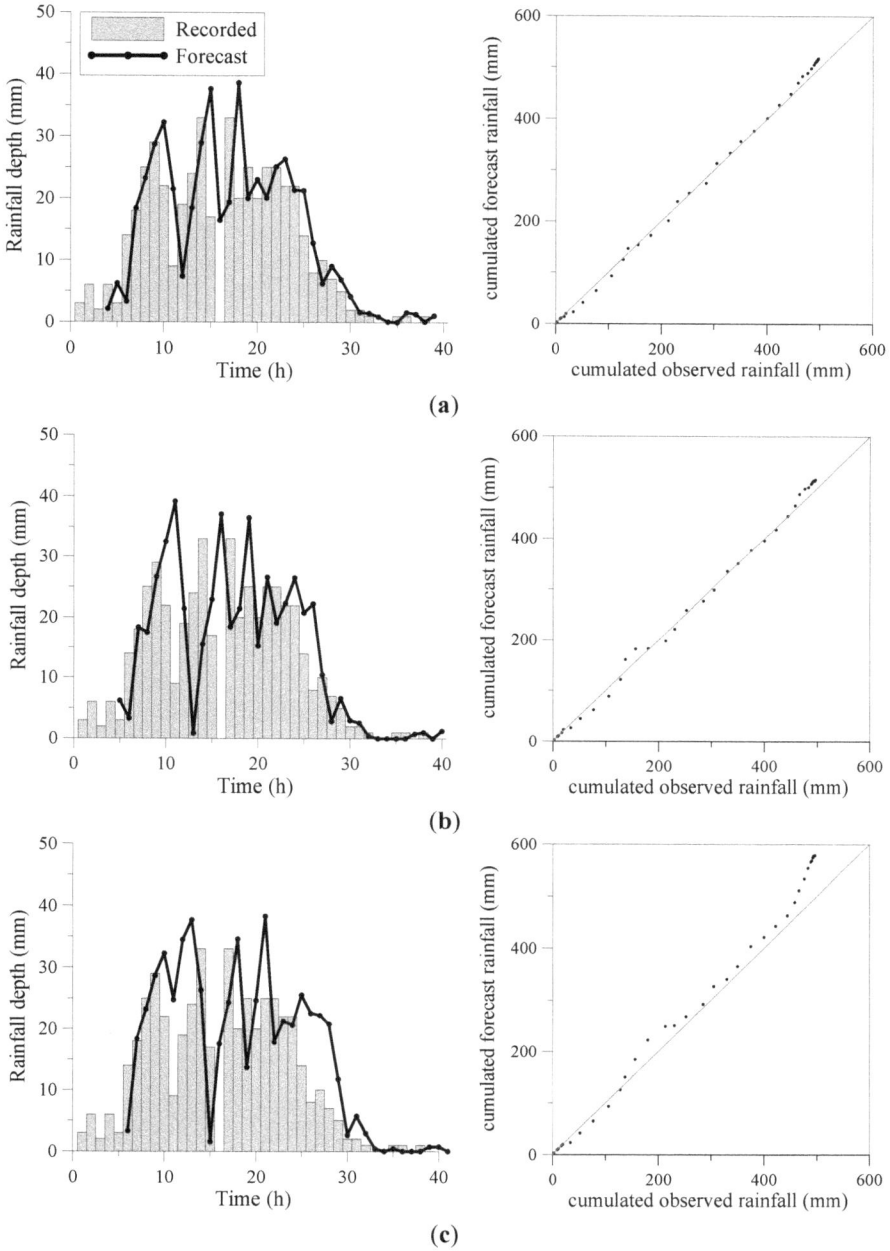

Figure 5. Grey model for rainfall forecasting in San-Hsia watershed: (**a**) 1-h ahead; (**b**) 2-h ahead; (**c**) 3-h ahead.

3.3. Flow Forecasting

Four sets of tests were performed to evaluate the applicability of the proposed system for real-time flood prediction. The simulation results are detailed shown as follows.

(1) Flow forecasting by using measured rainfall and without flow updating

This set of tests was conducted to evaluate the performance of the KW-GIUH model for simulating rainfall-runoff. Observed rainfall data were inputted into the KW-GIUH model and the flow updating algorithm was not used in the simulation. Figure 6 shows the results of runoff simulations for the Goodwin Creek and San-Hsia watersheds. As shown in Table 4, the simulated and observed hydrographs are in relatively good agreement in the study watersheds. The CE_Q values of the simulated hydrographs for all storm events are greater than 0.82, and most of the EQ_P and ET_P are lesser than 10% and 2 h, respectively. The results indicate that the KW-GIUH model is reliable for rainfall-runoff simulation in these two watersheds. Figure 6a shows that the temporal distributions of the observed rainfall hyetograph and flow hydrograph were inconsistent; specifically, the rainfall peak occurred at 45 h, whereas the flow peak occurred at 57 h. The reason for this inconsistency is unknown. However, this unusual hydrological record could be used to test the effectiveness of the proposed flow updating algorithm.

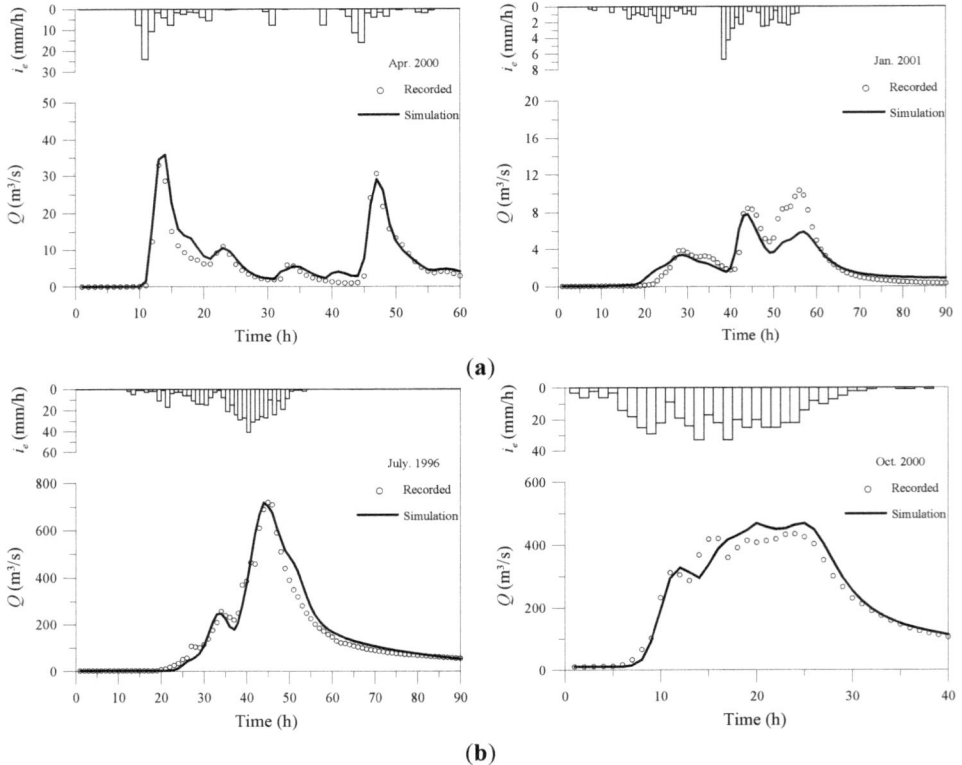

Figure 6. Flow forecasting using measured rainfall data and without flow updating in Goodwin Creek and San-Hsia watersheds: (**a**) Goodwin Creek watershed (STA 01); (**b**) San-Hsia watershed.

Table 4. Results of flow forecasting using measured rainfall and without flow updating technique.

Watershed	Event Date	CE_Q	EQ_p (%)	ET_p (h)
Goodwin (SAT01)	10/07/1989	0.83	6.29	1
	02/03/1991	0.92	2.56	0
	14/02/1992	0.88	4.33	1
	04/08/1995	0.86	7.81	−1
	29/11/1996	0.93	2.08	0
	23/12/1997	0.89	3.54	0
	15/02/1998	0.88	4.28	0
	13/03/1999	0.84	3.07	0
	01/04/2000	0.90	0.09	1
	17/01/2001	0.82	25.00	12
Heng-Chi	17/08/1984	0.92	2.00	−1
	16/09/1985	0.88	0.24	−1
	17/09/1986	0.85	1.82	0
	27/07/1987	0.86	4.16	0
	08/09/1987	0.92	3.46	0
	18/08/1990	0.85	4.52	−1
	05/06/1993	0.97	2.01	−1
	10/07/1994	0.86	1.25	−1
	30/07/1996	0.94	3.54	−1
	31/10/2000	0.95	3.01	−2
San-Hsia	17/08/1984	0.90	6.54	0
	16/09/1985	0.89	3.33	0
	17/09/1986	0.86	6.29	1
	27/07/1987	0.84	5.54	1
	08/09/1987	0.88	5.19	0
	18/08/1990	0.83	2.24	0
	05/06/1993	0.87	5.64	−1
	10/07/1994	0.95	2.13	0
	30/07/1996	0.96	1.32	−1
	31/10/2000	0.95	7.65	−3
Average		0.89	4.36	0.10

(2) Flow forecasting by using forecast rainfall and without flow updating

For the second set of tests, flow forecasting was performed by inputting the forecast rainfall (obtained from the grey model) into the KW-GIUH model. Table 5 and Figure 7 show that the flow forecasting accuracy decreased as the lead time increased from 1 to 3 h. For the $t + 1$ forecast, the forecast flow is in good agreement with the observed flow. For the $t + 2$ and $t + 3$ forecasts, the temporal variation of the flow hydrograph is adequately represented in the simulation although the simulated flow peak is higher than the observed flow peak because the forecast peak rainfall was overestimated in the hyetograph. Regarding the storm event at the Goodwin Creek watershed on 17 January 2001, the results shown in Figure 7a indicate that the KW-GIUH model forecast the first flow peak accurately. However, the second flow peak is underestimated because of the inconsistency between the rainfall hyetograph and flow hydrograph as mentioned.

Table 5. Results of flow forecasting using forecast rainfall and without flow updating technique.

Watershed	Event Date	CE_Q			EQ_p (%)			ET_p (h)		
		1-h Ahead	2-h Ahead	3-h Ahead	1-h Ahead	2-h Ahead	3-h Ahead	1-h Ahead	2-h Ahead	3-h Ahead
	10/07/1989	0.82	0.49	0.31	14.41	37.91	51.18	1	2	3
	02/03/1991	0.92	0.84	0.81	9.88	27.41	39.42	1	2	3
	14/02/1992	0.87	0.86	0.77	12.48	19.88	32.77	0	1	2
	04/08/1995	0.86	0.83	0.77	11.82	20.43	28.91	1	2	3
Goodwin	29/11/1996	0.92	0.85	0.83	8.97	14.81	17.94	0	1	2
(SAT01)	23/12/1997	0.89	0.86	0.83	18.13	29.87	41.09	1	1	2
	15/02/1998	0.87	0.81	0.69	14.30	28.99	45.17	1	2	3
	13/03/1999	0.82	0.74	0.70	7.69	12.90	18.09	0	1	2
	01/04/2000	0.90	0.55	0.03	8.95	45.27	62.98	1	2	3
	17/01/2001	0.82	0.81	0.80	24.75	1.27	30.97	12	12	12
	17/08/1984	0.90	0.86	0.81	4.81	11.85	19.28	1	2	2
	16/09/1985	0.87	0.81	0.74	3.29	8.74	20.32	1	1	2
	17/09/1986	0.83	0.79	0.71	10.93	24.31	31.88	1	2	3
	27/07/1987	0.85	0.83	0.78	8.49	18.41	24.31	1	2	2
Heng-Chi	08/09/1987	0.92	0.90	0.86	7.96	16.19	19.22	1	2	2
	18/08/1990	0.75	0.43	0.09	14.41	19.84	31.03	1	2	3
	05/06/1993	0.95	0.94	0.88	2.09	7.31	9.08	0	1	2
	10/07/1994	0.85	0.81	0.70	1.09	8.54	11.72	0	1	1
	30/07/1996	0.93	0.91	0.82	9.75	14.32	18.97	−1	0	0
	31/10/2000	0.95	0.94	0.86	4.71	5.47	7.93	−3	−2	−1
	17/08/1984	0.90	0.81	0.79	8.49	14.55	21.09	1	2	2
	16/09/1985	0.88	0.80	0.74	6.39	11.52	17.92	1	1	2
	17/09/1986	0.86	0.83	0.52	9.31	18.45	37.01	1	2	3
	27/07/1987	0.84	0.83	0.67	4.09	11.12	14.17	1	2	2
San-Hsia	08/09/1987	0.87	0.81	0.63	4.41	9.18	22.97	1	2	2
	18/08/1990	0.81	0.62	0.31	6.31	11.48	18.02	1	2	3
	05/06/1993	0.85	0.81	0.76	7.31	9.52	16.55	0	1	2
	10/07/1994	0.95	0.91	0.85	4.86	7.59	16.31	0	1	1
	30/07/1996	0.95	0.94	0.89	1.96	4.48	12.05	−1	0	0
	31/10/2000	0.94	0.92	0.80	8.67	13.71	16.58	−3	−2	−1
Average		0.88	0.80	0.69	8.69	16.18	25.16	0.73	1.60	2.23

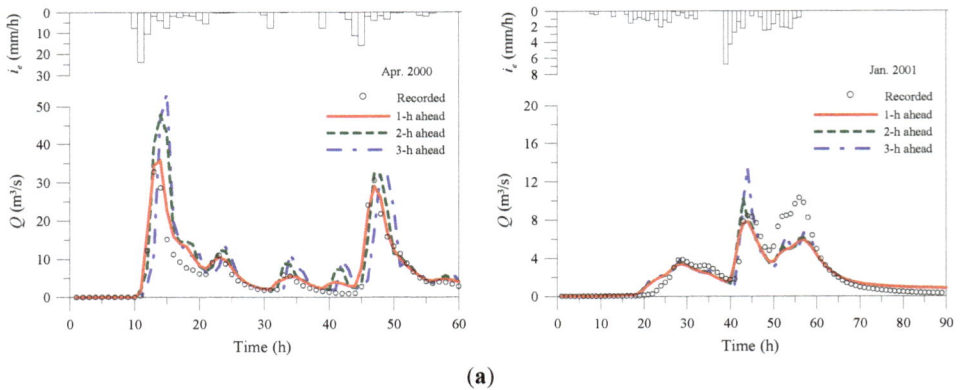

Figure 7. *Cont.*

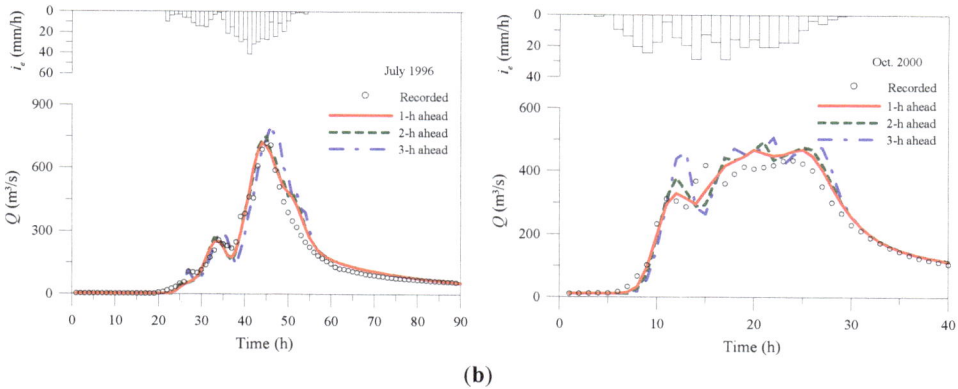

(b)

Figure 7. Flow forecasting using forecast rainfall and without flow updating in Goodwin Creek and San-Hsia watersheds: (**a**) Goodwin Creek watershed (STA 01); (**b**) San-Hsia watershed.

(3) Flow forecasting by using measured rainfall and flow updating technique

The third set of tests was conducted to evaluate the performance of the KW-GIUH model when the flow updating algorithm was used in the rainfall-runoff simulation, as shown in Equation (18). The measured rainfall at $t + 1$, $t + 2$, and $t + 3$ was inputted into the KW-GIUH model. Table 6 and Figure 8 show the simulation results, which were evaluated based on the coefficient of efficiency CE_Q, error of peak discharge EQ_P, and error of time to peak discharge ET_P. When the value CE_Q is approximately one and EQ_P and ET_P are approximately zero, good agreement between the recorded and simulated hydrographs is anticipated. The results in Figure 8 show that the CE_Q values are higher than 0.96, the mean EQ_P is 2.73%, and the mean ET_P is 0.17 h for the $t + 1$ simulation. For the $t + 2$ simulation, the CE_Q values are higher than 0.87, the mean EQ_P is 4.40%, and the mean ET_P is 0.67 h. Finally, for the $t + 3$ simulation, the CE_Q values are higher than 0.81, the mean EQ_P is 7.92%, and the mean ET_P is 1.23 h. Figure 9 shows that the forecast and recorded hydrographs are in good agreement for all storm events in this test, indicating that the proposed flow updating algorithm combined with the KW-GIUH model simulated the watershed runoff more accurately than do the KW-GIUH model alone. Moreover, regarding the storm event at the Goodwin Creek watershed on 17 January 2001, the flow hydrographs in Figures 7a and 9a show that the second peak was accurately forecasted when the flow updating algorithm is used, despite the recorded flow peak appearing to be unreasonable. The results show that using a purely deterministic approach to simulate watershed rainfall runoff is difficult without the assistance of a real-time adaptive algorithm.

Table 6. Results of flow forecasting using measured rainfall and flow updating technique.

Watershed	Event Date	CE_Q			EQ_p (%)			ET_p (h)		
		1-h Update	2-h Update	3-h Update	1-h Update	2-h Update	3-h Update	1-h Update	2-h Update	3-h Update
Goodwin (SAT01)	10/07/1989	0.97	0.93	0.89	2.54	5.77	8.43	1	1	1
	02/03/1991	0.98	0.94	0.90	0.14	3.43	4.95	1	1	2
	14/02/1992	0.96	0.91	0.84	3.83	5.46	5.57	0	0	1
	04/08/1995	0.96	0.92	0.83	2.53	4.59	7.33	0	0	1
	29/11/1996	0.96	0.91	0.85	3.64	4.22	8.36	1	2	2
	23/12/1997	0.97	0.92	0.85	4.81	5.65	8.78	−1	0	1
	15/02/1998	0.96	0.92	0.86	0.19	3.19	3.97	−1	−1	0
	13/03/1999	0.96	0.91	0.83	3.71	0.13	9.80	0	1	1
	01/04/2000	0.97	0.93	0.85	1.94	0.97	8.11	−1	−1	0
	17/01/2001	0.97	0.87	0.81	0.84	0.53	2.05	1	1	1
Heng-Chi	17/08/1984	0.96	0.92	0.88	4.75	5.69	10.54	0	0	1
	16/09/1985	0.97	0.93	0.89	4.55	6.29	14.12	0	0	1
	17/09/1986	0.97	0.92	0.90	2.30	1.89	4.92	0	1	2
	27/07/1987	0.96	0.91	0.88	0.76	2.69	5.50	0	1	1
	08/09/1987	0.96	0.92	0.89	1.62	5.86	8.80	1	2	2
	18/08/1990	0.97	0.93	0.91	0.50	3.40	4.14	−1	0	0
	05/06/1993	0.98	0.93	0.91	2.75	0.68	8.15	1	2	2
	10/07/1994	0.97	0.93	0.90	3.03	4.42	9.09	1	1	2
	30/07/1996	0.96	0.91	0.89	3.16	2.19	2.09	0	0	1
	31/10/2000	0.98	0.93	0.91	3.17	10.78	14.44	0	1	1
San-Hsia	17/08/1984	0.96	0.92	0.87	2.95	5.69	12.86	1	1	2
	16/09/1985	0.96	0.91	0.88	1.21	8.33	13.23	0	1	1
	17/09/1986	0.97	0.92	0.89	1.53	1.64	3.23	0	1	1
	27/07/1987	0.97	0.92	0.88	3.76	3.24	4.18	0	0	1
	08/09/1987	0.97	0.91	0.86	1.64	6.24	10.8	0	1	2
	18/08/1990	0.96	0.91	0.88	1.69	3.23	3.15	0	0	1
	05/06/1993	0.97	0.94	0.91	2.42	4.89	9.33	1	2	2
	10/07/1994	0.96	0.91	0.88	1.72	3.09	11.56	0	0	1
	30/07/1996	0.98	0.98	0.93	3.84	3.28	4.34	−1	0	1
	31/10/2000	0.99	0.96	0.95	6.22	7.35	9.42	1	2	2
Average		0.97	0.92	0.88	2.73	4.40	7.92	0.17	0.67	1.23

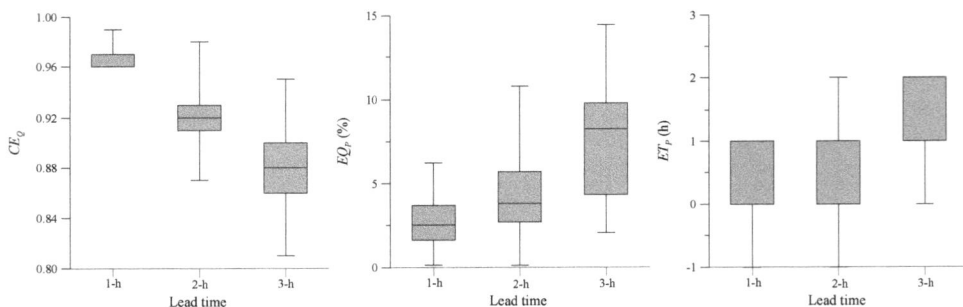

Figure 8. Results of evaluated criteria for flow forecasting using measured rainfall and flow updating technique.

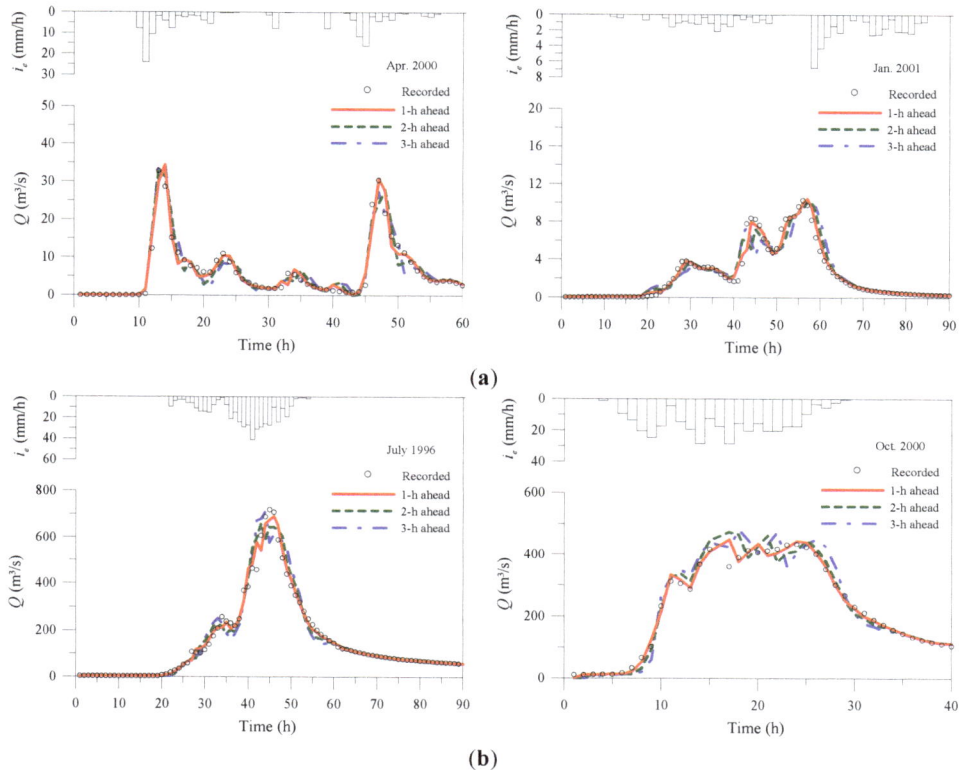

Figure 9. Flow forecasting using measured rainfall and flow updating algorithm in Goodwin Creek and San-Hsia watersheds: (**a**) Goodwin Creek watershed (STA 01); (**b**) San-Hsia watershed.

(4) Flow forecasting by using forecast rainfall and flow updating algorithm

The final set tests was conducted to confirm the performance of the proposed flood forecasting system. The forecast rainfall is generated by using the grey model, and the flow updating algorithm is included in the runoff simulation by using the KW-GIUH model to improve the forecasting accuracy. Table 7 and Figure 10 show that the mean CE_Q (EQ_P) values of the $t + 1$, $t + 2$, and $t + 3$ forecasts are 0.92 (4.50%), 0.80 (9.12%), and 0.72 (13.57%). The mean ET_P values of the $t + 1$, $t + 2$, and $t + 3$ forecasts are 0.70 h, 1.47 h, and 2.13 h, respectively. The results of the storm event simulations in Figure 11 shows that the recorded and simulated hydrographs are in good agreement for all the three watersheds under various geoclimate conditions, even as the lead time increases from 1 to 3 h.

Table 7. Results of flow forecasting using forecast rainfall and flow updating technique.

Watershed	Event Date	CE_Q			EQ_p (%)			ET_p (h)		
		1-h Ahead	2-h Ahead	3-h Ahead	1-h Ahead	2-h Ahead	3-h Ahead	1-h Ahead	2-h Ahead	3-h Ahead
	10/07/1989	0.94	0.82	0.80	3.81	11.21	13.91	1	1	2
	02/03/1991	0.95	0.87	0.77	1.00	3.60	7.33	1	1	2
	14/02/1992	0.89	0.69	0.66	4.22	1.89	4.04	1	2	2
	04/08/1995	0.88	0.70	0.69	1.01	8.67	12.59	1	2	3
Goodwin	29/11/1996	0.89	0.86	0.81	3.64	9.45	16.24	1	1	2
(SAT01)	23/12/1997	0.91	0.69	0.65	7.28	8.15	14.89	0	1	2
	15/02/1998	0.93	0.85	0.79	9.56	10.69	11.28	0	1	2
	13/03/1999	0.91	0.79	0.78	3.70	8.91	7.28	0	1	1
	01/04/2000	0.95	0.72	0.61	4.13	12.34	18.75	1	2	3
	17/01/2001	0.97	0.94	0.91	1.07	0.39	4.20	0	1	1
	17/08/1984	0.95	0.76	0.62	8.42	11.21	3.71	1	1	2
	16/09/1985	0.89	0.71	0.61	4.88	13.77	5.66	1	1	2
	17/09/1986	0.90	0.84	0.79	1.52	8.15	19.10	1	2	3
	27/07/1987	0.96	0.76	0.61	6.79	9.97	11.52	1	2	2
Heng-Chi	08/09/1987	0.89	0.75	0.62	0.04	7.44	16.60	1	2	3
	18/08/1990	0.91	0.78	0.66	3.21	0.22	9.67	0	1	1
	05/06/1993	0.88	0.77	0.61	7.93	12.73	19.02	1	2	3
	10/07/1994	0.92	0.74	0.64	3.28	11.82	23.11	1	1	2
	30/07/1996	0.96	0.90	0.83	1.70	3.62	6.61	1	2	2
	31/10/2000	0.95	0.89	0.82	3.68	5.03	10.02	1	2	2
	17/08/1984	0.93	0.76	0.63	9.31	11.59	17.42	1	2	3
	16/09/1985	0.89	0.74	0.61	5.81	14.60	19.88	1	2	2
	17/09/1986	0.91	0.91	0.78	8.44	18.00	22.30	0	1	2
	27/07/1987	0.89	0.72	0.59	7.32	11.52	15.39	1	2	3
San-Hsia	08/09/1987	0.96	0.83	0.74	1.75	5.47	14.50	0	1	1
	18/08/1990	0.91	0.75	0.65	1.68	3.13	9.50	1	2	2
	05/06/1993	0.88	0.71	0.63	6.03	22.14	27.56	1	2	3
	10/07/1994	0.92	0.78	0.69	1.32	13.36	28.36	0	1	2
	30/07/1996	0.98	0.97	0.92	4.60	4.83	5.03	1	1	2
	31/10/2000	0.98	0.95	0.94	7.75	9.65	11.62	0	1	2
Average		0.92	0.80	0.72	4.50	9.12	13.57	0.70	1.47	2.13

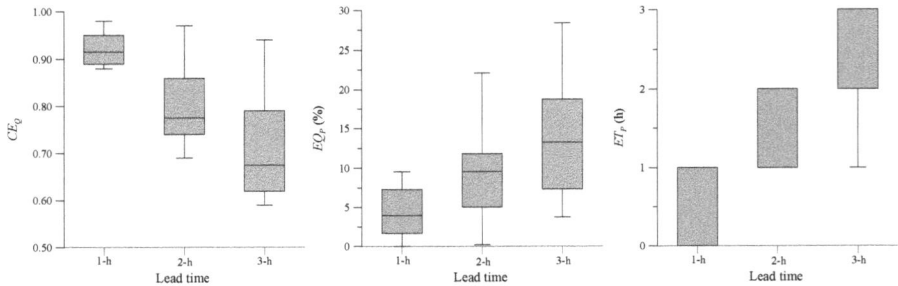

Figure 10. Results of evaluated criteria for flow forecasting using forecast rainfall and flow updating technique.

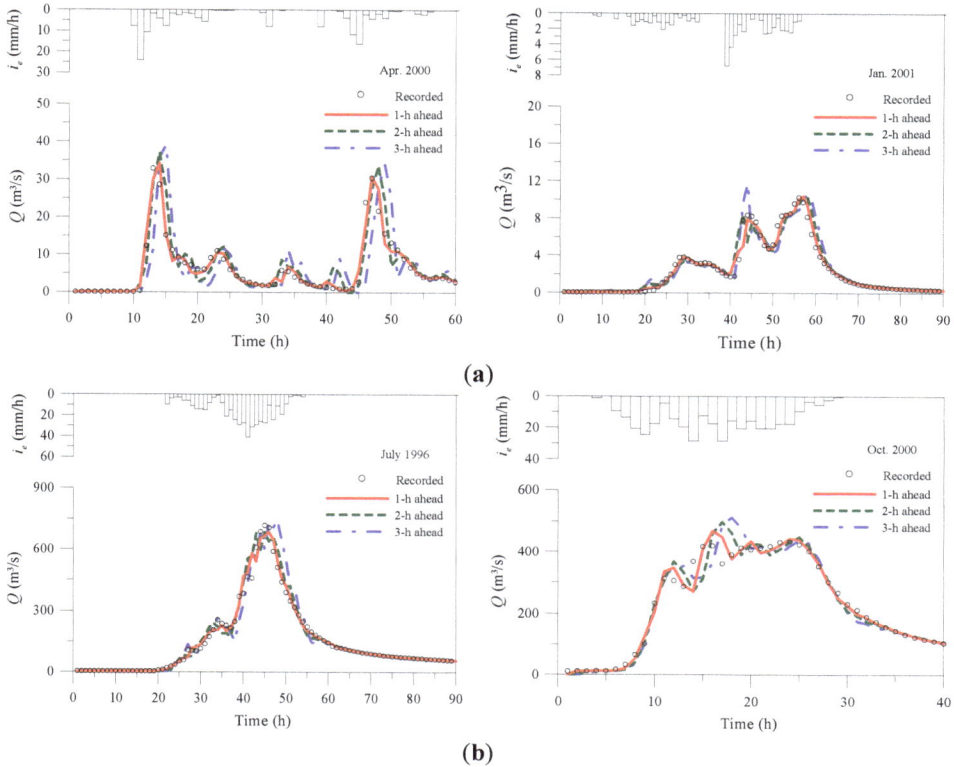

Figure 11. Flow forecasting using forecast rainfall and flow updating algorithm in Goodwin Creek and San-Hsia watersheds: (**a**) Goodwin Creek watershed (STA 01); (**b**) San-Hsia watershed.

4. Conclusions

This study developed an integrated framework for flood forecasting by using a rainfall forecasting model, watershed rainfall-runoff model, and real-time flow updating algorithm. Considering that current numerical meteorological models used in Taiwan cannot provide a 3-h prediction of the temporal distribution of rainfall, this study adopted a grey rainfall forecasting model. Using the KW-GIUH model for runoff simulation is advantageous because it can be developed based on only geomorphologic factors of the watershed. Moreover, a real-time flow updating algorithm was incorporated into the KW-GIUH structure to account for the uncertainty of watershed runoff processes. The proposed flood forecasting system was tested based on hydrological records from three watersheds under different geomorphological and hydrological conditions. For the 1-h, 2-h, and 3-h ahead forecast cases, the simulated mean coefficient of efficiency (error of peak discharge) is 0.92 (4.5%), 0.80 (9.12%), and 0.72 (13.57%). The mean ET_P values of the $t + 1$, $t + 2$, and $t + 3$ forecast cases are 0.70 h, 1.47 h, and 2.13 h, respectively. These results indicate that the proposed flood forecasting system can provide credible warning information for authorities. Furthermore, the proposed flow forecasting system can operate with high efficiency to meet the requirements of real-time flow forecasting. Nevertheless, in considering that the forecast rainfall is assumed to have the same tendency as previous rainfall; hence, only short-term prediction is applicable for this rainfall forecasting system. Since spatially-uniform rainfall is used in the KW-GIUH model, the proposed flow forecasting may be not used in a large watershed. Further validations to account for watersheds with various hydrological and geomorphologic characteristics are still required in future research.

Acknowledgments: This research was supported by the Ministry of Science and Technology, Taiwan, under grants MOST 103-2625-M-492-007 and 101-2218-E-006-003. The authors acknowledge the financial support provided by the Ministry of Science and Technology.

Author Contributions: Jui-Yi Ho was validated proposed model. Kwan Tun Lee was designed and performed the model. Both authors contributed about equally to compose this paper, discussed the results, and commented on the manuscript at all stages.

Conflicts of Interest: The authors declare no conflict of interest

References

1. Brath, A.; Burlando, P.; Rosso, R. Sensitivity analysis of real-time flood forecasting to on-line rainfall predictions. In *Selected Papers from the Workshop on Natural Disasters in European-Mediterranean Countries*; Siccardi, F., Bras, R.L., Eds.; National Research Council: Perugia, Italy, 1998; pp. 469–488.
2. Borga, M.; Anagnostou, E.N.; Frank, E. On the use of real-time radar rainfall estimates for flood prediction in mountainous basins. *J. Geophys. Res.* **2000**, *105*, 2269–2280. [CrossRef]
3. Plessis, L.D. A review of effective flood forecasting, warning and response system for application in South Africa. *Water SA* **2002**, *28*, 129–137. [CrossRef]
4. Walser, A.; Schär, C. Convection-resolving precipitation forecasting and its predictability in Alpine river catchments. *J. Hydrol.* **2004**, *288*, 57–73. [CrossRef]
5. Toth, E.; Brath, A.; Montnari, A. Comparison of short-term rainfall prediction models for real-time flood forecasting. *J. Hydrol.* **2000**, *239*, 132–147. [CrossRef]
6. Garbrecht, J.; Ogden, F.L.; DeBarry, P.A.; Maidment, D.R. GIS and distributed watershed models. I: Data converges and sources. *J. Hydrol. Eng.* **2001**, *6*, 506–514. [CrossRef]
7. Moore, R.J.; Bell, V.A.; Jones, D.A. Forecasting for flood warning. *Comptes Rendus Geosci.* **2005**, *337*, 203–217. [CrossRef]
8. French, M.N.; Krajewski, W.F.; Cuykendall, R.R. Rainfall forecasting in space and time using a neural network. *J. Hydrol.* **1992**, *137*, 1–31. [CrossRef]
9. Burlando, P.; Rosso, R.; Gadavid, L.G.; Salas, J.D. Forecasting of short-term rainfall using ARMA models. *J. Hydrol.* **1993**, *144*, 193–211. [CrossRef]
10. Lardet, P.; Obled, C. Real time flood forecasting using a stochastic rainfall generator. *J. Hydrol.* **1994**, *162*, 391–408. [CrossRef]
11. Kelly, K.S.; Krzysztofowicz, R. Precipitation uncertainty processor for probabilistic river stage forecasting. *Water Resour. Res.* **2000**, *36*, 2643–2654. [CrossRef]
12. Krzysztofowicz, R. Integrator of uncertainties for probabilistic river stage forecasting: Precipitation-dependent model. *J. Hydrol.* **2001**, *249*, 69–85. [CrossRef]
13. Lin, G.F.; Wu, M.C. A hybrid neural network for typhoon-rainfall forecasting. *J. Hydrol.* **2009**, *375*, 450–458. [CrossRef]
14. Deng, J.L. Introduction to grey system theory. *J. Grey Syst.* **1989**, *1*, 1–24.
15. Xia, J. Research and application of grey system theorem to hydrology. *J. Grey Syst.* **1989**, *1*, 43–52.
16. Huang, Y.P.; Huang, C.C. The integration and application of fuzzy and grey modeling methods. *Fuzzy Sets Syst.* **1996**, *78*, 107–119. [CrossRef]
17. Yu, P.-S.; Chen, C.-J.; Chen, S.-C.; Lin, S.-C. Application of grey method toward runoff forecasting. *J. Am. Water Resour. Assoc.* **2001**, *37*, 151–166. [CrossRef]
18. ASCE Task Committee on Application of Artificial Neural Networks in Hydrology. Artificial Neural Networks in Hydrology, part I: Preliminary concepts. *J. Hydrol. Eng.* **2000**, *5*, 115–123.
19. ASCE Task Committee on Application of Artificial Neural Networks in Hydrology. Artificial Neural Networks in Hydrology, part II: Hydrologic applications. *J. Hydrol. Eng.* **2000**, *5*, 124–137.
20. Xu, Z.X.; Li, J.Y. Short-term inflow forecasting using an artificial neural network model. *Hydrol. Process.* **2002**, *16*, 2423–2439. [CrossRef]
21. Lin, G.F.; Chen, L.H. A non-linear rainfall-runoff model using radial basis function network. *J. Hydrol.* **2004**, *289*, 1–8. [CrossRef]

22. Chetan, M.; Sudheer, K.P. A hybrid linear-neural model for river flow forecasting. *Water Resour. Res.* **2006**, *42*. [CrossRef]

23. Chen, W.; Chau, K.W. Intelligent manipulation and calibration of parameters for hydrological models. *Int. J. Environ. Pollut.* **2006**, *28*, 432–447. [CrossRef]

24. Muttil, N.; Chau, K.-W. Neural network and genetic programming for modelling coastal algal blooms. *Int. J. Environ. Pollut.* **2006**, *28*, 223–238. [CrossRef]

25. Chau, K.W. An ontology-based knowledge management system for flow and water quality modeling. *Adv. Eng. Softw.* **2007**, *38*, 172–181. [CrossRef]

26. Toth, E.; Brath, A. Multistep ahead streamflow forecasting: Role of calibration data in conceptual and neural network modeling. *Water Resour. Res.* **2007**, *43*, W11405. [CrossRef]

27. Taormina, R.; Chau, K.W. Neural network river forecasting with multi-objective fully informed particle swarm optimization. *J. Hydroinform.* **2015**, *17*, 99–113. [CrossRef]

28. Wu, C.L.; Chau, K.W.; Li, Y.S. River stage prediction based on a distributed support vector regression. *J. Hydrol.* **2008**, *358*, 96–111. [CrossRef]

29. Cheng, C.T.; Chau, K.W.; Sun, Y.; Lin, J. Long-term prediction of discharges in Manwan Reservoir using artificial neural network models. *Lecture Notes Comput. Sci.* **2005**, *3498*, 1040–1045.

30. Hapuarachchi, H.A.P.; Wang, Q.J. *A Review of Methods and Systems Available for Flash Flood Forecasting*; Report for the Bureau of Meteorology, Australia; Commonwealth Scientific and Industrial Research Organisation (CSIRO): Dickson, Austrilia, July 2008.

31. Burnash, R.J.C.; Ferral, R.L.; McGuire, R.A. *A Generalized Streamflow Simulation System: Conceptual Modeling for Digital Computers*; U.S. Department of Commerce: Washington, DC, USA, 1973.

32. Burnash, R.J.C. The NWS river forecast system-catchment modeling. In *Computer Models of Watershed Hydrology*; Singh, V.P., Ed.; Water Resources Publications: Highlands Ranch, CO, USA, 1995; pp. 311–366.

33. Sugawara, M. Automatic calibration of the tank model. *Hydrol. Sci. Bull.* **1979**, *24*, 375–388. [CrossRef]

34. Bergstrom, S. The HBV model. In *Computer Models of Watershed Hydrology*; Singh, V.P., Ed.; Water Resources Publications: Highlands Ranch, CO, USA, 1995; pp. 443–476.

35. Zhao, R.J. The Xinanjiang model applied in China. *J. Hydrol.* **1992**, *135*, 371–381. [CrossRef]

36. Jain, V.; Sinha, R. Derivation of unit hydrograph from GIUH analysis for a Himalayan river. *Water Resour. Manag.* **2003**, *17*, 355–375. [CrossRef]

37. Zhang, B.; Govindaraju, R.S. Geomorphology-based artificial neural networks (GANNs) for estimation of direct runoff over watersheds. *J. Hydrol.* **2003**, *273*, 18–34. [CrossRef]

38. Shadeed, S.; Shaheen, H.; Jayyousi, A. GIS-based KW-GIUH hydrological model of semiarid catchments: The case of Faria Catchment, Palestine. *Arabian J. Sci. Eng.* **2007**, *32*, 3–16.

39. Chiang, S.; Tachikawa, Y.; Takara, K. Hydrological model performance comparison through uncertainty recognition and quantification. *Hydrol. Process.* **2007**, *21*, 1179–1195. [CrossRef]

40. Kumar, A.; Kumar, D. Predicting direct runoff from hilly watershed using geomorphology and stream-order-law ratios: Case Study. *J. Hydrol. Eng.* **2008**, *13*, 570–576. [CrossRef]

41. Rodriguez-Iturbe, I.; Valdes, J.B. The geomorphologic structure of hydrologic response. *Water Resour. Res.* **1979**, *15*, 1409–1420. [CrossRef]

42. Lee, K.T.; Yen, B.C. Geomorphology and kinematic-wave based hydrograph deviation. *J. Hydraul. Eng.* **1997**, *123*, 73–80. [CrossRef]

43. Yen, B.C.; Lee, K.T. Unit hydrograph derivation for ungauged watersheds by stream order laws. *J. Hydrol. Eng.* **1997**, *2*, 1–9. [CrossRef]

44. Clark, M.P.; Rupp, D.E.; Woods, R.A.; Zheng, X.; Ibbit, R. P.; Slater, A.G.; Schmidt, J.; Uddstrom, M.L. Hydrological data assimilation with the ensemble Kalman filter: Use of streamflow observation to update states in a distributed hydrological model. *Adv. Water Resour.* **2008**, *31*, 1309–1324. [CrossRef]

45. Liu, Y.Q.; Weerts, A.H.; Clark, M.; Hendricks Franssen, H.J.; Kumar, S.; Moradkhani, H.; Seo, D.-J.; Schwanenberg, D.; Smith, P.; van Dijk, A.I.J.M.; *et al.* Advancing data assimilation in operational hydrologic forecasting: Progresses, challenges, and emerging opportunities. *Hydrol. Earth Syst. Sci.* **2012**, *16*, 3863–3887. [CrossRef]

46. Refsgaard, J.C. Validation and intercomparison of different updating procedures for real-time forecasting. *Nordic Hydrol.* **1997**, *28*, 65–84.

47. Reed, D.W. *A Review of British Flood Forecasting Practice*; Report 90; Institute of Hydrology: Wellington, UK, 1984.

48. Bobinski, E.; Mierkiewicz, M. Recent developments in simple adaptive flow forecasting models in Poland. *Hydrol. Sci. J.* **1986**, *31*, 297–320. [CrossRef]

49. Nayak, P.C.; Sudheer, K.P.; Ramasastri, K.S. Fuzzy computing based rainfall-runoff model for real time flood forecasting. *Hydrol. Process.* **2005**, *19*, 955–968. [CrossRef]

50. Chatfield, C. *The Analysis of Time Series an Introduction*; Chapman and Hall: London, UK, 1989.

51. Seo, D.J.; Koren, V.; Cajina, N. Real-time variational assimilation of hydrologic and hydrometeorological data into operational hydrologic forecasting. *J. Hydrometeorol.* **2003**, *4*, 627–641. [CrossRef]

52. Valstar, J.R.; McLaughlin, D.B.; te Stroet, C.B.M.; van Geer, F.C. A representer-based inverse method for groundwater flow and transport applications. *Water Resour. Res.* **2004**, *40*. [CrossRef]

53. Da Ros, D.; Borga, M. Adaptive use of a conceptual model for real time flood forecasting. *Nordic Hydrol.* **1997**, *28*, 169–188.

54. Madsen, H.; Skotner, C. Adaptive state updating in real-time river flow forecasting-a combined filtering and error forecasting procedure. *J. Hydrol.* **2005**, *308*, 302–312. [CrossRef]

55. Weerts, A.H.; el Serafy, G.Y.E. Particle filtering and ensemble Kalman filtering for state updating with hydrological conceptual rainfall-runoff models. *Water Resour. Res.* **2006**, *42*. [CrossRef]

56. Wang, D.; Cai, X. Robust data assimilation in hydrological modeling-a comparison of Kalman and H-infinity filters. *Adv. Water Resour.* **2008**, *31*, 455–472. [CrossRef]

57. Matgen, P.; Montanari, M.; Hostache, R.; Pfister, L.; Hoffmann, L.; Plaza, D.; Pauwels, V.R.N.; de Lannoy, G.J.M.; de Keyser, R.; Savenije, H.H.G. Towards the sequential assimilation of SAR-derived water stages into hydraulic models using the Particle Filter: Proof of concept. *Hydrol. Earth Syst. Sci.* **2010**, *14*, 1773–1785. [CrossRef]

58. DeChant, C.M.; Moradkhani, H. Examining the effectiveness and robustness of data assimilation methods for calibration and quantification of uncertainty in hydrologic forecasting. *Water Resour. Res.* **2012**, *48*. [CrossRef]

59. Nash, J.E.; Sutcliffe, J.V. River flow forecasting through conceptual models part I—A discussion of principles. *J. Hydrol.* **1970**, *10*, 282–290. [CrossRef]

60. Henderson, F.M.; Wooding, R.A. Overland flow and groundwater flow from a steady rainfall of finite duration. *J. Geophys. Res.* **1964**, *69*, 1531–1540. [CrossRef]

61. Thiessen, A.H. Precipitation averages for large areas. *Mon. Weather Rev.* **1911**, *39*, 1082–1084. [CrossRef]

62. Lee, K.T. Generating design hydrographs by DEM assisted geomorphic runoff simulation: A case study. *J. Am. Water Resour. Assoc.* **1998**, *34*, 375–384. [CrossRef]

MDPI AG

St. Alban-Anlage 66

4052 Basel, Switzerland

Tel. +41 61 683 77 34

Fax +41 61 302 89 18

http://www.mdpi.com

Water Editorial Office

E-mail: water@mdpi.com

http://www.mdpi.com/journal/water